ISBN 0-930406-13-3
UNDERSEA AND HYPERBARIC MEDICAL SOCIETY, INC.
10531 Metropolitan Avenue
Kensington, MD 20895-2627
(301) 942-2980

DIVING PHYSIOLOGY

IN

PLAIN ENGLISH

JOLIE BOOKSPAN, Ph.D.

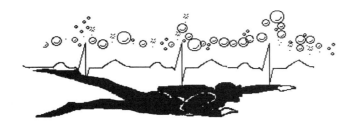

UNDERSEA & HYPERBARIC MEDICAL SOCIETY

DIVING PHYSIOLOGY
IN
PLAIN ENGLISH

Nothing in this book is meant as specific medical advice or
diving instruction. See your physician and get training
before attempting anything presented.å

REVIEWERS

Sincere thanks to the reviewers:

OVERALL REVIEW

The UHMS publications committee: Enrico Camporesi, M.D., Caroline Fife, M.D., Lee Greenbaum, Ph.D., Bill Hamilton, Ph.D., Paul Sheffield, Ph.D., and Hugh Van Liew, Ph.D.

Peter Bennett, D.Sc., Divers Alert Network.

G. D. Golden, physicist, pilot, engineer. World class, fine-tooth fussing over every detail in Chapters 1, 3, 4, and the glossary.

Dan Orr, Divers Alert Network.

CHAPTER 1 DECOMPRESSION TABLES AND COMPUTERS

John Crea. Pressure units, non-Haldane models.

Bill Hamilton, Ph.D. Detailed review, entire chapter.

Ron Nishi, DCIEM, Canada. Series Model section.

Mark Robinson, engineer with a sense of humor. Complete review and equation checking.

CHAPTER 2 IMMERSION EFFECTS

David Hsu, Ph.D., U. Pittsburgh School of Medicine.

CHAPTER 3 DIVING IN COLD AND HEAT

Al Paolone, Ed.D., environmental physiology professor, Biokinetics Research Laboratory Temple University.

CHAPTER 4 GENDER FACTS AND FOLKLORE

Alan Berg, Ph.D., M.D., housecall doctor.

Maurice Cross M.D., Diving Diseases Research Center, Plymouth, England.

Kelly Hill M.D., Our Lady Of The Lake Regional Medical Center Hyperbaric Medicine, Baton Rouge.

Richard Vann, Ph.D., Duke University Medical Center. Mammary implant section.

CHAPTER 5 DIVING INJURIES

Fred Bove, M.D., Ph.D., Chief of Cardiology Temple University Medical School. Lung injury information.

Jim Clark, M.D., University of Pennsylvania Institute of Environmental Medicine. Lung injury information.

David Hsu, Ph.D. Oxygen toxicity section.

Philip James, M.D., Wolfson Hyperbaric Medicine Unit Dundee, Scotland. Decompression sickness and lung injury sections.

Rev. Ed Lanphier, M.D., Dept. of Preventive Medicine University of Wisconsin. Headache section.

Lawrence Martin, M.D., Chief of Pulmonary and Critical Medicine Mt. Sinai, Cleveland. Lung injury and headache sections.

CHAPTER 6 EXERCISE

Audrey Tannenbaum, M.Ed., A.T.C., C.S.C.S., Maccabean Games Triathlon Gold Medalist.

CHAPTER 7 NUTRITION

Carl Gisolfi, Ph.D., authority on fluid regulation during exercise in the heat. Several issues in electrolyte drink section.

Audrey Tannenbaum, M.Ed., A.T.C., C.S.C.S., Maccabean Games Triathlon Gold Medalist.

GLOSSARY

John Crea, decompression guru. Gases and decompression.

Russ Gazzara, Ph.D., extra tall, extra Italian, FDA neurophysiology researcher. Physiology entries.

David Josephson, audio engineer. Physical science entries, SI and English (Common) systems of measurement.

Mark Robinson. Physics entries.

Larry 'Harris' Taylor, Ph.D. Gas issues.

PROOFREADING

Ann Barker, Associate Editor, Undersea and Hyperbaric Medical Society.

PREFACE
WHAT'S IN THIS BOOK

Finally. A book on diving physiology written in plain English.

This book is for all scuba divers and those interested in diving, regardless of diving certification level or academic background. The purpose is to present the interesting concepts behind the physiology, so all can understand and enjoy.

Topics in each chapter were selected from questions divers ask most frequently. In non-technical language this book explains the mysterious terminology of decompression tables and computers, reasons for the interesting changes in your body underwater, effects of diving in cold water and in hot conditions, the interesting hows and whys behind diving maladies, how to get in shape for diving, and important nutrition topics for divers. Although most scuba books and magazines have sections only about women, this book includes issues for men divers, too. There is a large, annotated glossary at the end of the book. More than a handy reference of definitions, it includes word derivations, key concepts, and fun stories behind the people and information.

With the information in this book you will be better equipped to make sense of the many claims and counterclaims in diving physiology. You will be better prepared to understand more advanced training classes. You will have information to make informed decisions concerning decompression tables and computers, be a healthier, fitter diver, and avoid diving injuries. You'll even learn neat scuba knowledge tidbits just for fun.

Happy reading and happy diving.

CONTENTS

REVIEWERS   iii

PREFACE   v
INTRODUCTION TO THE READER

CHAPTER 1   **1**
DECOMPRESSION TABLES AND COMPUTERS

PART I - BRIEF REVIEW OF PRESSURE   2
   Ambient Pressure, 2
   How Nitrogen Gets In and Out Of Your Body, 3

PART II - WHERE DECOMPRESSION TABLES AND COMPUTERS COME FROM 5
   History, 5
   Modern Practice, 6
   What Decompression Tables and Computers Calculate, 6

PART III - BASIC TERMS AND CONCEPTS   8
   Compartments, 8
   Partial Pressure, 10
   Nitrogen Tension, 12
   Half-times, 14
   Fast and Slow Compartments, 17
   Saturation and Desaturation, 19
   Saturation Diving, 20
   Supersaturation, 21
   Supersaturation Ratios, 21
   M-Values, 22
   Table-Based and Model-Based Computers, 23

PART IV - NON-HALDANE DECOMPRESSION MODELS   24
   Statistical Models, 24
   Series Model, 25
   EL Model, 27
   Slab Model, 27
   Varying Permeability Model, 28
   Reduced Gradient Bubble Model, 28

PART V - DIVING WITH GASES OTHER THAN AIR   29
Oxygen Enriched Air, 29
Heliox, 31
Trimix, 32
Gas Switching, 33

CONCLUSION   34

CHAPTER 2   35
IMMERSION EFFECTS

PART I - DIVE REFLEX   36
What Is The Dive Reflex? 36
Different In Humans and Marine Animals, 37
Role In Humans, 37
Individual Variation, 38
Mechanisms, 38
Preventing Problems From The Dive Reflex, 40
Summary, 42

PART II - THE P PHENOMENON   43
Why Does It Occur? 43
Mechanical Factors, 44
Chemical Factors, 45
Environmental Factors, 46
Personal Factors, 47
Factors Unknown, 47
Handling Diuresis, 49
Rehydrating Underwater , 50
Summary, 51

CHAPTER 3   53
DIVING IN COLD AND HEAT

PART I -WHY DO YOU GET COLD?   54
How You Lose Heat, 54
Key Concept In Heat Transfer, 57
Skin Temperature and Core Temperature Are Different, 57
How You Conserve Core Heat, 58
How You Gain Body Heat, 60
Summary, 63

PART II - SUSCEPTIBILITY TO COLD   64
What Is Hypothermia (and What Is It Not)? 64
Body Size and Shape, 65
Age, 67
Behavior, 67
Medication, 67
Rest and Exercise, 67

Physical Fitness, 68
Protective Clothing, 68
Gender, 69
Acclimatization, 69
Other Influences, 70
Summary, 71

PART III - EFFECTS OF DIVING IN THE COLD   72
Respiratory Effects, 72
Vascular Effects, 72
Manual Impairment, 73
Mental Function, 74
Cardiovascular Effects, 74
Metabolic Effects, 74
Renal Effects, 74
Thermostat Effects, 75
Fatigue, 75
Nitrogen Effects, 75
Preventing Cold Injury, 76
Summary, 78

PART IV - DIVING IN THE HEAT   79
Environmental Variables, 79
Human Variables, 80
Shirts or Skins? 82
Preventing Heat Injury, 83
Summary, 84

CHAPTER 4   85
GENDER FACTS AND FOLKLORE

PART I - ISSUES SPECIFIC TO MEN   86
Penile and Testicular Implants, 86
Infertility, 87
Offspring Gender, 87
Hair Restoration, 87

PART II - ISSUES SPECIFIC TO WOMEN   89
Pregnancy, 89
Oral Contraceptives, 89
Breast Implants, 89

PART III - ISSUES AFFECTING BOTH WOMEN AND MEN   91
Work Load, 91
Diving Accidents, 93
Cardiovascular Health, 93
Spontaneous Pneumothorax, 94
Flexibility and Joint Injury, 94
Joint Structure and Injury, 94
Diver's Acne, 95
Back Pain, 95
Overweight, 96

Eating Disorders, 97
Anabolic Steroids and Steroid Substitutes, 98
Air Consumption, 98
Slipping Weight Belt, 99
Hernia, 99

PART IV - THE FOLKLORE   100
Decompression Sickness, 100
Hypothermia, 101
Hyperthermia, 103
Dehydration, 104
Drag, 105
Sharks, 105

CONCLUSION   106

CHAPTER 5   **107**
DIVING INJURIES

PART I - LUNG INJURIES   108
Breath-hold Injury, 108
Pneumothorax, 109
Bronchitis, 110
Emphysema, 111
Asthma, 111
Pneumonia, 111
Preventing Diving Lung Injury, 112

PART II - DECOMPRESSION SICKNESS   113
How Decompression Sickness Occurs, 113
Where Are The Bubbles? 114
Mechanical Effects Of DCS, 115
Biochemical Effects Of DCS, 116
Where Do Bubbles Hurt You? 116
Is It DCS or AGE? 118
Factors Affecting Risk of Decompression Sickness, 119
Bubbles Not All Bad? 121
Preventing Decompression Sickness, 121
Summary, 122

PART III - OXYGEN TOXICITY   123
Defenses Against Oxygen, 123
Free Radicals, 125
Pulmonary O_2 Toxicity, 126
Central Nervous System (CNS) O_2 Toxicity, 127
An Intriguing Twist, 127
When Is O_2 Toxic? 127
Susceptibility to Oxygen Toxicity, 129
Treating Oxygen Toxicity, 130
Preventing Oxygen Toxicity, 130
Summary, 131

PART IV - DIVING HEADACHES   133
    Does Diving Cure A Headache? 133
    Does Diving Cure A Hangover? 133
    Does Diving Cause A Headache? 134
    Preventing Headaches, 136

PART V - SWIMMER'S EAR   138
    What Is Swimmer's Ear? 138
    Symptoms, 138
    Causes, 138
    Treating Swimmer's Ear, 140
    Preventing Swimmer's Ear, 141

PART VI - MARINE STINGS   142
    Poison and Venom, 142
    Why Do They Sting Us? 142
    What Happens When They Sting Us? 143
    Treating Stings, 144
    Preventing Stings, 146

CHAPTER 6   147
EXERCISE FOR DIVERS

PART I - FAT'S NOT ALL BAD   148
    When Fat Helps In Sports, 148
    When Fat Hinders Sports, 148
    What About Diving? 148
    Summary, 149

PART II - WHY SHOULD DIVERS GET FIT?   150
    Increased Heat Tolerance, 150
    Increased Cold Tolerance, 150
    Better Health, 151
    Diving Safety, 151
    Injury Reduction, 151
    Delayed Aging, 152
    Positive Mood, 152
    Fat Loss, 153
    Summary, 153

PART III - ASPECTS OF FITNESS   154
    What Is Fitness? 154
    Why Different Aspects Of Fitness? 154
    What Are The Different Aspects Of Fitness? 155
    Summary, 156

PART IV - HOW TO GET FIT   157
    Cardiovascular Endurance, 157
    Anaerobic Capacity, 158
    Strength, 158
    Muscular Endurance, 160

Power, 160
Flexibility, 161
Size, 163
Firm, 163
Can You Have It All? 163
Summary, 164

PART V - TAILORING FITNESS FOR DIVING   165
Results Are Specific To The Exercise, 165
Don't Worry About Being Exact, 165
Some Exercises Are Counterproductive, 166
Getting In Shape For Diving, 166
Summary, 167

PART VI - GETTING OUT OF SHAPE AND HOW TO AVOID IT   168
How To Get Out Of Shape, 168
What Goes Bad? 169
How Long Does It Take? 170
Does It Hurt? 170
Preventing Getting Out Of Shape, 171
Summary, 171

CHAPTER 7   172
NUTRITION FOR DIVERS

PART I - DIVERS AND DIETING   173
Poor Food Habits, 173
Dehydration, 174
Fatigue, 174
Reduced Cold Tolerance, 174
Possible Risk of Heart Disease, 174
Summary, 175

PART II - HOW TO LOSE WEIGHT WITHOUT DIETING   176
Cut Fats, 176
Substitute, 176
Don't Go Hungry, 177
Less Sugar, 177
Be Prepared, 177
Take Your Time, 177
More Physical Activity, 177
Summary, 178

PART III - BONE HEALTH   180
What Is Osteoporosis? 180
Why Young Divers Need to Know, 181
Factors Affecting Risk, 181
Where Diving Fits In, 182
How Much Calcium Do You Need? 182
Calcium Sources, 182
Preventing Osteoporosis, 183
Summary, 183

PART IV - FLUID REPLACEMENT FOR DIVERS   185
  Why Not Dehydrate? 185
  How You Lose Body Water, 186
  How You Conserve Body Water, 187
  Why Replacement? 187
  Water, 187
  Electrolyte Replacers, 188
  Carbohydrate Loaders, 189
  Carbohydrate Replacers, 190
  Not Harmful To Divers, 191
  Alcohol, 193
  Caffeine, 194
  Preventing Dehydration, 194
  Summary of Fluid Replacement Options, 194

ANNOTATED GLOSSARY   **197**

APPENDIX   **231**
PRESSURE CONVERSIONS

FIGURES   **233**

INDEX   **235**

CHAPTER 1

DECOMPRESSION TABLES AND COMPUTERS

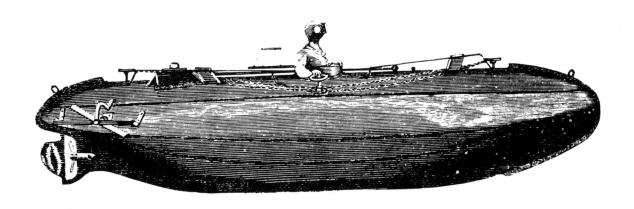

This book begins with the complex subject of decompression tables and computers because of high interest by divers. This chapter surveys basic concepts and terms, which can help you make diving decisions to reduce risk of decompression sickness. The chapter does not detail specific decompression tables and computers, nor make recommendations for particular models. Understanding their fundamentals will help you make your own decisions. Topics are from questions divers ask most frequently, and from common misconceptions. Because of large demand, numbers and equations are explained conceptually so all can enjoy, even without a background in math.

Understanding of decompression theory is still incomplete, and more involved than explained here, but begins with these basics.

- Brief Review of Pressure
- Where Decompression Tables And Computers Come From
- Basic Terms & Concepts
- Introduction to Non-Haldane Decompression Models
- Diving With Gases Other Than Air

CHAPTER 1
PART I

BRIEF REVIEW OF PRESSURE

Divers use decompression tables and computers to minimize risk of decompression sickness (DCS). Decompression sickness is covered in Chapter 5. For now, DCS results from extra inert gas, usually nitrogen, forming bubbles in blood and other areas of your body after ascent. The source of nitrogen is the pressurized air you breathe from your scuba tank or other air supply during a dive. The goal of decompression computation is to determine how long and how deep you can dive without undue risk of DCS after ascent. It also determines if you can ascend directly to the surface, or need to stop during ascent before reaching the surface, to release enough dissolved nitrogen so it doesn't become bubbles.

- Ambient Pressure
- How Nitrogen Gets In And Out Of Your Body

AMBIENT PRESSURE

Ambient Pressure – Surrounding Pressure. On land, exerted by the weight of air above you. Under water, by both atmospheric and water pressure. As distance down increases, pressure increases.

With sea level as a zero starting point, pressure under water, or in a tank, is called gauge pressure and does not include atmospheric pressure (14.7 psi, 760 mmHg, or 101.3 kPa). When including atmospheric and water pressure together, it is called absolute pressure.

In the near vacuum of space, there is just about no air and no air pressure. On land, the atmosphere around you exerts pressure on your body. The pressure is from the weight of miles of air above you. It doesn't take much effort to draw a breath of air. The pressure of your air supply is external, or ambient pressure.

With depth underwater, pressure continues increasing from the combination of air and water pressure. Water weighs more than air. You don't have to go very deep before ambient pressure is considerably higher than at the surface. If you've ever tried to breathe under water through a long snorkel or tube extended to the surface, you know this doesn't work past a few feet. You can't expand your chest against the overpowering ambient pressure.

Your scuba regulator avoids this problem by sensing ambient pressure. It delivers air to your mouthpiece at ambient pressure, making breathing possible. You breathe air at greater than atmospheric pressure. This higher-than-normal air pressure is the source of decompression problems.

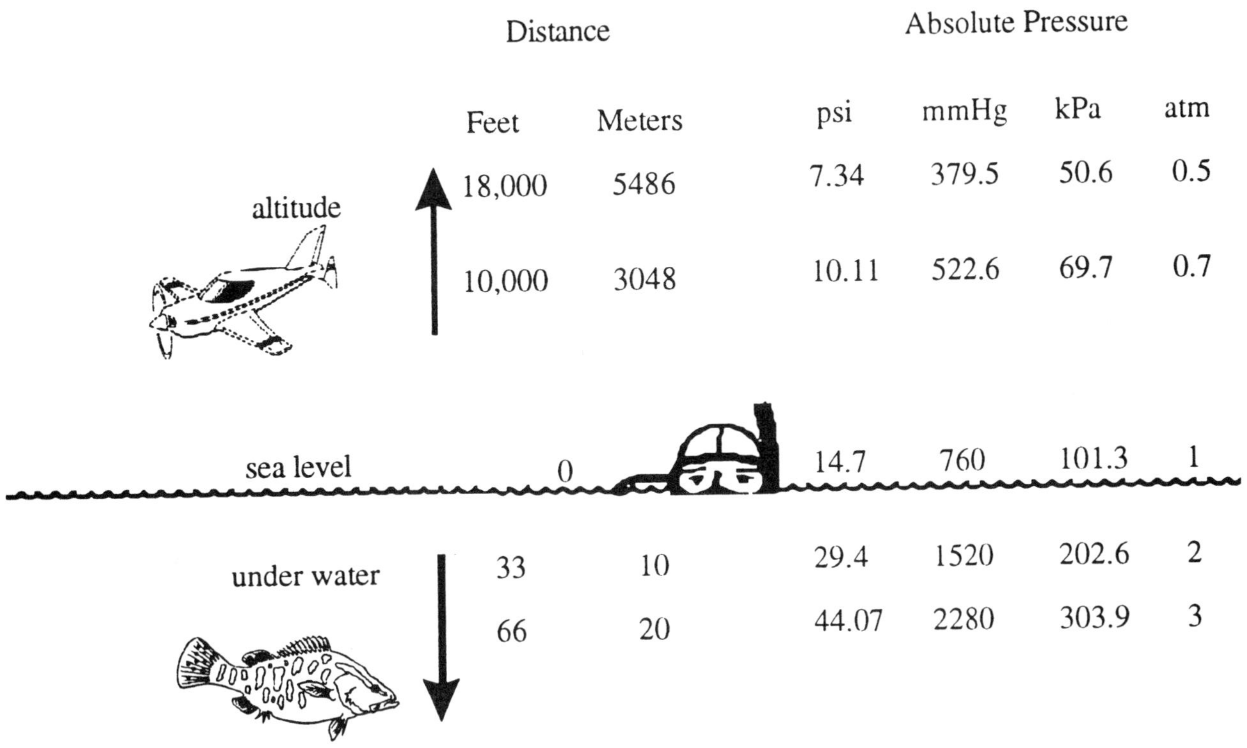

	Distance		Absolute Pressure			
	Feet	Meters	psi	mmHg	kPa	atm
altitude	18,000	5486	7.34	379.5	50.6	0.5
	10,000	3048	10.11	522.6	69.7	0.7
sea level	0		14.7	760	101.3	1
under water	33	10	29.4	1520	202.6	2
	66	20	44.07	2280	303.9	3

Figure 1.1. As you go up, pressure decreases. As you go down pressure increases. Pressures underwater are for sea water. Fresh water values are slightly less.

How Nitrogen Gets In and Out of Your Body

Uptake - Transfer of dissolved gas into the body. Also called ongassing or ingassing.
Elimination - Transfer of dissolved gas out of the body. Also called offgassing or outgassing.

Nitrogen is the inert gas most commonly considered in decompression theory. Nitrogen in the air you breathe from your scuba tank or other air supply passes from your lungs to blood vessels in your lungs. Nitrogen changes from gaseous to dissolved form. Dissolved nitrogen travels with your blood to your body tissues. Other inert gases behave similarly. The process of absorbing dissolved nitrogen into your body tissues is called nitrogen uptake, also called ongassing, and ingassing.

Overall movement of gas molecules during ongassing is from areas of higher concentration and pressure to lower concentration and pressure, from lungs to blood to body tissue, Figure 1.2.

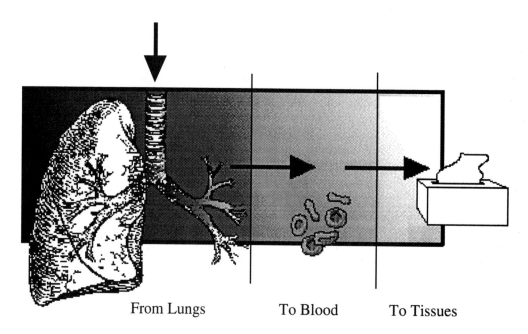

From Lungs   To Blood   To Tissues

Figure 1.2. Overall movement of gas molecules is from areas of higher concentration and pressure to lower concentration and pressure, from lungs to blood to body tissues.

Greater pressure with increasing depth dissolves more gas. This is a fundamental principle of chemistry summarized by Henry's Law. As you dive deeper, your regulator increases the pressure of the air you breathe to match ambient pressure, so you can breathe. The deeper you go, the more nitrogen from each breath dissolves in your body. The longer you stay, the more time nitrogen has to dissolve.

When you ascend, an opposite chain of events occurs. Ambient pressure decreases as you get shallower. Your regulator reduces the pressure of your air supply to match decreasing ambient pressure. Ambient pressure becomes less than your accumulated internal nitrogen pressure. Nitrogen in your body begins coming back out of you. Nitrogen transfers first from your tissues to your blood, then from your blood back to your lungs where you breathe it out. This elimination process is called offgassing or outgassing. What we hope happens is that nitrogen remains dissolved in the blood until it gets to the lungs without reforming into gas. This is not always the case.

Nitrogen can come out of solution to become a gas again before it gets to your lungs, if your internal nitrogen pressure exceeds a maximum amount relative to ambient pressure, during or after ascent. Gaseous nitrogen forms tiny bubbles that are accepted to be the basis of decompression problems.

CHAPTER *1*
PART *II*

WHERE DECOMPRESSION TABLES COME FROM

This section gives a brief history of decompression theory, and summarizes what most current decompression tables do.

- History
- Modern Practice
- What Decompression Tables And Computers Calculate

HISTORY

Illness from pressure change was first recorded in the late 1600's by physicist and chemist Robert Boyle, who exposed animals to changes in pressure. One of his more famous observations, among many, was a gas bubble in the eye of a snake when he lowered pressure in a vacuum chamber. In other work, he explained change in gas volume from change in pressure, summarized by Boyle's Law.

The first description of pressure-related illness in humans was in 1841 by Triger, before modern scuba was invented. Laborers worked in mines and under bodies of water, in pressurized tunnels and water-tight boxes called caissons. The tunnels and caissons were pressurized with air to keep water and mud out. As work progressed deeper, workers began breathing air at greater pressures, and returning to the surface with pain and sometimes paralysis. Triger wrote of limb pain, and described the treatment – alcohol applied externally and internally. Later, during construction of the Brooklyn Bridge and other bridges, the bent over posture to ease pain from this "caisson disease" popularized the name "the bends." More than a hundred workers suffered serious bends during the Brooklyn bridge construction from 1869 to 1883.

Several researchers participated in unraveling a series of issues to explain this disease, where Pol and Watelle noted in 1854, "One pays only upon leaving." By 1878, French physiologist Paul Bert had determined the connection between bends and nitrogen bubbles, and showed that pain could reverse with recompression. The British Royal Navy needed to minimize decompression sickness among fleet divers, and commissioned John Scott Haldane and co-workers Arthur E. Boycott and British naval officer Guybon C. Damant. In 1908, they published their work along with three sets of tables of time and depth schedules. These tables were adapted and used by the British Royal Navy and the United States Navy.

According to Haldane:

- Different areas of your body absorb and release nitrogen at different rates.

- Rates of nitrogen absorption and elimination can be estimated using a fairly easy mathematical equation. The equation is exponential, which means that each area gains (or loses) a fixed percentage of how much it has left after every passing unit of time. See the glossary for explanation of exponentials.

- A diver could ascend without decompression problems so long as pressure reduction was not by more than half.

MODERN PRACTICE

Most dive tables and computers currently used by divers are based on concepts initiated by Haldane, and added to by followers. Most do the same four things, explained next in Part III, Terms and Concepts:

- They estimate the partial pressure of inert gas, usually nitrogen, that would accumulate in different body areas, handled computationally as "compartments".

- They compare estimates of internal nitrogen partial pressures to their supposed maximum tolerated pressures, usually called M-values.

- They state depth and time limits on ascents so you don't exceed these maximums in any compartment. Pressure reduction may be more or less than the half originally proposed by Haldane.

- If compartments would exceed their M-values on ascent, they tell the diver to make a decompression stop, to let compartments drain down until they are below M before ascending further.

WHAT DECOMPRESSION TABLES AND COMPUTERS CALCULATE

It is said that some divers believe that the decompression computer worn on the body somehow measures nitrogen in the body. Decompression computers, like tables, do not measure the nitrogen, they estimate it through calculation. Most decompression tables and computers currently used by divers use the same base equation derived by Haldane, modified by number and speed of compartments selected for the model, and compare it to what different modelers select as the maximum amount of nitrogen each compartment can hold on ascent.

The equation for Haldane-based computation has several parts, explained next in Part III:

- How much gas partial pressure you start with already in your body

- Pressure around you at each depth, and how long you stay there

- Percentage of nitrogen, or other inert gases, in your breathing gas

- Partial pressure of nitrogen in each compartment at each depth, which is determined by the percentage of nitrogen and depth.

- Speed of gas uptake and elimination in each compartment (half-times)

- Maximum amount of nitrogen each compartment is thought to tolerate upon ascent, called M-values.

The final formula, or algorithm, defines the model and is often proprietary information. We don't yet have algorithms that exactly match what is thought to be happening in the body.

Decompression tables and computers are not just number fiddling. Decompression algorithms are tested on divers. The equations are then modified where needed, to reflect, as much as possible, data found during diving.

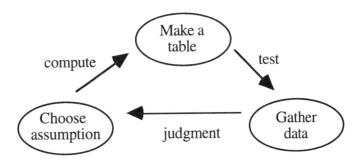

Reports exist of divers turning off their computer between repetitive dives so the computer will allow them more time on the next dive, or hanging it over the side of the boat after a dive if it says they should not yet surface. These are good ways to get expensive trips to a medical facility for decompression sickness treatment. Use your computer only as directed in the instructions.

"Hello, I am a decompression model.
I will tell you what you tell me to tell you."

CHAPTER 1
PART III

BASIC TERMS & CONCEPTS

This section summarizes the sometimes mysterious vocabulary of decompression science. Understanding these basics helps understand decompression in general, the Haldane-based tables mentioned in Part III, the non-Haldane tables introduced in Part IV, and use of gas mixtures other than air, Part V.

- Compartments
- Partial Pressure
- Nitrogen Tension
- Half-times
- Fast and Slow Compartments
- Saturation
- Supersaturation
- Supersaturation Ratios
- M-Values
- Table-Based and Model-Based Computers

COMPARTMENTS

In anatomy, tissues are body areas that are structurally and cellularly similar, for example, muscle tissue.

In decompression, compartments are areas similar in rate of inert gas uptake. They are sometimes called "tissues" but compartment is preferred because they are not specific anatomic entities.

Your entire body absorbs nitrogen under pressure. Some body areas absorb gas faster than others, for example, 5 and 10 minute compartments, compared to 60 and 120 minute compartments, further explained in the section on half-times.

Contemporary researchers prefer the term compartment rather than tissue, since decompression compartments are not whole body tissues like muscle or nerve. Because so many divers and researchers use the term tissue, confusion sometimes results. Anatomically, there are only four tissues in the human body: muscle, connective, epithelial, and nervous tissue. Everything in your body is made of combinations of those four. For decompression work, the body is divided computationally into any number of compartments. How many is up to the modeler.

Even though decompression compartment divisions do not
correspond one to one with anatomic tissues, they reference existing
areas (theoretically) wherever they might be, that behave alike.

Although blood flow may change with activity or other events in the body, thereby changing an anatomic tissue's speed, decompression models account for many compartments, which we hope account for most of the possibilities. At least one dive computer so far, the Uwatech (Bühlmann) Aladin "Air-X," tries to deal specifically with changes in blood flow due to exercise (determined by air consumption) and cold.

Compartment Identifying Experiments. Divers often ask how the different compartments were identified. The numbers naming decompression compartments derive not only from theory, but experiment.

If you came up from a dive and breathed out each breath into a collection bag for a set time and analyzed the gas, you could find how much nitrogen you released from your entire body. If you put dots on a chart showing how much nitrogen came out every few minutes, it would draw a particular type of curve called an exponential curve, which means that you lost a fixed percentage of the resulting value with every passing unit of time (see the glossary for explanation of exponentials). This, more or less, estimates a measurement called total body nitrogen washout. Total washout curves, like most composite descriptions, don't tell how much nitrogen came from different parts of you, just an average amount over all. You wouldn't have information about washout rate in your different compartments.

Decompression researchers use many techniques to try to identify how fast specific areas of your body ongas and offgas. Some experiments measure blood flow to different parts and draw inferences about how much gas will be carried to them. This method is limited by the fact that blood flow is only part of how different amounts of gas wind up in your anatomic tissues. Some work takes a different tack by putting a radioactive marker on nitrogen introduced into specific areas, then determining how much goes in and out. Other work identifying different speed tissues came from Naval submarine work. Escapes from submarine towers after short, deep exposures, and experimental dives with longer decompression using regular compressed air, showed certain washouts proceed faster than others.

Multi-Compartment Models. Different compartments take up nitrogen at different rates. Each compartment also tolerates a different amount of nitrogen before it accumulates too much to ascend directly to the surface without stopping to let some out. By including several compartments, decompression tables and computers are thought to do a better job of accounting for the various areas of the body.

Multi-compartment decompression tables and computers limit your time underwater so no one compartment gets too much. Almost all decompression tables and computers are multi-compartment models.

PARTIAL PRESSURE

> *Partial Pressure – The part of total pressure exerted by only one gas in a mixture of several gases. All the partial pressures together make up total pressure. Partial pressure of a gas is the total pressure times the fraction (percentage) of that gas. Partial pressures determine how much inert gas you will take up and eliminate.*

Understanding partial pressure is an important part of understanding decompression. Spend some time to get familiar with this section, if you aren't already.

On land, the weight of the air column above you presses on you. Nitrogen makes up about 78% of air, so nitrogen exerts about 78% of the pressure. That's why it's called a partial pressure. Another 21% of the pressure on you comes from oxygen. The sum of all the partial pressures equals the total pressure. That is Dalton's Law. Argon makes up almost 1% of the pressure, and is usually lumped with nitrogen and tiny amounts of helium, neon, krypton, xenon, and others to give 79% inert gas in decompression calculations.

Partial pressure of nitrogen is commonly abbreviated PN_2 (pronounced pee-enn-tu). Sometimes pPN_2 is used, particularly in engineering. FO_2 is partial pressure of oxygen.

You may occasionally see the expression FiO_2, (pronounced eff-eye-oh-tu), rather than just FO_2. FiO_2 means the fraction of inspired oxygen. That is different from what you breathe back out, which is the fraction of expired O_2, written FeO_2 (eff-eee-oh-tu). Usually FiO_2 is inferred when you see FO_2.

Partial Pressures Of Gases In Air

The sum of partial pressures = total pressure

nitrogen	0.78	(just over 78%)
oxygen	0.21	(just under 21%)
argon, carbon dioxide, water & trace gases	0.01	(around 1%)
	1.00 atmosphere abs	100%

Partial Pressure Determines Gas Exchange. Partial pressure of nitrogen in your breathing mixture determines how much nitrogen you ongas and offgas. As PN_2 of the air you breathe increases with depth, nitrogen ongassing increases. When you reduce water pressure around you by ascending, nitrogen pressure that you have built up in your body then exceeds the PN_2 of water around you. You offgas nitrogen.

Units of Partial Pressure. There are several units for partial pressure. Figure 1.1 shows relative scale of a few common units.

Medical people often measure partial pressure in millimeters of mercury (mmHg). For decompression, the unit of partial pressure is often atmospheres absolute (ATA or atm abs), defined in Part I. Calculations using atmospheres are simple and relate easily to diving because they compare to total sea level pressure at one ATA. For example, PO_2 at the surface is 0.21 ATA, because air is 21% oxygen. PN_2 of regular air with 79% nitrogen is 0.79 ATA at the surface.

In scientific applications, the term "atm abs" or the International System (SI) pressure units pascals (Pa) and kilopascals (kPa) are preferred over "ATA." The term ATA may also be confused with the technical atmosphere sometimes used in Europe, abbreviated "at," or if absolute "ATA." In this chapter, ATA is used because you will see it so commonly. The glossary further explains atmospheres, atmospheres absolute, technical atmospheres, and the SI system and units. A table of pressure conversions is in the Appendix.

Interesting Note. Because the term ATA stands for atmospheres absolute, and is already plural, the term is ATA, not ATAs.

PN_2 of regular air with 79% nitrogen is 0.79 ATA at the surface.
PO_2 of regular air with 21% oxygen is 0.21 ATA at the surface.

Fraction of Gas Does Not Change With Depth. Composition of any breathing gas does not change with depth, just the pressure on it. The percentage of oxygen stays 21% for regular air, and nitrogen stays 79%, so FO_2 stays 0.21 and FN_2 stays 0.79. The fraction only changes if you change the mix (Part V).

Partial Pressure Changes With Depth. When you dive to 33 feet (10 m), or two atmospheres absolute, you are under twice the total pressure than at the surface at one atmosphere absolute. Doubling total pressure doubles the partial pressure of oxygen in regular air from 0.21 to 0.42 ATA, and PN_2 from 0.79 to 1.58. Tripling pressure by diving to 66 feet triples PO_2 to 0.63 ATA.

Once you know total pressure, you can calculate partial pressure. For depths that are not convenient multiples, find absolute pressure by dividing the depth in feet by 33, then adding 1. The 1 is for atmospheric pressure, which is part of absolute pressure:

$$\frac{D}{33} + 1 \qquad \text{so, at 100 feet:} \quad \frac{100}{33} + 1 = 4.03 \text{ ATA (or atm abs)}$$

Calculating Partial Pressure. Partial pressure of a gas equals the fraction (percentage) of that gas times total pressure, or $PO_2 = FO_2 \times ATA$, Table 1.1.

Table 1.1. Fraction of gas times total pressure = partial pressure.

Percentage (fraction) O_2	Depth (feet	meters)	Pressure (ATA or atm abs)	$FO_2 \times ATA = PO_2$
	Surface		1	$0.21 \times 1 = 0.21$
	33	10	2	$0.21 \times 2 = 0.42$
21% oxygen	66	20	3	$0.21 \times 3 = 0.63$
(air)	99	30	4	$0.21 \times 4 = 0.84$
	132	40	5	$0.21 \times 5 = 1.05$
	Surface		1	$0.32 \times 1 = 0.32$
	33	10	2	$0.32 \times 2 = 0.64$
32% oxygen	66	20	3	$0.32 \times 3 = 0.96$
(NOAA Nitrox I)	99	30	4	$0.32 \times 4 = 1.28$
	132	40	5	$0.32 \times 5 = 1.60$
	Surface		1	$1.00 \times 1 = 1.0$
	33	10	2	$1.00 \times 2 = 2.0$
100% oxygen	66	20	3	$1.00 \times 3 = 3.0$
	99	30	4	$1.00 \times 4 = 4.0$
	132	40	5	$1.00 \times 5 = 5.0$

Why You Use Partial Pressures. Partial pressure calculations let you know how much nitrogen and other inert gases you uptake and offgas. How this is done is covered next in Nitrogen Tension.

Mixtures with high oxygen partial pressure are sometimes breathed on decompression stops to shorten decompression stop time after long, deep dives. Reducing PN_2 in the mix by increasing PO_2 promotes nitrogen elimination, while total gas pressure outside the body is kept high enough to resist bubble formation, by the sum of the nitrogen and oxygen partial pressures.

Just as raising PN_2 increases nitrogen uptake, raising PO_2 can increase oxygen uptake. Too much causes toxicity, discussed in Chapter 5; knowing partial pressure calculations for oxygen helps prevent it.

NITROGEN TENSION

Nitrogen Tension – Partial pressure of nitrogen in the body.

Partial pressure of nitrogen in the mix you breathe is usually just called nitrogen partial pressure. Partial pressure of nitrogen dissolved in your body is commonly called nitrogen tension. In other words, ambient nitrogen partial pressure determines compartment tensions. Division of these terms is not standardized. You may also hear the term gas loading.

Units of Nitrogen Tension. Nitrogen tensions are partial pressures, so use partial pressure units, often feet of sea water (fsw). Haldane defined sea level pressure in fsw. Much of his and his followers' math use 33 fsw as sea level pressure, so a depth of 33 feet has a pressure of 66 fsw. You may also see meters of sea water (msw), mmHg, torr, bar, atmospheres (atm), and atmospheres absolute (ATA or atm abs), which is air plus water pressure together (see previous section – Units of Partial Pressure). Scientific writing uses International System (SI) units of pascals (Pa) and kilopascals (kPa). All are units of pressure. Don't confuse the units of pressure; fsw and msw, with the units of distance; feet and meters. It's not as difficult as it sounds. A conversion table of common units appears in the Appendix. English and SI systems are explained in the glossary. Also see the glossary for more on the important distinctions between atm, ATA, and technical ATA.

The point is just to understand that nitrogen tensions in your body are pressures, not volumes of gas as sometimes thought, and that you may see the result of many dive computer calculations of nitrogen tension in fsw, a common pressure unit.

Starting Nitrogen Tension On Land. The weight of the air column at sea level makes air pressure equivalent to the pressure of 33 fsw, even though you are at zero elevation. Nitrogen partial pressure is the fraction of gas times total pressure, so nitrogen partial pressure is 0.79×33, or 26.07 fsw.

Nitrogen tensions in your body vary from this because the air you breathe in gets "diluted" by water vapor and carbon dioxide from your body. Subtracting water vapor pressure and arterial CO_2 values gives the blood tension. Tensions in your various compartments will eventually match, or equilibrate with inert gas tension in your blood.

This, more or less, is the compartment nitrogen tension you start with. If you go up in an airplane or to the mountains, your internal nitrogen tensions will all gradually decrease, as there is less ambient pressure, and less nitrogen partial pressure to drive nitrogen uptake. When you go diving, tensions rise from your starting point, because of increased pressure underwater.

Nitrogen fraction is 79%. Total pressure at sea level is 33 fsw.
Partial pressure of nitrogen (inspired) is:

0.79×33 fsw = approx. 26 fsw

Nitrogen Tension Underwater. At 33 feet down, for example, nitrogen partial pressure would be around 52 fsw. How is that number determined? Total pressure at 33 feet of depth is 66 fsw (33 ocean plus 33 for the atmosphere). Partial pressure is percentage times pressure, or $0.79 \times 66 = 52.14$ fsw.

All your compartment tensions will eventually reach (equilibrate with) external pressure, more or less, given general conditions, individual physiology, and subtracting out water vapor and carbon dioxide pressures. These numbers are not exact in the body, so don't worry about the decimal places. Calculations are often done with inspired gases. Pulmonary gases are not ignored, just sort of held constant, so many models do not consider them separately.

Nitrogen fraction is 79%. Total pressure at 33 feet is 66 fsw.
Partial pressure of nitrogen (inspired) is:

$$0.79 \times 66 \text{ fsw} = \text{approx. } 52 \text{ fsw}$$

Deeper depth increases pressure to drive nitrogen ongassing, increasing compartment nitrogen tensions. Longer bottom time increases tensions. Longer surface intervals decrease tensions. Conservatism with these variables reduces your compartment nitrogen tensions.

Compartments Reach Different Tensions. When you dive, you suddenly increase ambient nitrogen partial pressure. However, it takes time to ongas enough nitrogen so that internal N_2 tensions equilibrate with external N_2 partial pressure. Each compartment takes up gas at different rates, meaning each will have a different nitrogen tension after the same period of time. Not all will have enough time to ongas all they can and arrive at equilibrium with ambient pressure. Faster compartments equilibrate, or come close to it, on an average recreational dive. Slower ones remain relatively low. Mid-speed compartments have mid-range nitrogen tensions. Information about half-times allows decompression tables and computers to calculate nitrogen tensions in each compartment at each point in time during your dive.

HALF-TIMES

> *In decompression equations, half-times describe the rate of nitrogen or other inert gas transit into and out of the body.*

A 5 minute half-time compartment fills with inert gas to half the maximum it can hold in 5 minutes. A 10 minute compartment half fills in 10 minutes, a 20 minute compartment half fills in 20 minutes, and so on.

Half-time Gas Uptake. At sea level before your dive, compartment tensions are all equilibrated with sea level pressure, described earlier in Nitrogen Tension. Pressure at depth drives more gas uptake, and compartment tensions will become equal to the new pressure after enough time. Compartments get halfway to that new equilibration point, or half 'full' after one half-time. After the next half-time, the remaining half fills by half. The quarter that's left will then fill by 50%, then the remaining eighth, and so on.

Figure 1.3 shows compartments reach 50% of capacity (equilibrium) after one half-time, 75% after two half-times, 87.5% after three half-times, 93.75% after four half-times, and 96.87% after five half-times. By convention, after six half-times, compartments are considered completely equilibrated with the pressure at depth, or "full," explained later in Saturation.

Gas Elimination: The Haldane model figures offgassing at the same half-time rate as ongassing, although several factors can slow nitrogen release from your body. Each compartment loses half the remaining amount with each passing half-time, until they all eventually reach equilibrium with sea level pressure again. Faster compartments do this faster than slower ones, Figure 1.4.

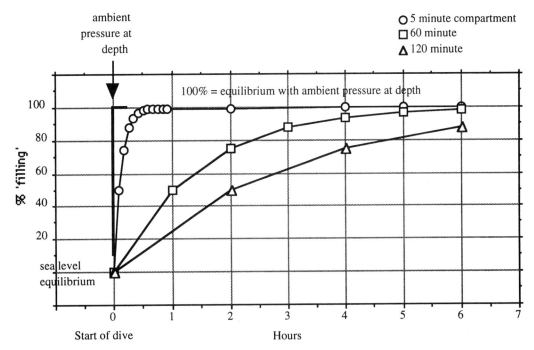

Figure 1.3. Ongassing in the 5, 60, and 120 minute compartments over a six hour dive to any depth. All reach 50% after one half-time: 5 minutes in the 5 minute compartment, 60 minutes (1 hour) in the 60 minute compartment, and 120 minutes (2 hours) in the 120 minute compartment.

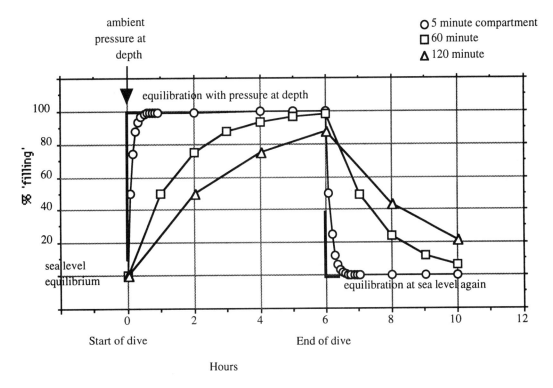

Figure 1.4. Inert gas elimination in the 5, 60, and 120 minute compartments, after first ongassing for 6 hours. All lose 50% of what they started with after one half-time. Slow compartments are slower to gain and lose inert gas, and therefore slower to become equal with surrounding pressure.

The Half-time Equation. Tensions in each compartment, at each part of your dive, are estimated using the exponential equation for half-time rate of change (exponents explained in Parts I, II, and the glossary). Then you plug in numbers for starting compartment tensions, inert gas partial pressures at your depth, and time exposed (plus or minus various other factors up to the modeler).

$$Pt = Po + (Pa - Po)(1 - e^{-0.693t / T^{1/2}}) \pm \text{stuff}$$

Pt	=	Total compartment pressure (tension)
Po	=	Starting compartment pressure (P sub-zero)
Pa	=	Ambient partial pressure of nitrogen
t	=	Time exposed to the ambient pressure
$T^{1/2}$	=	Compartment half-time

Which Half-times Are Used? Parts of you take up nitrogen with half-times ranging from seconds to hours, not only at specific intervals of time like 5 or 10 minutes. To reduce the multitude of half-times to workable units, modelers group them into specific times. The grouping is similar to test grades where the scores may range from zero to 100. All scores from 90 to 100 are grouped together to be called an "A." All those from 80 to 89 get a "B," etc.

Some decompression tables and computers use variations on a standard group of half-time compartments: the 5 minute half-time, the 10 minute, 20 minute, 30, 40, 60, 80, 90, 120, and 240. Others use completely different half-times. How many and which ones are up to the modeler. The more half-time compartments considered, the more information the model gives. More compartments do not necessarily make models more accurate. Some samples follow:

US Navy Standard Air Tables: 5, 10, 20, 40, 80, 120

Orca Edge: 5, 11, 17, 24, 37, 61, 87, 125, 197, 271, 392, 480

Dacor Micro Brain: 4, 11, 31, 86, 238, 396

Beuchat Aladdin: 4, 12, 26, 54, 108, 304

Bühlmann ZHL-12: 4, 7.94, 12.2 18.5, 26.5, 37, 53, 79, 114, 146, 185, 238, 304, 397, 503, 635

Half-times Are Not Just Theoretical. A frequent question by divers is if the half-times used in decompression are only theoretical, or if they are an actual phenomenon. Half-times describe the rate of change of many natural processes, Figure 1.5.

Radiation is one example of a natural phenomenon that behaves according to half-times, although for radiation we call it a half-life. A half-life is the time for a radioactive sample to decay to half its original value. Drug metabolism also behaves according to half-times. Your body takes predictable units of time to eliminate one-half of a standard dose of substances like Valium, other drugs, or carbon monoxide, to name only a few. In pharmacology it's common to call this unit time either a half-time or a biologic half-life. Valium, for instance, has a half-life of about 24 hours to clear from your body. In one day, half will be gone. Drugs with short half-lives of 1.5 to 3 hours like penicillin must be taken several times a day to keep them from falling below therapeutic level. The local anesthetic Novocain is chosen for dental work for its half-time – long enough to last until completion of dental work, but short enough to eliminate soon after.

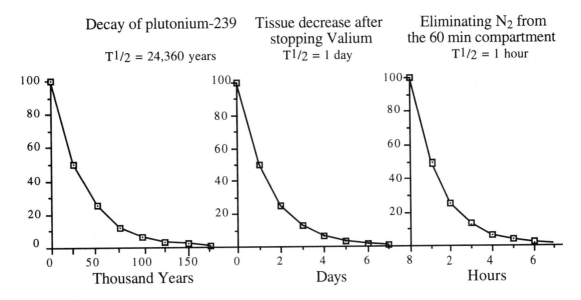

Figure 1.5. Half-time behavior is common in nature.

FAST AND SLOW COMPARTMENTS

> *Fast compartments absorb and release inert gas quickly. Slow compartments absorb and release slowly. In anatomic tissues, rate depends on blood flow and solubility of gas in that area. In Haldane decompression models, blood flow is the main factor establishing compartment speed.*

During most dives, nitrogen tensions become higher in fast compartments than in slow ones, because they take up more gas in the same amount of time. When compartments eliminate gas during surface intervals, faster compartments quickly return to starting pressure. Slower compartments are not much affected by stops or short surface intervals, because they offgas too slowly, Figure 1.6.

Which is Which? Confusion sometimes occurs when divers ask which anatomic tissue corresponds to which half-time compartment. Exact half-times are not known for anatomic structures in your body. Experiments and educated "guesstimation" generalize about which body areas are faster or slower.

Body areas well supplied by blood, such as lungs and abdominal organs, absorb nitrogen quickly. Slower tissues are usually considered to include bone, because of low blood supply, and fat and fatty bone marrow. Fat and fatty tissues are slow tissues, but not necessarily for lack of blood supply.

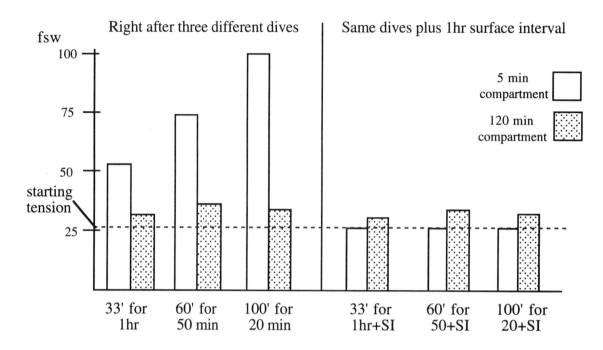

Figure 1.6. Fast and slow compartment nitrogen tensions (fsw) right after three different dives, compared to tensions after the same three dives plus a surface interval of 1 hour.

Nitrogen is more soluble in fatty than watery tissues. It takes longer for nitrogen to fill and leave fatty tissue. This is a property of fat, and true even for fatty areas with similar blood supply as leaner tissue. Very slow tissues are thought to be avascular areas like cartilage and certain joint structures including the joint fluid called synovial fluid.

Many body structures are made of several different anatomic tissues, with different properties. The heart, for example, probably has several different areas that take up and give off gas at all different rates. It does not matter to the decompression equations which anatomic tissue is what speed compartment. Decompression compartments cover, or attempt to cover, the spectrum of possibilities in gas exchange.

Do You Only Offgas On Ascent? Divers often ask if all your compartments outgas on ascent or "safety stops" because ambient pressure is lower than during the dive. That's not the case for all compartments.

Slow compartments can take up gas during ascent, at the same time that faster compartments are getting rid of theirs. Slower compartments can still have lower pressures than the surroundings, because they don't have time during typical recreational dives to become equal to ambient pressure. During ascent, pressure drives nitrogen in the air you breathe into any compartments with lower than ambient pressure. At the same time, fast compartments with higher tensions offgas. Gas can go in both directions, Figure 1.7.

The utility of safety stops is to quickly lower tensions in the faster compartments. Remember that these numbers cannot exactly describe what happens in the body. They show, in general, which tensions would go higher, which lower.

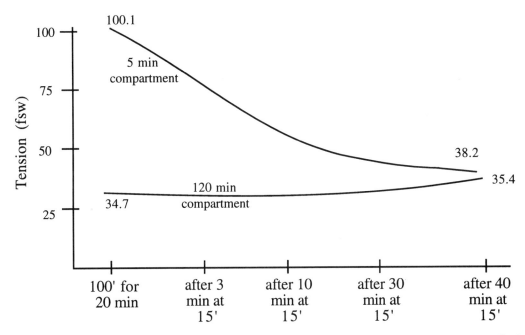

Figure 1.7. Slower compartments can take gas on at the same time that fast compartments are eliminating gas on a stop or when spending time in the shallows after a deeper dive.

SATURATION AND DESATURATION

> *Saturation – When the body contains all the nitrogen or other inert gas it can hold at a given pressure (depth). Occurs when compartments have enough time to become equal with inspired inert gas partial pressure.*

You are saturated with nitrogen right now on land. Your body has all the nitrogen it can hold at the elevation where you live because of air pressure around you. In other words, you are equilibrated with ambient pressure.

The amount of dissolved gas compartments can hold changes with pressure. That is Henry's Law. If you go one foot underwater, increased pressure drives more nitrogen uptake. After sufficient time, your tensions will be the same as the ambient pressure at 1 fsw, and compartments are saturated. If you descend any deeper, you will absorb more nitrogen. After time, you equilibrate with ambient pressure, and are saturated at the new depth.

A typical one hour no-stop recreational dive would saturate
only your fastest compartments –
those with half-times of 10 minutes or less.

When Are You Saturated? Divers often ask how long it would take to completely saturate your whole body during a dive. Compartments are 98.44% saturated or desaturated after six half-times. For practical purposes, almost 99% is considered close enough. No matter what the depth, the 60 minute (one hour) compartment would be considered saturated in 6 hours (6 half-times x 60 minutes = 360 minutes or 6 hours). The slower 120 minute compartment would take 12 hours (6 half-times x 120 minutes = 720 minutes or 12 hours). A fast compartment like a 5 minute compartment saturates in only 30 minutes (6 half-times x 5 minutes = 30 minutes). If you dived deeper, it would take another 6 half-times for compartments to saturate at the new depth.

An easy way to figure saturation (or desaturation) for any half-time is to divide the half-time speed by ten, then change the answer to hours:

5 minute half-time:	5 becomes 0.5, or 0.5 ($^{1/2}$) hour
10 minute half-time:	10 becomes 1.0, or 1 hour
60 minute half-time:	60 becomes 6.0, or 6 hours
120 minute half-time:	120 becomes 12.0, or 12 hours

When Are You Desaturated? How long does it take to get all that extra gas back out of you? Several complicated factors slow desaturation, but most Haldane models figure offgassing at the same half-time rate as ongassing. After any dive, it takes 6 hours for your 60 minute compartment to return to its starting amount of nitrogen, 12 hours for your 120 minute half-time compartment, and 24 hours for your 240 minute compartment. This is true no matter how short the dive, because whatever amount of gas compartments start with, it takes six half-times to get rid of it. Certain non-Haldane models, discussed in Part III of this chapter, allow more time for desaturation.

Determined by the Longest Half-time. The longest compartment considered by the U.S. Navy (USN) Standard Air Decompression Tables, and tables based on them such as the Jeppesen, NAUI, Nu-Way, NASDS, and Dacor, is the 120 minute compartment. It takes 12 hours for the 120 minute compartment to be considered desaturated, and all faster compartments will desaturate more quickly. That's why there's a 12 hour minimum between dives to end the repetitive dive category, and be considered as starting a new dive when using these tables. The DSAT Recreational Dive Planner uses 6 hours as the minimum between dives, and is limited to no-stop diving. It is a variation on the USN-based tables. It takes 24 hours to desaturate the 240 minute (4 hour) half-time. Dives within 24 hours of a previous dive are calculated as repetitive dives. Several dive computers use half-times up to 480 minutes. The 480 compartment takes 48 hours to desaturate. Some models use still longer half-time compartments.

SATURATION DIVING

> *Saturation Diving – Alternative method to repeated decompression after repeated underwater work bouts. Divers remain underwater, working, living, and sleeping, using dry bells and habitats for periods of days, weeks, or longer, becoming saturated with nitrogen or other inert gas in the breathing mixture. Decompression time is the same regardless of length of stay.*

With long, deep diving, nitrogen tensions rise too high to surface without decompression trouble. You must make a stop before surfacing, in some cases several stops at several depths, to lower nitrogen tensions below a critical amount, explained below in the section on M-values. The stops are called decompression stops.

Some commercial, military, and scientific applications require long underwater stays. Long exposures require long decompression stops. Length of the decompression stops often exceeds length of the bottom time. Rather than decompress after each task, science, military, and commercial divers can remain under pressure for the duration of their work. Scientists may live in dry habitats underwater, venturing out to work. Commercial saturation divers can stay in a pressure chamber and "commute" to work underwater in a pressurized bell. In both cases, they remain under pressure and become saturated. Once saturated, they don't absorb more nitrogen, no matter how much longer they remain at that depth. Decompression stop time is the same if they stay under pressure a day or a week. Saturation diving requires extensive support operations and equipment.

SUPERSATURATION

> *Supersaturation – When compartment tensions exceed ambient pressure, the compartment has more nitrogen than it can contain in equilibrium. Occurs when ambient pressure drops on ascent. Past a point, bubbles form.*

On ascent, ambient pressure drops. Ambient pressure may become lower than nitrogen tensions that have built up in certain compartments (but not all). These compartments will then have more nitrogen than they can contain in equilibrium. Whether that's dangerous depends on how much supersaturation exists for how long. Past a point bubbles form. That point is called critical supersaturation. Some researchers believe bubbles are probable after any degree of supersaturation.

Fast ascents may allow too much nitrogen to come out of solution too fast, forming bubbles and decompression problems. One decompression accident report quoted a diver who stated he ascended rapidly to meet a no-decompression time limit, thinking it would reduce his risk of DCS. Such accelerated ascent may increase risk of a decompression problem. It's better to make a slower ascent with slightly more total time.

SUPERSATURATION RATIOS

> *Supersaturation Ratio – Compartment nitrogen tension at depth compared to (divided by) total pressure at the surface or decompression stop. Exceeding the supersaturation ratio produces bubbles or likelihood of bubbles. Each half-time compartment has a different supersaturation ratio.*

Haldane did not distinguish between the point where bubbles form and decompression sickness. His work was symptom based. He found that direct ascent to the surface (one atmosphere absolute) was possible from unlimited time at two atmospheres absolute, or to two from four, without decompression symptoms. He assumed the tolerance to pressure halving held for all compartments. His decompression tables limited supersaturation ratios in all compartments to two. This is now called a 2:1 supersaturation ratio. Today we believe that fast compartments tolerate higher supersaturation ratios than slow compartments before bubbles become a problem. The literature on the whole development of these ratios is confusing. Some look at ratio of internal nitrogen tensions to total ambient pressure, others to ambient partial pressure of nitrogen. Some use nitrogen, others use air. Each arrives at different numbers. We also now know that bubbles often form with no symptoms. M-values, covered next, take the supersaturation concept further and try to define when your compartments have had enough.

Divers aren't the only ones who have to know about supersaturation ratios. When you ascend from land to altitude, ambient pressure drops. Pressure does not drop as much per distance as underwater, because air is lighter than water. You have to go to 18,000 feet before pressure drops to half that of sea level. That's a good thing – you wouldn't want to get decompression sickness every time you took a fast elevator. There have been cases of decompression sickness in flight crews who experienced large, rapid cabin depressurization during a flight emergency (as well as air embolism and ear equalization trauma). Decompression sickness is also a concern in extravehicular travel during space flight. The space shuttle is kept at one atmosphere absolute of regular air. The pressure inside space suits is less than one atmosphere absolute. To get into the suits, astronauts first breathe oxygen to outgas nitrogen.

M-VALUES

> *M-values – Maximum nitrogen (or other inert gas) tensions that various compartments are thought to tolerate before supersaturation produces a harmful amount of bubbles.*

The 2:1 supersaturation ratio for all compartments worked well for the applications for which they were developed, but did not prevent problems as well in other exposures. The US Navy began work to modify the Haldane tables. By the late 1950's, R.D. Workman of the US Naval Experimental Diving Unit (NEDU) systematized work done by others and experimentally determined maximum nitrogen tensions in different compartments before bubbles are thought to form. These maximum tensions are called M-values. (M is for maximum). M-values exist for any inert gas used. M-values in this chapter refer to nitrogen, unless noted.

Decompression tables and computers limit depth and time so no compartment exceeds its M-value at any point during the dive. This is accepted to reduce decompression problems. Bubbles have been found in recreational divers after profiles that don't exceed established limits. M-values are not magic limits that prevent bubbles. Avoid diving the time and depth limits of your tables or computer. The numbers can only approximate what is happening.

M-Value Units. M-values are pressures, so units are pressure units. The unit fsw is used, as it is convenient to have M-values in the same units as the dive for easy comparison.

Different M-Values for Different Compartments. Fast compartments tolerate higher supersaturation ratios than slow compartments, so have higher M-values. According to the US Navy Standard Air Decompression Tables for example, a five minute compartment was empirically observed to tolerate a maximum nitrogen tension at the surface of 104 fsw, a 120 minute compartment, only 52 fsw.

Table 1.2 compares half-time compartments and their corresponding M-values in two models. For perspective, remember that all your compartments start with a nitrogen tension approximately 26 fsw at sea level (79% of 33 fsw).

Table 1.2. Comparison of M-values (fsw) in two different models, the US Navy Standard Air Decompression Tables, and the DSAT RDP. In both, fast compartments are considered to tolerate higher supersaturation ratios than slow tissues, so have higher M-values.

	Half-time ($T_{1/2}$)								
	5	10	20	30	40	50	60	80	120
US Navy	104	88	72	–	56	–	–	54	52
DSAT	99.08	82.68	66.89	59.74	55.73	–	51.44	49.21	46.93

Different M-Values for Different Depths. Each compartment has different M-values for different depths.

Recreational no-stop diving is based on being able to ascend directly to the surface. Your decompression table or computer tells you to surface before any of your compartments reach M-values allowed at the surface. Surface M-values are written M_0, pronounced M sub zero. If compartments would exceed M_0, you make a decompression stop to let your compartments drain down until they are below M_0.

M_{10} is the maximum tension you can build up and get to within 10 feet of the surface, with acceptable risk. If you have built such high nitrogen tensions that you should not ascend as far as the decompression stop at 10 feet, you do a deeper stop to offgas enough to ascend further.

Controlling Compartments. M-Values allow decompression tables and computers to determine depth and time limits for different compartments, then base the limit for the entire body on the compartment that would first reach its maximum. That compartment is called the controlling compartment.

TABLE-BASED AND MODEL-BASED COMPUTERS

Table-Based Computer – Looks up the dive profile against values already determined by a decompression table.

Model-Based Computers – Calculates decompression for the actual depth-time profile in real time.

The many Haldane based decompression computers give their final answer in two ways. A very few look up the dive profile against values that have already been determined by a decompression table. They assign the actual dive profile to a predetermined depth-time profile that is closest. These are called Look-Up or Table-Based Computers. The majority of computers are Model-Based – programmed with the decompression calculation algorithm. They calculate decompression for the actual depth time profile.

CHAPTER 1
PART IV

INTRODUCTION TO
NON-HALDANE MODELS

Some decompression models view gas transport or bubble formation different from the Haldane model. Their development grew from need to reduce decompression problems in dive profiles not covered by the Haldane model, and because several issues in decompression dynamics remain unexplained by existing decompression theory. As mentioned in Part II, the tables are not just number fiddling, but based and adjusted from experience. Concepts behind a few of several non-Haldane models are briefly summarized.

- Statistical Models
- Series Model
- EL Model
- Varying Permeability Model
- Reduced Gradient Bubble Model
- Slab Model

STATISTICAL MODELS

> *Statistical Model – Decompression tables that approach decompression statistically; out of so many dives of a specific type, so many DCS incidents are expected.*

Some decompression models approach decompression statistically, that out of a given number of dives of a specific type, a certain number of DCS incidents is expected. The US Naval Medical Research Institute (NMRI) in Bethesda developed several statistical tables using maximum likelihood calculations developed by Dr. Paul Weathersby.

One table for air diving gives dive profiles with 1% risk of decompression sickness. A second table for air diving has longer profiles with 5% predicted risk. Which profile is chosen depends on priority and length of the dive mission. Other tables use gases other than nitrogen, also profiling dives with 1% or 5% risk. According to decompression physiologist Dr. Bill Hamilton, statistical models are the coming wave in decompression models.

SERIES MODEL

> *Series Model – Decompression model where inert gas is assumed to pass serially from compartment to compartment. Only one compartment is considered exposed to the ambient pressure reached in the blood stream. The Canadian DCIEM tables are calculated with a series model. Also called serial model*

In 1962, researchers D.J. Kidd, a Canadian Navy surgeon, and R.A. Stubbs, a Canadian Air Force scientist, began work to develop a dive computer. They started with a Haldane parallel model and later decided that a series (serial) model better represented the human body.

Decompression tables and computers based on the Haldane model assume that compartments ongas and offgas separately but at the same time directly to and from your blood. The idea of separate, simultaneous, gas transfer is called parallel gas transfer. In a parallel model, no gas transfer is assumed between compartments, Figure 1.9.

It's unlikely that all gas diffuses to and from compartments in parallel. Adjacent compartments are often of different half-times. Higher nitrogen pressure areas reside next to lower pressure areas. Nitrogen would flow from higher to lower pressure areas. Gas transit from compartment to compartment is called series transfer. Only one compartment is considered to be exposed to the ambient pressure reached in the blood stream, Figure 1.10. The phenomenon of serial transfer has been observed in pharmaceuticals. A series model may account for nitrogen transfer as well. According to decompression modeler Dr. Hugh Van Liew of SUNY Buffalo, "Both kinds of model attempt to describe reality. Reality may be more complex than either model."

The first Kidd-Stubbs "computers" were built before microprocessors. Their first model, simulating a parallel model, was made of pipes of different lengths connected with small orifices to simulate gas diffusion into the compartments. The short pipes were fast half-time tissues because they filled quickly. The long pipes were slow tissues, taking longer to fill. A pressure gauge on each pipe showed the pressure within each "compartment." These computers were called pneumatic because the only driving force required was the gas pressure. Their series model took several different forms in the prototypes. Later versions were machined compartments of the same volume connected up by "pneumatic resistors" controlling rate of flow into and out of the compartments.

The two laboratories where Kidd and Stubbs worked (Canadian Forces Institute of Environmental Medicine and the Defence Research Medical Laboratory) merged in 1971 to form DCIEM – the Defence and Civil Institute of Environmental Medicine in Canada. The Kidd-Stubbs computers, first the pneumatic-mechanical, and later, pneumatic-electronic devices were used for much of the experimental diving at DCIEM in the 1970's. As microprocessor and digital technology replaced pneumatic technology, DCIEM converted to a digital microprocessor-controlled computer using the mathematical algorithm from the Kidd-Stubbs series model.

The present DCIEM Kidd-Stubbs tables were developed by the DCIEM group led by Ron Nishi. They use four compartments in a series. These compartments don't have set half-times. Compartments ongas and offgas to each other. Different filling times result for each, depending on depth and conditions.

Parallel Gas Transfer

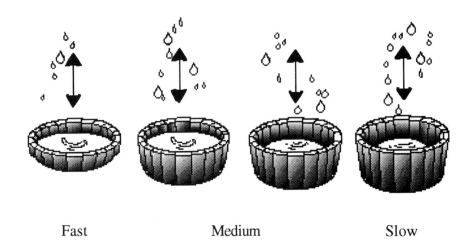

Fast   Medium   Slow

Figure 1.9. Compartments are considered to be exposed separately to ambient pressure from the blood, and ongas and offgas separately to and from your blood. No gas transfer is assumed between compartments. Haldane models assume parallel gas transit.

Series Gas Transfer

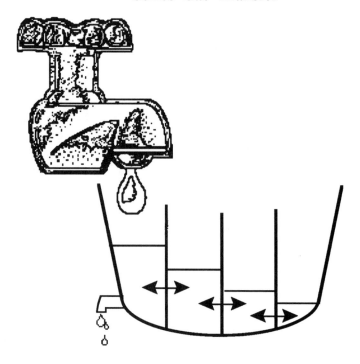

Figure 1.10. Only one compartment is assumed to be exposed to the ambient pressure reached in the blood. Compartments do not have set half-times, and ongas and offgas to each other.

EL MODEL

> *EL Model – Decompression model where inert gas uptake is calculated as exponential (E), and offgassing as linear (L).*

EL stands for Exponential and Linear. The EL model is a variation of the Haldane model. The EL is a parallel model that describes ongassing at exponential rate, as in Haldane models, but as soon as supersaturation occurs, a slower linear offgassing is used, Figure 1.8 (Part III explains these terms). Haldane decompression models calculate ongassing and offgassing at the same exponential rate. Linear offgassing requires longer stays during decompression stops.

The Haldane model assumes no bubble formation on ascent, however it does occur, and when bubbles occur, they slow offgassing. Haldane models then cannot accurately predict offgassing time. This slowed offgassing may produce more bubbles. Another factor changing offgassing dynamics is that blood flow normally changes rapidly all over the body. Slower ascent times using the EL model are believed to limit bubble formation.

Capt. Ed Thalmann of the Naval Experimental Diving Unit (NEDU) and his group developed the EL model as a basis for a US Navy diver-carried computer for combat swimmers.

They found that the profiles generated by the exponential offgassing of the USN tables were not conservative for the depth/time dive profiles they needed.

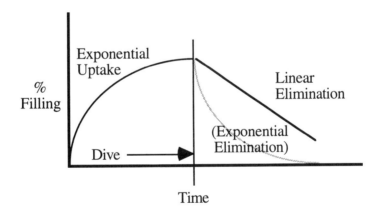

Figure 1.8. Filling and emptying curves for the EL model.

SLAB MODEL

> *The slab model uses one compartment, called a slab, rather than several separate compartments. Gas diffuses through one area of the slab to get to another.*

The slab model describes decompression dynamics in the body using one compartment, called a slab, rather than several separate compartments. Gas diffuses through one area of the slab to get to another.

The fastest area is considered exposed to the ambient pressure of gas in the blood. The slowest, farthest away.

The British Sub-Aqua Club (BSAC) tables use the slab model. They were developed by Dr. Tom R. Hennessy of London.

VARYING PERMEABILITY MODEL

> *Varying Permeability Model – Decompression model limiting bubble size on ascent to a critical volume, and quantity to below a critical number. Also called the Tiny Bubble model.*

Haldane-based tables and computers calculate limits for dives based on eliminating gas that is dissolved in your body, not gas that has come out of solution to form a free gas phase and bubbles. When bubbles form in your body they slow further nitrogen exit by several mechanical and chemical means. To account for free phase bubbles, several bubble models were developed. One is the Varying Permeability Model developed by a group of University of Hawaii researchers led by Drs. Yount and Hoffman. Their work descended from experiments of bubbles in supersaturated gelatin. They believe the size and number of bubbles is important, and that the body can tolerate a certain amount for long periods of time. Their research group is called the Tiny Bubble Group.

They base their model on very small gas phases stable enough to remain bubbles, but small enough to remain in solution. Surface-active molecules on the bubble skin keep them stable. The varying permeability model limits bubble size on ascent to a critical volume, and number to below a critical number, called delta-n, which changes with depth and time. For short decompressions times, bubbles don't have time to grow very large. The model allows many small bubbles. With long decompressions, bubbles have time to get big. The model restricts ascent to only allow a few. Based on this, the model calls for safety stops or shallow swimming, shorter no-stop times, ascent rates not over 60 ft/min, and restrictions on deep repetitive dives, 'spike' (shallow to deep) dives, and muti-day diving. All of these are consistent with conservative table use in general.

REDUCED GRADIENT BUBBLE MODEL (RGBM)

> *Reduced Gradient Bubble Model (RGBM) – Decompression model using reduced surface gradient on repetitive dives.*

Another free phase bubble model is the Reduced Gradient Bubble Model descended from the tiny bubble model described above. It was developed by theoretical physicist Dr. Bruce Wienke, and partly based on the work of Yount and Hoffman. The RGBM reduces the surface gradient on repetitive dives. Surface gradients are much like M-values, where shorter half-times have larger values than longer half-times. Reduced allowable surface gradients shorten no-stop diving time on repetitive dives. The RGBM also tries to account for diving deep after a previous shallow dive, and for multi-level diving.

CHAPTER 1
PART V

DIVING WITH GASES
OTHER THAN AIR

Diving with gas mixtures other than regular air is not a new idea. Commercial, scientific, and military applications have long used helium, nitrogen, and oxygen in varying concentrations, and occasionally hydrogen, argon, and neon combinations with oxygen for depth and time exposures not suitable for regular air.

Breathing mixes have high technical, equipment, and training requirements. Get training through mixed gas training organizations before you try it.

- Oxygen Enriched Air
- Heliox
- Trimix
- Gas Switching

OXYGEN ENRICHED AIR

Oxygen Enriched Air (OEA) – Breathing mixtures with higher oxygen percent or fraction and lower nitrogen fraction than regular air. Used to reduce decompression sickness risk on the same profile as an air dive, or to extend bottom time with similar risk. Because of increased oxygen, OEA mixes are not used to extend depth range. Also called Enriched Air Nitrox (EAN).

The term nitrox historically referred to mixtures with less than 21% oxygen, commonly used in habitats and saturation situations to avoid oxygen toxicity problems. When oxygen percentage is above the normal 21% of regular air it is called enriched air nitrox (EAN or EANx) and/or oxygen enriched air (OEA). All the terms are often interchanged, which is sometimes confusing. Two EAN mixes are currently popular. NOAA Nitrox I, called EAN32, has 32% oxygen and 68% nitrogen. NOAA Nitrox II, or EAN36, is 36% oxygen, 64% nitrogen.

Mixtures with more oxygen and less nitrogen than air incur less nitrogen uptake, compared with air. Compared with air, you can dive longer, or increase your safety margin for the same profile.

Equivalent Air Depth (EAD). Equivalent Air Depth (EAD) is the depth defined by the partial pressure of nitrogen you breathe, rather than your actual depth. For a mix with less nitrogen than air, EAD is shallower than if you were breathing air. Understanding EAD helps you see how less nitrogen allows you to dive longer or deeper, with nitrogen tensions as if at shallower depths, Table 1.3.

EAD is calculated with a partial pressure equation:

$$EAD \ (fsw) = \frac{(1\text{-}F_{O_2}) \ (D+33)}{0.79} - 33$$

$(1\text{-}F_{O_2})$ is the fraction of nitrogen, because F_{O_2} is the fraction of oxygen, so subtracting it from 1 gives what's left, or nitrogen.
D   is your actual depth in feet of sea water (fsw).
$(D+33)$ adds 33 fsw (for the atmosphere) to the measured depth to get absolute depth.
    Dividing by 0.79, the fraction of nitrogen in air, gives the equivalent absolute depth.
    Subtracting 33 fsw gives the measured depth to use in dive tables.

Table 1.3. Equivalent air depth (EAD) examples. EAD is shallower than actual depth because there is less nitrogen in the mix.

Breathing Mix	Actual Depth (fsw)	Equivalent Air Depth (EAD) with respect to nitrogen (fsw)
Air	80	80
EAN32 with 32% O_2	80	64
EAN32 with 32% O_2	100	81.5
EAN36 with 36% O_2	80	58.5
EAN36 with 36% O_2	100	75

EAN mixes are not used to extend depth range. The higher oxygen content creates risk of oxygen toxicity at shallower depths than air. The maximum operating depth (MOD) for nitrox is shallower than for air. MOD varies with application and work load. Maximum operating depth (varying with conditions) for EAN32 is approximately 130 feet. For EAN36, 110 feet. Oxygen toxicity, and variables affecting maximum operating depth are described in Chapter 5, Diving Injuries. EAN diving requires additional training specifically for nitrox.

Enriched air nitrox diving uses special nitrox decompression tables and computers. Because nitrox tables are currently based on the same Haldane model as many air decompression tables, EAD can also figure the equivalent depth with respect to nitrogen to apply regular air decompression tables to enriched air nitrox dives.

Calculating EAD is a good mental exercise on land, but it is simpler and less prone to calculation error to use tables for nitrox diving where EAD is done for you.

Enriched Air Nitrox Misconceptions:

• A misconception that has made the rounds of divers is that decompression sickness from an enriched air nitrox dive is somehow less serious, or that enriched air nitrox bubbles in the body are less injurious than those from air diving. There is no good evidence that the bubbles or consequences differ in each.

• Breathing enriched air nitrox does not rule out hyperbaric chamber treatment in case of decompression sickness. The increased oxygen would not add appreciably to risk of oxygen toxicity during chamber treatment. Treatment for DCS after diving with EAN is the same as after diving with air.

• Divers often ask if oxygen has mood-elevating qualities. Such questions stem from reports of feeling better after enriched air nitrox diving than air diving, and after oxygen treatment for diving injury. There is good evidence that oxygen does not cause euphoria, but often relieves physical symptoms, which could improve spirits. High nitrogen burden may contribute to fatigue after dives. Extreme fatigue that is due to bubbles is a type of decompression illness. Reducing the nitrogen burden with more oxygen reduces the likelihood of nitrogen related fatigue and feeling unwell. Studies of breathing 100% oxygen before and after exercise at sea level show no physical mood-boosting effects, although a percentage of experimental subjects who were told they were breathing oxygen, but received room air, reported elevated mood. Football players often breathe oxygen believing it will help them, but several studies show oxygen has no beneficial physical effect before, during, or after short, intense efforts such as football. Mood effect of oxygen under hyperbaric pressures is less well studied.

HELIOX

> *Heliox – Mixture of helium and oxygen. Helium replaces some or all nitrogen, and part of the oxygen. Reduces or eliminates nitrogen narcosis on deep dives, and allows oxygen level to be controlled to reduce risk of oxygen toxicity.*

Originally only in military, commercial, and scientific diving realms, very deep dives are now done by well-trained, well-equipped, private citizens for fun. These dives often use helium-oxygen mixes, called heliox. Helium replaces part of the oxygen in air, and some or all of the nitrogen. Less oxygen reduces oxygen toxicity. Helium causes less narcosis than nitrogen (some say none), meaning it can be used at depths that would incapacitate a diver with nitrogen narcosis. Helium is easier to breath than nitrogen at depths of hundreds of feet, reducing the work of breathing that would otherwise be a substantial hindrance and health hazard. Helium causes Donald Duck voice. Applications where the diver must communicate with others by speech use helium speech unscramblers. Use of heliox requires special heliox training.

Helium Misconceptions:

• Helium does not necessarily reduce decompression time. Helium does not dissolve as well in your tissues because it is naturally less soluble than nitrogen.

However, the helium that dissolves passes into your tissues faster than nitrogen. Technically speaking, helium is less soluble but more diffusible than nitrogen, making helium half-times over 2½ times faster than nitrogen half-times. According to decompression physiologist Dr. Bill Hamilton, ascent after saturation diving is faster with helium than nitrogen, everything else being the same, but since helium loads faster, decompression may be faster with nitrogen than helium for short exposures. All the variables make it complex.

• It is not the case that Donald Duck voice is due to the vocal folds (cords) vibrating faster in helium than in air. Two main reasons for voice change are speed of sound and impedance match. These two don't account for everything, but do account for most of it. The main consideration is the different speed of sound in different gases. Sound travels faster in low molecular weight gases like helium. The second factor is the shift in low frequency vocal resonances in gases of different density. The shift results in the nasal voice of deep chamber dives, but that is different from Donald Duck voice. The fundamental pitch of vocal fold (cord) vibration doesn't change with density of the breathing gas. Dr. David Doolette of Australia points out that if it did, the Donald Duck voice would gradually lower to normal at depth while breathing helium, and your normal voice would rise to Donald Duck pitch when going to altitude while breathing air.

• There is much discussion whether you get colder breathing helium than breathing air. Helium has greater thermal conductivity than air. Undeniably, you lose more heat when surrounded by helium than by air, because heat conductance is the major factor in skin heat loss. Therefore helium is not used in dry suits. However, respiratory heat loss depends on heat capacity, and not at all on conductance. The thermal capacity of helium per gram is higher than that of air. However, there are fewer grams of helium for the same volume breathed because it is far less dense, making thermal capacity less compared to the same volume of air. Less heat would be lost breathing helium, so it should not chill you to breathe, as commonly thought. In a helmet or full face mask, your face may feel cool, making it hard to separate out the lesser loss through breathing. Depth affects gas density, and so heat loss through the breathing medium, and to be more confusing, you also need to account for interactions of respiratory heat loss through convection and evaporation. With helium you may also be more aware of the cold that is so common in diving, than when dulled by narcosis while breathing non-helium mixes. Remember too, it is generally not feasible to breathe air at depths where helium is used, so hard to compare in actual use. The short answer seems to be that breathing mixtures of helium at depths encountered by technical divers does not result in greater cooling than breathing air. Helium feels colder to your skin than air, but it carries away less heat when you breathe it.

TRIMIX

> *Trimix – Mixture of three gases for diving beyond the air range, usually helium, oxygen, and nitrogen.*

Trimix is a helium-nitrogen-oxygen breathing mix. Helium replaces some of the nitrogen and oxygen to reduce narcosis and oxygen toxicity, as explained above in the section on heliox.

Because helium is expensive, some nitrogen is kept in the mix, popularizing trimix over heliox for many but not all deep pleasure dives. Because of narcosis that may occur, divers using trimix must consider depth and conditions to determine suitability of nitrox for their dive. These considerations and others are covered in special training that divers need before trying trimix.

Another application for a trimixture is extreme depth diving. At depths past 600 feet or so, pressure begins to exert an excitatory effect on the nervous system called High Pressure Nervous Syndrome (HPNS). Pressure itself seems to cause HPNS, not helium, as sometimes thought. Adding a small amount (5-10%) of nitrogen back into the mix reduces HPNS. Nitrogen is a neural depressant at high pressure. Some consider trimix the choice over heliox for deeper work, but others don't agree.

GAS SWITCHING

> *Gas Switching – Changing the breathing gas during a dive, sometimes several times, to keep gas partial pressures within acceptable ranges and/or assist inert gas elimination. Requires much training and logistics.*

Divers can't breathe the same mix at all depths during deep diving. Divers switch from higher percentage oxygen mixes during descent, to lower percentage "bottom mix" to keep PO_2 within acceptable range. They switch again to higher "travel" mixes during ascent, then sometimes higher mixes again for decompression hangs. Such switching require training, complicated and large equipment set-ups, gas logistics, and special decompression calculations, often custom "cut" by decompression table experts.

Hypoxic and Normoxic. Gas mixes like heliox and trimix used at great depth must have a lower oxygen percentage than regular air to reduce risk of oxygen toxicity. Sometimes PO_2 is so low it would not keep you alive if you breathed it on land. That is called a hypoxic mix. At depth, the increased partial pressure provides enough oxygen molecules to support your life.

Consider a hypoxic mix containing only 2% oxygen. It would not keep you alive on land. At 313.5 feet, PO_2 rises to the equivalent of a 21% mixture of air ($PO_2 = 0.21$ ATA). A 5% oxygen mix, also too low to sustain your life on land, becomes normoxic at 105.6 feet. Normoxic means that the partial pressure approximates that at sea level, 0.21 ATA, regardless of true fraction. Divers doing profiles so deep they require gas switching must plan their equipment to get the right mix for their depth. A bottom mix with low O_2 will suffocate you when shallow. A higher O_2 travel or decompression mix can result in oxygen toxicity if used when deep.

Decompression Mixes. Decompression mixes are high oxygen mixes of varying percentages up to 100%. They are used during decompression stops of deep and technical dives to reduce decompression "hang" times and risk of decompression sickness. They are also called intermediate mixes and hang mixes.

High oxygen mixes increase the nitrogen offgassing gradient, to reduce decompression hang times and risk of decompression sickness. They are not for use at depth. Tragedies have occurred when divers mistook their high oxygen mix regulator for the backup regulator at depth, and suffered an oxygen toxicity convulsion.

For any breathing mix other than compressed air, make sure every tank you use is analyzed for oxygen content. Changes in temperature and pressure when filling tanks can change the mix. Oxygen content may not be what you expect. Read about ideal gas behavior in the glossary.

Without training, it is risky to dive with special gas mixtures. Get good training before you try non-air mix diving.

CONCLUSION

There is much more to decompression theory than presented here. This chapter will get you started with the basics. Whether you use decompression equations or not, it is helpful to understand the concepts behind them. A good understanding of what is known allows you to make better decisions about decompression tables and computers to dive more safely. You will also be better able to spot misinformation.

The object of all decompression tables and computers is to maximize diving time, minimize physiologic problems of breathing oxygen, nitrogen, and other gases, and do it reliably which means repeatedly with similar results. Decompression tables and computers vary on a continuum of conservative to liberal. No tables or computers are risk free. In decompression theory, as in pharmacology or any other physiologic issue involving dose of a substance and its response, we do not yet have the perfect way to describe nitrogen leaving your body, thereby completely preventing decompression sickness. In decompression theory, more is unknown than known. The models that are the basis for current decompression computers and tables are rough approximations of the complex biologic system that is your body.

Many decompression sickness cases result from improperly using tables and computers. Major considerations in your risk are depth, time, and ascent rate (Chapter 5). You can easily control these, and use your tables and computers conservatively to increase your safety margin. The responsibility to use tables and computers properly is yours.

CHAPTER 2

IMMERSION EFFECTS

The capacity of water immersion to cause bodily changes has been known for a long time. Over three thousand years of medical writings of Persians, Hindus, Greeks, Egyptians, and Chinese have documented various effects of immersion. In the past three hundred years, scientists have collected data explaining the physiology behind these varied effects.

Scuba diving involves immersion in varied conditions: full-body immersion, head-out immersion, with exercise, cold exposure, breathing different gas densities and pressures, and full body exposure to pressure. Snorkeling and free diving add breath-holding. Each component has interesting physiologic effects, singly and combined with other components. Two major results of immersion are the dive reflex, which occurs without you being aware of it, and the P Phenomenon, which is more apparent. Both have been heavily studied.

- The Dive Reflex
- The P Phenomenon

CHAPTER 2
PART I

THE DIVE REFLEX

When you go underwater, your heart rate usually decreases, and blood vessels of your arms and legs constrict. Blood leaves your arms and legs and shunts into the central area of your body. Several misconceptions surround these effects, collectively called the dive reflex. When a child survives 30 minutes under icy water was the dive reflex responsible? Does it lower metabolism? Does it protect your brain against low oxygen states? The answer seems to be no to all three.

- What Is the Dive Reflex?
- Different In Humans And Marine Animals
- Role In Humans
- Individual Variation
- Mechanisms
- Preventing Problems From The Dive Reflex

WHAT IS THE DIVE REFLEX?

The dive reflex consists of decreased heart rate and blood flow to the limbs. It is a cardiovascular response to immersion. Other associated responses are not part of the dive reflex. For instance, although breathing rate often slows during scuba diving at depth, it is not part of the dive reflex, it is due to other influences: Increased partial pressure of oxygen when breathing compressed air at depth reduces the need to maintain normal rate of ventilation, and at great depths, the increased work of breathing dense gas causes your body to slow breathing rate. Divers also sometimes attribute slowed breathing rate to inert gas narcosis, particularly in warm water narcosis, although studies do not bear this out.

Manifestations of the Human Dive Reflex

- Limb blood vessels constrict, reducing limb blood flow
- Decreased heart rate

DIFFERENT IN HUMANS AND MARINE ANIMALS

In both humans and marine mammals, the dive reflex reduces heart rate and limb blood flow. Yet the human dive reflex is different in several ways from the dive reflex in marine animals. The extent of difference between human and animal response to immersion led dive reflex researcher Paulev to state that it may be inappropriate to extend the term "dive reflex" to human response to immersion.

Not Protective in Humans. In aquatic mammals like whales and seals, the dive reflex plays a major role in conserving oxygen. Some whales are known to submerge for up to 120 minutes, elephant seals even longer. The dive reflex seems to have developed far back in evolution as a protective measure in animals. Heart rate even drops in fish when they are removed from the water.

Unlike marine mammals, humans don't seem to retain an oxygen-conserving benefit during immersion. In cold water, although heart rate decreases in humans, that does not reduce metabolism or oxygen demands of the body's vital organs. Just the opposite. One of the immediate responses to cold immersion is increased metabolism and oxygen consumption. Metabolism increases as an immediate adaptation to dealing with the work of staying warm in the cold.

Breath Holding. Human breath-holding time is normally very short compared to those of aquatic mammals. Human breath-holding time is also usually shorter in cold water than in air or in warm water, more evidence of the lack of protective effect against hypoxia. Marine mammals like whales, seals, dolphins, and sea otters also have anatomic variations allowing them to collapse their lungs with submersion, displacing air away from pulmonary blood to reinforced upper airway passages. This protects them from oxygen toxicity, nitrogen narcosis, and decompression sickness. Humans typically inspire deeply before submersion. Humans can get decompression sickness with deep, repeated free-diving because air remains in the lung, exposed to the pulmonary blood at pressure.

Heart Rate and Limb Blood Flow. In seals, heart rate drops to about 10% of rates on land, and blood flow to their flippers nearly stops. Human heart rate can decrease to half that of normal land values — from 70-80 beats per minute (bpm) on land, for example, to 35-40 bpm during immersion, although individual variation is wide. Humans constrict blood vessels in the limbs, but not nearly to such an extent as aquatic mammals. Also unlike animals, human heart rate and limb blood flow decreases as water temperature decreases.

Arrhythmias. Humans normally have occasional irregular heart beats, called arrhythmias. These usually do no harm, and are not noticed. Incidence of arrhythmias increases during cold immersion, increased blood returning to the chest, called venous return, and when heart rate slows greatly. In extreme cases, very low heart rate from the dive reflex, or arrhythmias from any factors during immersion, such as low heart rate, cold, and increased venous return, can result in blackout or death.

ROLE IN HUMANS

Occasional cases of human survival after very cold water near-drowning do not seem to be due to the dive reflex. Extreme cold exposure in an unconscious, non-breathing person is the likely mechanism behind the reduced metabolism that permits survival in occasional cases. The purpose of the dive reflex in human divers seems to be to reduce heat loss through blood vessel constriction in the limbs.

Role Of The Dive Reflex In Humans

- The dive reflex does not seem to reduce your body's oxygen demands. In conscious humans, cold water immersion raises oxygen consumption due to the work of keeping warm.

- The dive reflex does not increase breath-holding time in cold water. Cold immersion reduces it compared to non-immersion in neutral temperature.

- The purpose of the dive reflex in human divers seems to be to reduce heat loss by constricting blood vessels in the limbs.

INDIVIDUAL VARIATION

Human cardiovascular reaction to diving varies among conditions and individuals. Some people respond profoundly, others not at all. Those unfamiliar with the water may override the dive reflex with a fear response that increases heart rate, although considerable drop in heart rate has been observed in good and poor swimmers. The dive reflex even blunts the heart rate rise from underwater exercise.

MECHANISMS

A flurry of dive reflex studies appeared in the 1960's and early 70's. Many centered on the largest fleet of commercial divers in the world – the women breath-hold divers of the Orient, the Ama. After more than a decade of little research, studies are resurfacing, particularly by the military interested in cold water operations. Military and Ama studies have isolated several interacting and competing influences.

Temperature. Cold water reduces heart rate in at least two ways. Cold receptors, particularly those around the mouth and nose send a direct signal to lower heart rate. Heart rate also drops as an indirect result of blood vessels constricting in the limbs. Blood shunts away from the limbs into the thorax, increasing blood volume returning to the heart, called venous return. More blood returning to the heart makes the heart pump more back out with each beat. This amount is called stroke volume. Your body likes to keep total amount of blood pumped out per minute constant at rest. When stroke volume increases, it causes a reflex drop in heart rate.

The dive reflex becomes stronger as the water temperature drops, but only up to a point. Very cold water can increase heart rate. At around 5°C (41°F) a pain response to the cold raises heart rate. Warm and hot water increase heart rate. Water at body temperature is usually considered thermoneutral, and has no effect.

Immersion. Immersion increases the volume of blood and fluids returning from lower limbs to thorax. Increased venous return increases stroke volume, reflexively decreasing heart rate, as described above in Temperature. How does immersion do this?

When you are standing up on land, a portion of your circulating blood volume pools in the veins of your legs because of gravity. With leg movement, contracting muscles squeeze the vessels, helping pump blood back up. You also have valves in your veins that help keep blood from falling back down. Still, gravity works against you, your veins are distensible, and air pressure around your legs is not enough to counter it, so blood tends to pool. (If your blood vessels were lead pipes, you would not have pooling, no matter how great the gravity, but you would have other, more serious problems.) Water pressure counteracts venous pooling. See Venous Pooling in the glossary.

It is often assumed, since pressure increases with distance under water, that in a person upright in the water, greater water pressure on the feet compared to the head squeezes blood headward from the feet. But, blood centralization (increased venous return) occurs upside down underwater with feet above the head. Blood is not squeezed from head to feet. Centralization also occurs when lying down in the water. It is not the pressure gradient from foot to head that squeezes blood upward. It is the water pressure nearly matching the pressure increase down the column of your own blood vessels, removing venous pooling (See Mechanical Factors, Part II of this chapter, and Hydrostatic Pressure in the glossary).

Full immersion is not required for the dive reflex. Head-out immersion induces the reflex, although less than when the face is also immersed. Some researchers submerged only the subjects' feet and found heart rate did not change, but peripheral blood flow decreased. Another study progressively lowered subjects on a platform and found heart rate dropped as water level rose. The rising water level increasingly counteracted leg blood pooling, increasing blood flowing back to the heart, which increased venous return, and reflexively lowered heart rate.

Face immersion alone also triggers the reflex. In one study, just covering the face of a human subject with a wet, cold face cloth was sufficient. Other studies concluded that specific neural receptor sites around the nose and mouth are more responsive than other parts of the face.

Wetting. If face immersion alone triggers the dive reflex, what is it about face immersion? Is wetting with water a factor? One investigation compared subjects with wetted faces to other subjects whose faces were covered with a plastic film during face immersion. The film prevented wetting but allowed cold transmission. Other studies tried insulated coverings. Still more studies looked at immersion with and without face masks. Cold was more a factor than wetting. Wetting was important because water conducts heat. It's still unclear if wetting is or is not a factor in warmer water.

Breath-Holding. Breath-holding by itself lowers heart rate. In one study, subjects breathed normally but the oxygen and carbon dioxide levels in their breathing mixture were changed to simulate breath-holding. Heart rate slowed with both increasing carbon dioxide and decreasing oxygen levels. In another study, subjects held their breath but were artificially maintained with normal levels of oxygen and carbon dioxide in their blood. Heart rate dropped. It was concluded that stretch receptors in the lung are involved, because stopping breathing movement contributes to the dive reflex.

Partial Pressure of the Breathing Gas. Depth of submersion has not been found to be a factor in the dive reflex in breath-hold divers. Studies of subjects breathing compressed air found increased gas partial pressure with depth decreases heart rate, a phenomenon different from the dive reflex, called hyperbaric bradycardia (the word root *brady* means slow, *cardia* refers to the heart). Further work revealed that both increased oxygen and nitrogen partial pressures participated in heart rate slowing, as well as increased density of the breathing gas.

Other Factors. Researchers have harassed subjects to look at the contribution of emotion. Some studies found an anticipatory drop in heart rate when human subjects knew they were about to submerge. This interesting effect was also noted in a sea lion trained to dip his face in a pan of water on command. Some studies conclude that the reflex dies out with increasing age, others find the opposite. A maneuver commonly, though incorrectly, called the Valsalva maneuver (see the glossary for explanation) has components that both raise and lower heart rate. Divers sometimes use the Valsalva maneuver to equalize pressure in their middle ear when descending to prevent ear pressure injury. There is also a difference if subjects were breathing in or out when breath holding commenced for testing.

What's Not Related To The Dive Reflex? Some things don't affect the dive reflex. One is body position underwater. Whether you're head up or head down underwater does not alter the response. On land if you lie down or turn upside down, gravity greatly increases venous return which lowers heart rate. Early dive reflex studies of face immersion had subjects lean forward to put their face in a pan of water. When the heart rate decreased it was incorrectly concluded that posture was a factor in heart rate decrease during the dive reflex. When studies were conducted with subjects completely submerged, regardless of posture, it was found that buoyancy underwater negates the gravity effect to pool blood volume in the legs. The dive reflex is also unrelated to the *oculocardiac reflex* in which heart rate slows upon pressing the eyeball.

PREVENTING PROBLEMS FROM THE DIVE REFLEX

Sudden vasoconstriction, decrease in heart rate, increase in the volume of the heart from increased venous return, and occurrence of abnormal heart rhythms are not well tolerated by everyone's cardiac system, particularly older males and in colder water.

- Avoid diving in "all at once" – get in slowly

- Try gently wetting your face and hands before you get in

- Wear thermal protection

- Keep in good cardiovascular shape. Get regular checkups that include cardiac evaluation at rest and during exercise

Factors In The Dive Reflex

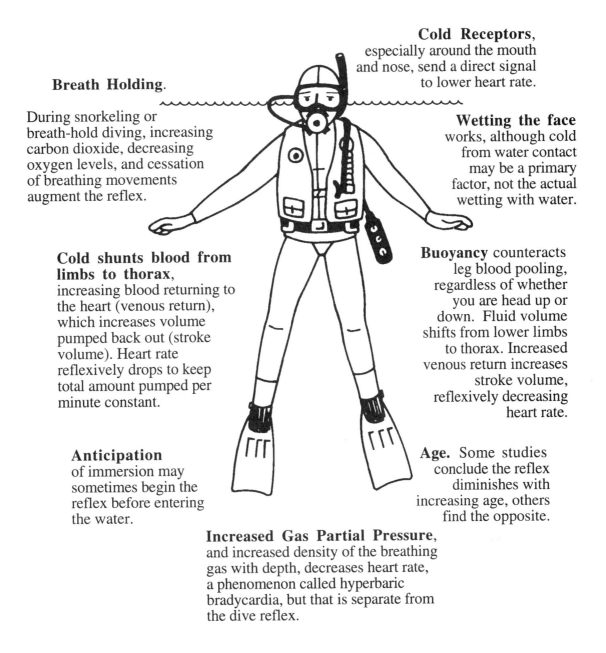

Cold Receptors, especially around the mouth and nose, send a direct signal to lower heart rate.

Breath Holding.

During snorkeling or breath-hold diving, increasing carbon dioxide, decreasing oxygen levels, and cessation of breathing movements augment the reflex.

Wetting the face works, although cold from water contact may be a primary factor, not the actual wetting with water.

Cold shunts blood from limbs to thorax, increasing blood returning to the heart (venous return), which increases volume pumped back out (stroke volume). Heart rate reflexively drops to keep total amount pumped per minute constant.

Buoyancy counteracts leg blood pooling, regardless of whether you are head up or down. Fluid volume shifts from lower limbs to thorax. Increased venous return increases stroke volume, reflexively decreasing heart rate.

Anticipation of immersion may sometimes begin the reflex before entering the water.

Age. Some studies conclude the reflex diminishes with increasing age, others find the opposite.

Increased Gas Partial Pressure, and increased density of the breathing gas with depth, decreases heart rate, a phenomenon called hyperbaric bradycardia, but that is separate from the dive reflex.

Figure 2.1. Several factors influence the dive reflex.

SUMMARY

Heart rate and limb blood flow decrease from many factors resulting from cool or cold water immersion. The dive reflex is different in humans than in animals. It has not been shown to be useful to humans for protection from hypoxia, for extension of breath-holding time in cold water, or to aid survival after cold-water near drowning. The role of reduced limb blood flow in humans seems to be to reduce heat loss to protect from cold. Heart rate slows for two main reasons: a direct response of cold receptors in the skin, particularly around the nose and mouth, and from increased blood returning to the heart. Venous return to the heart increases from cold-induced blood vessel constriction in the limbs, and because buoyancy reduces blood pooling in the lower limbs, regardless of whether you are head up or head down. Breath holding, exercise, anticipation of immersion, partial pressure of the breathing gas, and temperature all act and interact in the dive reflex. Arrhythmias may occur with cold immersion, which may be benign or serious. Keep in good cardiovascular shape to help prepare for the bodily changes occurring with immersion.

CHAPTER 2
PART II

THE P PHENOMENON:
WHY DOES DIVING MAKE YOU HAVE TO "GO"?

"James Crook of Long Acre, had dropsy, jaundice, palsy, rheumatism, and an inveterate pain in his back. In three immersions, the swelling of his legs sunk, so did the pain of his back, as did the jaundice, blowing from his nose a great quantity of bilious yellow matter. From the rigidity and the pressure of the fluid we may account for his pissing more than he drank."

— A. Sutherland, 1764

Since Sutherland's 18th century experiment, the capacity of immersion to increase urine output, politely termed diuresis (rhymes with 'try-a-thesis'), has undergone intense scientific scrutiny. The resulting knowledge helps explain blood volume regulation in renal (kidney) and cardiovascular disease states, the effects of extended commercial and scientific diving missions, and weightlessness during space travel. It's also a topic of intrigue to scuba divers who want to know why diving makes you have to go.

- Why Does It Occur?
- Mechanical Factors
- Chemical Factors
- Environmental Factors
- Personal Factors
- Factors Unknown
- Handling Diuresis
- Rehydrating Underwater

WHY DOES IT OCCUR?

Due to its effect, immersion diuresis has been called the P Phenomenon or PP for short. The P Phenomenon is usually explained by the capacity of immersion to shift blood away from the legs to the chest (thorax). Volume detectors in the heart notice the increase in fluid and, to normalize volume, signal your body to move some fluid out.

Does the fluid shift from the legs explain everything? A study attempted to answer that by comparing amputees who had lost both legs at the hip with non-amputees during immersion. Diuresis was mostly accounted for by leg volumes, but not entirely. There is more to it than that. Stand on your head. Or lie on your back with your feet up. Blood also shifts away from your legs without the immediate event that accompanies immersion. What else is going on?

MECHANICAL FACTORS

Upright Position. More diuresis occurs in a person immersed in water up to the neck than up to the hips. Many divers state that because pressure increases with depth, greater water pressure on the legs compared to the upper body squeezes blood volume upward. That is contradicted by the fact that diuresis occurs when horizontal in the water, and during microgravity during space flight, two conditions where there is no difference between the pressure on the head and feet. Diuresis also occurs upside down underwater, where the water pressure difference, called hydrostatic gradient, is reversed. Blood is not squeezed into the feet. What else might be involved?

Negative Pressure Breathing. When you sit in a tub of water up to your neck, air pressure at your mouth is lower than water pressure on your chest. Breathing in against lower pressure at your mouth than chest is called negative pressure breathing. The feeling is like trying to drink through a straw. It takes a bit of effort to inhale. Many effects occur from breathing against such resistance. One is blood drawn into the chest area, for a number of reasons, resulting in diuresis to offset the extra fluid.

When you breathe underwater from a scuba regulator, negative pressure breathing is slight, with less, if any effect. The single-hose, two-stage regulator in use today has the second stage at your mouth level. The second stage is designed to deliver air at the same pressure as water surrounding your mouth, so you can breathe easily. When you are upright in the water, your mouth is higher than your chest, so this pressure is slightly less than surrounding pressure on your chest. A slight negative pressure breathing develops, depending on how easy-breathing your regulator model. If you turn upside down during scuba diving, the second stage of your regulator delivers air to your mouth at greater pressure than the ambient pressure on your chest. The resulting positive pressure breathing reverses the complicated processes that drew blood into the thorax with negative pressure breathing. Thorax blood volume decreases, slightly reducing diuresis.

The effect of negative pressure breathing during scuba diving is small, and diuresis occurring while upside down underwater is still left unexplained, along with that occurring in any position in a space vehicle during zero gravity. What else could be involved?

Reduced Effect Of Gravity. Gravity is not reduced when you're underwater. Gravity still acts in full, but due to buoyancy, its effects on your blood volume are mostly counteracted. In space the pull of gravity is weak, so blood does not pool.

When you stand up on land, blood pools in your legs because of gravity, and because your veins (much more so than arteries) can expand to hold more blood. Less blood flows back to your heart when you stand up than lie down, because some blood stays a while in your legs. If you measure blood pressure in your arms and legs while lying down, they are about equal. When you stand up on land, blood pressure is higher in your legs because of the weight of blood in the vessels above. Air pressure can't counteract it, so you get pooling. Microgravity in space removes the increased blood pressure in the legs, whereas underwater, it is still there, but immersion counteracts it. See Venous Pooling in the Glossary.

Astronauts and mission control scientists refer to the headward fluid volume shift during space flight in a technical and scientific manner. They call it the "Fat-Face-Chicken-Legs-Effect."

Figure 2.2. In the microgravity of space, and buoyancy under water, blood doesn't pool in the legs as it does on land. Volume increases in the thorax, contributing to diuresis.

Since pressure increases with distance under water, it is often mistakenly stated that this hydrostatic gradient squeezes blood headward from the feet. It is the blood pressure equalization effect, not any progressive squeezing, that increases thorax blood volume, and subsequently diuresis. Reduced leg blood pooling even occurs upside down; the hydrostatic gradient does not squeeze blood into the feet. "Pressure of the surrounding water" does not mean that blood is squeezed up, but that you cancel the venous pooling effect, which is the lower blood vessels stretching from outward pressure on the vessel walls, uncompensated by air pressure. In water, this outward pressure is almost exactly canceled by inward pressure of the surrounding water (See Immersion Mechanisms, Part I of this chapter, and Hydrostatic Pressure in the glossary).

CHEMICAL FACTORS

This part may look technical, but it's not hard. The blood centralization just described, causes your body to release chemicals that produce and regulate the diuresis. These chemicals also regulate the excretion of sodium that occurs, called natriuresis (nay-tree-you-REE'-sis), and excretion of potassium, called kaliuresis (ka-lee-you-REE'-sis). Chemical factors are an interesting part of the story. They are summarized below, with more detail in the glossary for the curious.

Antidiuretic Hormone. One of the main chemicals of the body for controlling fluid output volume is a hormone called vasopressin. One action of vasopressin is to concentrate and decrease fluid volume output. Vasopressin's common name is antidiuretic hormone (ADH), because it suppresses diuresis. ADH is important in daily life so you don't dry out. Immersion usually cuts back ADH secretion. Without the suppressive influence of ADH, diuresis increases, at least temporarily.

Another familiar influence suppresses ADH with similar effect – strong alcohol. Less concentrated alcohols like beer have limited effect on ADH. Alcohol is covered in Chapter 7 Part IV, Fluid Replacement.

ANF. Another chemical is more important to diuresis during immersion than ADH. When immersion shifts blood volume centrally, the upper chambers of your heart, called atria, distend because of the extra blood flowing into them.

To reduce all this extra volume, the atrial cells secrete a substance that increases diuresis. It also suppresses thirst, increases natriuresis, and releases a counterbalancing set of chemicals that fine-tune blood volume regulation. Because it is secreted in the atria, and is a major factor in natriuresis, scientists creatively call it atrial natriuretic factor, or ANF for short. Because ANF is a protein molecule called a peptide, it is alternately called atrial natriuretic peptide (ANP).

Renin-Angiotensin-Aldosterone System. This important system counterbalances the ANF-ADH system, and is the main agent to help keep too much sodium and water from making their escape.

When your kidney senses reduced blood flow from fluid loss or reduced blood pressure, it sends out an enzyme called renin to start a cascade of events to fix the problem. Renin makes a substance that makes another substance called angiotensin. Angiotensin constricts blood vessels raising blood pressure. In only a few minutes the increased blood pressure stimulates your nearby adrenal gland to secrete a hormone called aldosterone (al-DOSS'-ter-own). Aldosterone tells the kidney to save sodium so you can keep more water. The renin-angiotensin-aldosterone system makes sure you don't go overboard losing water in normal day-to-day activities. Immersion suppresses this system, causing diuresis. Decreased fluid and sodium from diuresis and natriuresis stimulates the system to try to restrict this loss, in a continuing feedback cycle.

ENVIRONMENTAL FACTORS

Time of Day. Diuresis is higher during the day than at night. Suppression of diuresis at night is a helpful thing your body does to let you get a night's sleep, immersed or otherwise. Immersion experiments have looked into circadian variation (regular change over each 24 hour cycle) in ANF that may inhibit diuresis at night. These experiments find that variations in ANF don't explain all differences. Time of day is probably a minor factor in diving diuresis.

Fluid Density. Salt water, being denser than fresh water, slightly increases buoyancy and the diuretic effect of fluid shifting (increased density enhances the pressure equalization effect, described earlier in Reduced Effect of Gravity). Density, like time of day, is a minor factor in the magnitude of the P Phenomenon.

Temperature. Temperature is a big contributor. Not much diuresis occurs in hot water, such as in a hot bath, if blood vessels expand in your arms and legs in response to the heat. This peripheral vasodilation shifts blood to your limbs and reduces thoracic blood volume, so there is less stimulus for diuresis.

With cold water immersion so common in diving, vasoconstriction shifts blood away from your limbs toward the center of your body. When added to the other effects of immersion you feel the need in a big way. Temperature is such an important contributor that you can feel the effect when stepping into a cool shower with no immersion at all.

PERSONAL FACTORS

Hydration. If you are not well hydrated your body decreases water loss. Deliberate dehydration to reduce the P Phenomenon is not recommended. Staying well hydrated is important to diving health.

Age. More and faster diuresis occurs in older (62-74) compared to younger subjects (21-28) in experiments of age and immersion, even with the same central blood shift.

Emotion. Fear, apprehension, or other emotional stress from difficult or unknown conditions during a dive, add to neural signals to the kidney, increasing output. The signals are the catecholamines called norepinephrine and epinephrine, your body's chemical message transmitters, explained in the glossary.

Exercise. Exercise reduces diuresis by a complex series of reactions.

FACTORS UNKNOWN

Although diuresis does not change with depth underwater, it increases in dry hyperbaric chambers during deep saturation studies. This remains incompletely explained, but may relate to increased gas pressure and density, and reduced water loss through the skin. Your body uses the alternate route to remove water.

P PHENOMENON MYTH

It is not true that putting a sleeping person's hand in water will invoke the P Phenomenon during sleep.

What Actions Increase Your P Phenomenon?
Try Each. Be Scientific.

- Lie on your back with your feet up

- Stand on your head

- Step into a warm shower

- Now make the water cold in the same shower

- Immerse yourself in a warm bath

- Immerse yourself in a cold bath

Factors In The P Phenomenon

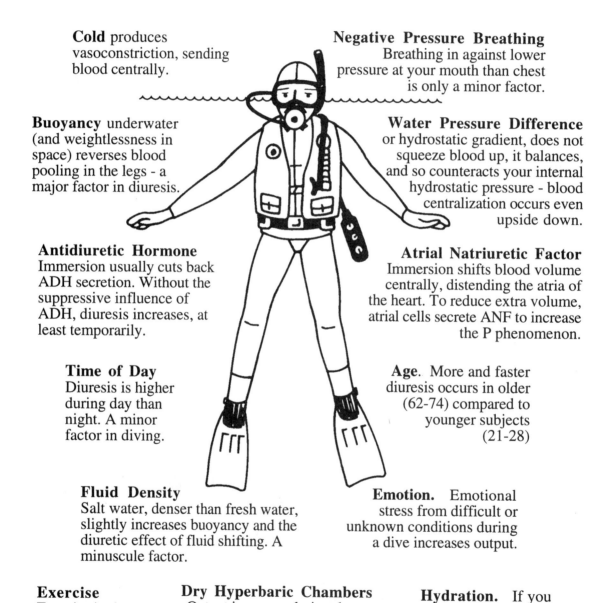

Cold produces vasoconstriction, sending blood centrally.

Negative Pressure Breathing Breathing in against lower pressure at your mouth than chest is only a minor factor.

Buoyancy underwater (and weightlessness in space) reverses blood pooling in the legs - a major factor in diuresis.

Water Pressure Difference or hydrostatic gradient, does not squeeze blood up, it balances, and so counteracts your internal hydrostatic pressure - blood centralization occurs even upside down.

Antidiuretic Hormone Immersion usually cuts back ADH secretion. Without the suppressive influence of ADH, diuresis increases, at least temporarily.

Atrial Natriuretic Factor Immersion shifts blood volume centrally, distending the atria of the heart. To reduce extra volume, atrial cells secrete ANF to increase the P phenomenon.

Time of Day Diuresis is higher during day than night. A minor factor in diving.

Age. More and faster diuresis occurs in older (62-74) compared to younger subjects (21-28)

Fluid Density Salt water, denser than fresh water, slightly increases buoyancy and the diuretic effect of fluid shifting. A minuscule factor.

Emotion. Emotional stress from difficult or unknown conditions during a dive increases output.

Exercise Exercise in the cold reduces output.

Dry Hyperbaric Chambers Output increases during deep saturation studies. May relate to increased gas density and reduced water loss through the skin, but the mechanism is not resolved.

Hydration. If you are not well hydrated your body decreases water loss.

Figure 2.3. Several factors contribute to the P Phenomenon.

HANDLING DIURESIS

The common saying regarding the P Phenomenon underwater is, "There are those who do and those who lie." For some, diuresis while diving is no concern. They just let 'er rip. In other situations, divers find that idea less than attractive. In a drysuit, for instance. Even in wetsuits, some divers resist if they have recently eaten asparagus or taken megadoses of vitamins, both known for aromatic effect on fluid output. What about before you even get in the water while aboard dive boats with no plumbing? What are your options?

Let 'er Rip. The "Let 'er Rip" option is usually a wetsuit or bathing suit option. Most output harmlessly dilutes away. Some divers deliberately superhydrate themselves for the wetsuit heating bonus that follows. A few go as far as superhydrating with caffeine drinks. Caffeine is not recommended. High levels may promote diuresis to the extent that you put out more than you drank. There is some indication that if dehydration results, it may increase risk of decompression sickness. Otherwise, a good soapy scrub after diving, for the wetsuit and for you, is the main consideration. Commercial products, available in spray or liquid, are available from home medical suppliers and dive shops, specifically to deodorize and reduce urine scald.

Drysuit Options. Technical and deep diving sometimes requires decompression stops extending dive time to hours. Such long immersions create uncomfortable situations for the drysuit diver. Various outlets, with valves called p-valves to divert output outside the suit, have been built into wetsuits and drysuits with mixed results. Other options are becoming more popular.

One solution is a device worn by women and men in long surveillance operations, and sometimes by adults with incontinence. It is worn under the drysuit, consisting of a funnel that diverts output through a tube to a collection bag strapped to one leg. It is usually called a sheath urinal kit, alternately called a condom catheter or external catheter. They are available under various trade names from product suppliers for home medical care, law enforcement, and the military. Variations for divers include overboard dump or collection bags.

Another increasingly common, accessible, and convenient option is incontinence pants, pads, and adult diapers. Air Force women U-2 pilots wear a "space-diaper" during their 10-12 hour surveillance missions. There are varied commercial products on the market. Incontinence pants look like ordinary underwear with extra removable absorbent pads and water-resistant liners. Adult diapers look more like traditional disposable diapers. They are sold in drug stores, shopping markets, and home medical suppliers.

Divers using these products have experimented with technique for maximum efficiency. They recommend short spurts rather than "letting 'er rip" for absorption without leakage. A minor problem with incontinence pants and diapers, and sometimes with frequent application of let 'er rip with wetsuits, is diaper rash, also called nappy rash.

Dive Boat Options. On dive boats without plumbing facilities, one option is to jump in the water. Small boats in tropical waters make this easy and sometimes unnoticed. This is not always feasible, particularly in cold waters. Another option is to try your hand at "going" over the downwind side of the boat. Both women and men divers may be reluctant to try this in mixed company.

Small hand-held urinals are inexpensive, fairly discreet, matter-of-fact ways to handle this normal activity. Receptacles vary from home made to commercially produced. The male version looks like a flower vase, sometimes with a handle. The female version adds a simple, small, slanted funnel, easily used standing. Any flexible kitchen funnel will do in emergencies. Commercial versions have a variety of names like female urinal, urinary output director, camping funnel, female adapter, Lady J™, The Complete Freshette™ System, and camping Jane.

They are available from camping and outdoor supply companies, and home and medical suppliers. Variations of commercial collection bags are the Piddle Pack, a small container housing a dehydrated sponge, and the Buddy Bag™, a small plastic bag lined with chemically treated paper that converts liquids to spill-proof gel. Piddle Packs are used in fighter jets by pilots.

All these devices are convenient in moving vehicles like automobiles, boats, and small planes, but caution is recommended in planes. At least two American fighter jets are confirmed to have crashed after loss of control using the Piddle Pack.

There are reports of divers using antidiuretic drugs that are commonly prescribed for bed-wetting. These drugs are variations of vasopressin, which reduce diuresis, as described earlier in this section. Their safety and effectiveness for diving is not known.

REHYDRATING UNDERWATER

Some divers deliberately restrict fluids before diving. Don't do that. Dehydration has negative effects on general health, and reduces diving health through reduced tolerance for exercise, heat, and possibly decompression stress (Chapter 7). Being well hydrated keeps urine dilute, a courtesy to your wetsuit, drysuit, those around you, and reduces nappy rash.

Drink plenty of non-alcoholic liquids before diving. Increasing numbers of divers on long profiles, such as technical and cave divers, drink during the dive. At least one commercial product is available, called SCUDA, or Self Contained Underwater Drinking Apparatus.

Commercial beverage carriers for camping and travel could be taken underwater with good results, such as Bota™ Bags and Camelbaks® (use Cordura®, not leather), and water belts with good push-sealing nozzles. These are available at camping and military supply stores.

Commercial fruit drinks in soft-pack bags have been reported as workable, but avoid boxes – they get too soft to insert the straw. In theory, any flexible bag with a tube and well-sealing nozzle should work.

Some divers deliberately restrict fluids before diving to reduce the P Phenomenon. Dehydration has negative effects on general health and diving health. Stay well hydrated.

SUMMARY

Immersion is not a single condition. Therefore diuresis has multiple underlying mechanisms. Several effects of immersion shift blood and fluids into the chest area.

Negative pressure breathing is a small factor. Buoyancy from water pressure is a major contributor. It is not the hydrostatic gradient that squeezes blood upward. Fluid shifts occur regardless of posture underwater. Buoyancy counters gravity-induced blood pooling in the legs.

Volume detectors in your heart signal your body to release atrial natriuretic factor (ANF), to normalize volume by increasing diuresis. Another body chemical involved is antidiuretic hormone (ADH). The renin-angiotensin-aldosterone system counter-balances the ANF-ADH system to prevent you from losing too much sodium and water.

Diuresis increases in cold water and decreases with exercise. It is influenced to a large extent by your state of hydration, and to a small extent by the time of day, density of the water, your age, emotional state, and other factors. Staying comfortably warm while diving reduces the need to handle diuresis on long dives.

It's not healthy to deliberately dehydrate yourself to reduce diuresis. Stay well hydrated by drinking water or juice before diving. Increasing numbers of divers even drink during extended dives, using various simple devices from camping water bags, to commercial soft-pack juices, to SCUDA. Several options exist to handle diuresis on dive boats without facilities and in drysuits, easily used by both females and males.

Varying combinations of mechanical, neural, environmental, and chemical influences control the magnitude and time course of body fluid volume changes and their control. Intricate feedback loops constitute a continually changing set of interlaced influences. On the other hand, sometimes it's no more than "When you gotta go, you gotta go."

Summary of Options

- **Let 'er Rip**. The "let 'er rip" option is usually a wetsuit or bathing suit option. Most output harmlessly dilutes away.

- **Drysuit Options**. Strap on devices, like those worn under clothing by women and men in surveillance operations, or by those with incontinence, funnel output to a collection bag strapped to one leg or alternately, directed to an overboard dump. Another increasingly common, accessible, convenient option is incontinence pants and adult diapers.

- **Dive Boats Without Facilities Options.** Three main options: Jump in the water, try over the downwind side of the boat, or use small hand held urinals ranging from home made to commercial. The female version adds a simple, small funnel that woman can easily use standing. They are widely available from camping and outdoor supply companies, from military and law enforcement outfitters, and from home and hospital medical suppliers.

- **To Drink Underwater**. Options are the commercial product SCUDA, and various beverage carriers for camping and travel, such as Bota™ Bags, Camelbaks® (Cordura®, not leather), and water belts with good push-sealing nozzles. Commercial fruit drinks in soft-pack bags have been reported as workable, but avoid boxes – they get too soft to insert the straw.

CHAPTER 3

DIVING IN COLD AND HEAT

Why is even moderately cool water such a problem for divers? Why are men's hands and feet often warmer in winter than women's, and what does that have to do with penguins? What are the problems of diving in cold water or in hot weather and what can you do about them?

- Why Do You Get Cold?
- Susceptibility to Cold
- Effects of Diving in the Cold
- Diving In The Heat

CHAPTER 3
PART I

WHY DO YOU GET COLD?

Internal temperature of cold-blooded animals, like lizards and fish, changes with the temperature around them. For that reason they, and other cold-blooded animals, are called poikilotherms (POI'-kill-o-thurms) which comes from Greek words meaning "varying temperature." In cold environments their metabolic rate drops so low that they become inactive.

Warm-blooded animals, like birds and mammals, maintain internal temperature fairly constant in a wide range of external temperatures. They (and we) are called homeotherms, meaning "same temperature." To keep internal temperature more or less the same regardless of most external conditions, your body continually increases some heat transfers and decreases others. You have various insulations that remain fairly constant from minute to minute, like fat, and other insulation such as the thickness of your superficial layer, which changes greatly with blood flow to the skin. You can sweat and shiver, exercise, and go underwater. Each contributes physically and chemically to several heat gain and loss pathways. The interesting story of how your body maintains internal temperature given a wide variety of environmental temperatures and conditions follows.

- How You Lose Heat
- Key Concepts in Heat Transfer
- Skin And Core Temperature are Different
- How You Conserve Heat
- How You Gain Heat

HOW YOU LOSE HEAT

You lose heat all the time. Your body generates heat in the process of being alive. If you didn't lose heat your body would cook. For that reason, losing heat doesn't always mean you are in danger of hypothermia or any injury from cold. You need to lose some heat. Whether you stay comfortable or get cold depends how much heat you keep and how much you lose.

You gain and lose heat in four ways: radiation, conduction, convection, and evaporation. When you lose heat to the environment through breathing, sweating, peeing, and through your skin, you do it in combinations of those four ways. In respiration for instance, you lose heat though evaporation, conduction, and convection.

Radiation. When the sun comes out from behind a cloud, you suddenly feel warmer. There is no time for the sun to heat the air, which would then warm you by conduction and convection. The heat you feel is through radiation. Radiation transfers heat energy by electromagnetic waves. Because it does not depend on presence of matter, as with conduction and convection, radiant heat can transfer across a vacuum. That's how the sun's heat energy reaches us through space. Radiant heat can only go in a straight line. It can't go around corners. For that you need conduction and convection.

Above water, you lose heat through radiation by radiating it directly off your skin to your surroundings. Once underwater, heat transfer by radiation is nil compared to other heat transfer pathways.

Conduction. Conduction transfers heat directly from one material to another one touching it. Get up from your chair and feel the seat. It's warm. Heat left your body and transferred to each layer of your clothes in succession, then to your chair. Heat transfer by conduction results from molecular collisions. Because your behind was initially warmer than the chair, your behind increased the excitation or vibration of the molecules of your clothes. They, in turn, collided more often with molecules on the surface of your chair. Heat transfers out of you as long as your behind is warmer than the chair. Once temperatures equalize, there is no more gradient, and no drive to move more heat.

Some materials conduct heat better than others. You usually discover this on a cold morning when you put one bare foot on the bathroom mat and the other on the tile. Both surfaces are the same temperature, but the tile feels colder because it conducts more heat from your foot than does the mat. Cooking pot handles are made of poor conductors. A good conductor would quickly transfer heat from pan to handle, and burn your hand.

Water is a good conductor of heat. If you hold one hand in the air and the other in water of the same temperature, the hand in water feels colder because heat transfers out of that hand faster than the one in air. You conduct small amounts of heat to your clothes, bathing suit, wetsuit, or any materials in direct contact with your skin, that are cooler than your skin.

Convection. Convection involves heat loss by moving air or liquid. Blowing on hot food and slurping soup are examples of cooling by convection. Your body easily loses heat by convection, too. When you are in cold moving air or water, as soon as you lose heat to the air or water surrounding you, it moves out of contact with you. You lose more heat to each replacement layer. Convection is why wind feels so much colder than non-moving air of the same temperature. Air convection of wind, referred to in meteorology as advection, causes the wind-chill factor.

When you are in cold water without thermal protection, convection is the major way you lose heat. It occurs whether you move through still water or hold still in moving water. Without adequate thermal protection in extremely cold water you will probably not remain conscious long enough to narrow the temperature difference so that heat transfer can stop. Like radiation, you lose heat through convection only as long as you are warmer than the environment.

Evaporation. When you come up from a dive, you're wet. When that water evaporates it turns into water vapor. This process is called a liquid-to-vapor phase change, which requires heat. In this case, the heat comes from your body and you cool as a result.

Unlike heat loss through radiation and convection, your skin does not need to be warmer than the surroundings to lose heat through evaporation, so evaporation is important in high heat conditions.

Dogs pant for evaporative cooling. Antelope shunt venous blood through their large wet muzzles. Water evaporating from their wet snout cools blood before circulation to the brain, protecting the brain from the extreme heat of their African plains home. Human evaporative heat loss occurs in two places – the skin surface and respiratory tract.

Heat loss from breathing is minor during recreational diving. It becomes more a consideration during extreme depth diving. Most of your evaporative heat loss from diving occurs through your skin when you don't dry off after your dive. Another amount comes from sweating, particularly in the heat, discussed in Part IV of this chapter. Sweat must evaporate to cool you. Sweating by itself without evaporation accounts for little heat loss, because very little heat conducts into sweat. The phase change of evaporation takes away far more heat energy than if there was no phase change and you just wiped away the sweat. That's why melting ice cubes (changing phase from solid to liquid) cool a drink more than pouring in cold water at the temperature of ice, but not yet frozen. Under water you can't lose heat through your skin by evaporation. You can sweat underwater if you exercise enough to overheat, but without evaporation, but little heat is lost. The sweat washes away into the water.

You can't evaporate sweat as well when it's humid. That's why you feel hotter in humid environments. The air around you is already nearly saturated with water vapor. Little more can evaporate from your skin, reducing your ability to cool yourself in the heat.

Popular Heat Loss Myth. It's not true that you lose the majority of your heat through your head. Head heat loss is about one-third to one-fifth of total heat loss, and varies with the temperature around you, and whether you are at rest or exercising.

In 1957, Frose & Burton found head heat loss is linear with temperature, meaning that the lower the temperature, the higher the percentage head heat loss. They found that at 0 degrees Centigrade, up to 35% of heat could be lost through the head at rest. Dr. Sarah Nunneley measured head heat loss at about 30% of total at rest. When exercising at a work rate of about half of your maximum capacity, she found head heat loss fell to about 19% of total. That is a fair amount considering that the head is only about 7-9% of your total surface area. If you are cold and need to reduce head heat loss, wear a hat.

Ways You Lose Heat

• Radiation	• Conduction
• Convection	• Evaporation

KEY CONCEPTS IN HEAT TRANSFER

Hold an ice cube. It feels like cold is traveling into your hand, but it isn't. What you feel is heat transferring out of your hand to the ice. Cold is the absence of heat, but heat is not the absence of cold. That might sound nit-picky, but that important difference is key to understanding why your body loses heat when you dive in cold water.

The complex science of heat transfer can be simply summed up: heat energy flows naturally in only one direction, from areas of higher temperature to lower temperature. When the difference is large, more heat flows than when it is small. Think of the temperature difference between two areas as a force, pushing heat from the higher temperature area to the lower temperature area. This force is called a temperature gradient.

Temperature gradients exist all over your body. Two gradients are important to understanding body heat transfer. One is the "skin-to-environment" gradient, the temperature difference between the surface of your skin and the outside environment. The other is the temperature difference between the inner portion of your body, called the core, and your skin, called the "core-to-skin" gradient. Here is where thermoregulation gets interesting.

Just as nitrogen diffuses from higher to lower pressure areas,
heat energy flows from higher to lower temperature areas.

SKIN AND CORE TEMPERATURE ARE DIFFERENT

Your skin temperature is not 98.6°F (37°C). That familiar number is the average temperature of your core. From that average, your core temperature drops a degree or two in early morning while you sleep, and typically rises three to six degrees during exercise. Higher temperatures up to 106°F (41.1°C) have occurred without harm during record-breaking, long-distance runs. Healthy core temperature maintains itself within this narrow range despite wide changes in environmental temperature and activity. Part of your regulating mechanism for maintaining core temperature is to have a changeable skin temperature. Your body usually keeps skin temperature cooler than core temperature. In the cold, skin temperature quickly drops to that of surrounding air or water. If skin surface temperature is close to surrounding temperature, the gradient is small so heat loss is small. Two concepts follow:

- The surrounding temperature need not be 98.6°F to be thermoneutral
- People with cooler skin in the cold have a smaller skin-to-environment gradient to lose heat.

An analogy is if you stand outside your house in cold weather, touch the outside wall and find it warm, you would notice the expensive loss of heat and know your home needed better insulation. Polar bears demonstrate this well. They are so well insulated that infrared photographs show no heat at the surface of their bodies.

HOW YOU CONSERVE CORE HEAT

You body resists heat loss three main ways. Reduction in peripheral blood flow reduces warm blood flowing to the skin surface, layers of insulation act as barriers, and anatomic blood vessel arrangements short circuit warmth leaving your core and cold returning from your skin surface.

Vasoconstriction. Your body's first response to skin cooling is to slow heat loss by decreasing circulation to your skin. Blood vessels constrict in superficial layers called your "shell." Decreased skin blood flow from vasoconstriction increases your insulation by up to two inches, and keeps warm blood away from your skin. The resulting low skin temperature decreases your skin-to-environment gradient.

Changes In Shell Thickness

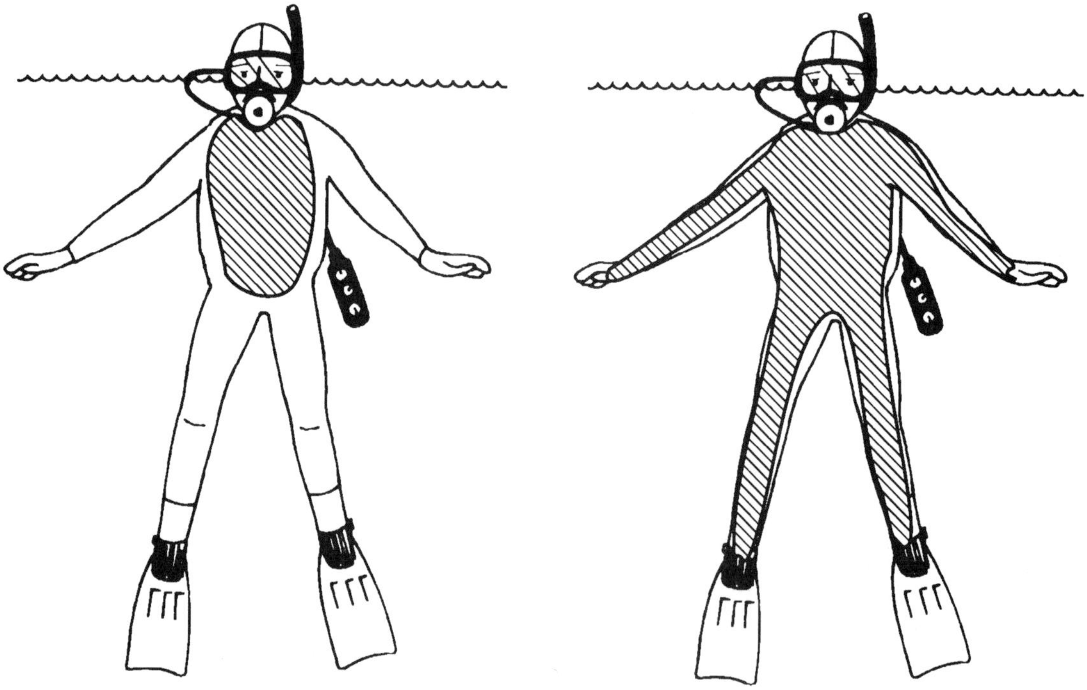

Vasoconstriction with cold   Vasodilation with heat

Figure 3.1. Shell thickness changes with amount of blood flowing through it. Skin blood vessels constrict from cold, thickening shell insulation, and decreasing heat loss. In the heat, vessels dilate and the shell thins, allowing heat loss.

Studies of cold water immersion report lower skin temperature in women than men. These studies are sometimes misinterpreted to mean women are at increased risk of hypothermia. This is not the case. Lower temperatures were of surface skin, not deep skin layers or, more important, the core. Deep skin temperatures remained higher compared to those of men under the same laboratory cold conditions. Both the men and women in these studies protected their core temperatures, although by different means. The men produced more heat and lost more heat. The women conserved heat through better insulation and vasoconstriction. Cool extremities are not, in this case, the result of poor circulation, as sometimes thought. Better insulation through more subcutaneous fat and vasoconstriction reduce heat loss.

One factor determining how much heat you lose is the difference between skin and water temperature, which in turn depends on many variables.

Insulation. You have three components to your non-clothing insulation: fat, muscle, and the thickness of your shell. Another form of insulation in non-humans is fluffing up fur or feathers. Humans can only manage goose bumps, where tiny muscles attached to hair follicles make them fluff up, called piloerection. Goose bumps are ineffective for heat conservation in humans.

Shell. It is oversimplified though useful to think of your body as a central core surrounded by an adjustable insulating shell. Shell thickness changes with amount of blood flowing through it. Your body's first response to skin cooling is to decrease circulation to your shell by constricting blood vessels as described above. Increased shell thickness lowers skin temperature and increases a core-to-skin baffle, restricting heat loss, Figure 3.1.

Muscle. Your muscle layers help insulate you at rest, although less than fat. During exercise, muscle generates heat, adding to body heat stores, but rapidly convects away the heat to the blood. Fat is a better insulator than muscle during exercise in cold water, such as scuba diving.

Fat. Fat is good insulation. Research consistently shows body fat is a major deterrent to heat loss. Body insulation increases directly with average thickness of the fat layer under the skin, and with deep body fat. People with thicker fat layers lose less core heat at rest and during exercise, both in cold air and cold water, tolerate a lower temperature before shivering, and have a slower drop in core temperature during swimming in cold water. Thin people raise their metabolic rate higher than fatter people in a none too successful attempt to keep as warm as those with more fat. Too much fat has health drawbacks in other areas, but keeping warm is not one of them. In this regard, fat is helpful. Ask any whale.

Body fat is a major deterrent to heat loss.

Counter-Current Heat Exchange. Penguins stand around in ice and snow in their little bare feet with negligible heat loss. One reason is that arteries and veins in their feet closely intertwine and exchange heat.

Warm arterial blood going to their feet warms the cool blood coming back. Cold venous blood returning from the feet cools the arterial blood (Figure 3.2). Remarkably little heat is lost to the feet, and cold blood from the feet does not appreciably cool the penguin's core. This is called counter-current heat exchange. It reduces convective heat loss through the blood. Penguin feet are nearly the temperature of the snow. In this case cold feet are a healthy adaptation to cold environments.

Counter-current heat exchange occurs between vessels in close proximity in the limbs of many animals including humans. Studies on Korean breath-hold divers suggest counter-current heat exchange allows extremities to stay warmer and better perfused, while conserving more heat than is possible with limb vasoconstriction alone.

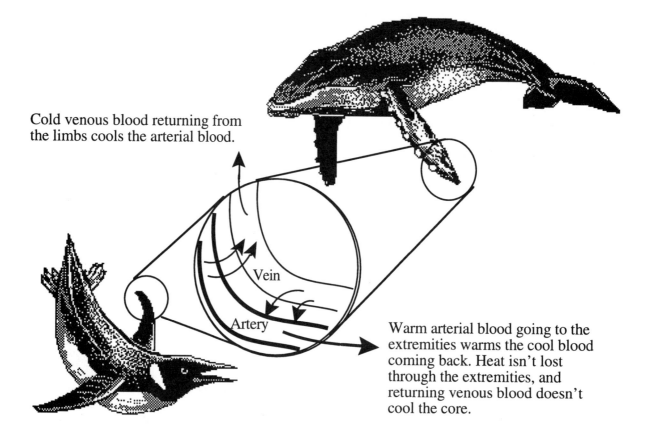

Cold venous blood returning from the limbs cools the arterial blood.

Vein

Artery

Warm arterial blood going to the extremities warms the cool blood coming back. Heat isn't lost through the extremities, and returning venous blood doesn't cool the core.

Figure 3.2. Counter-current heat exchange.

Ways You Conserve Heat

- Vasoconstriction

- Shell, muscle, and fat insulation

- Counter-current heat exchange

HOW YOU GAIN BODY HEAT

Your body gains heat through external heat sources, and by generating its own heat internally. External heat gain through radiation is usually through the sun, heat lamps, stoves, and other radiant heat devices. Heat gain occurs through conduction from directly applied heat packs or blankets heated to higher than skin temperature, and through convection of warm air or water. Your body cannot gain heat through evaporation. Evaporation only carries away your heat. The environment then gains the heat you lost through evaporation.

Your body makes heat physically through shivering and exercise, and chemically through boosting metabolism. The regulator in your brain, called the hypothalamus, is like a thermostat. It has a predetermined temperature setting. When cold receptors in your core and skin tell your thermostat you are getting below a certain temperature, it sends signals to reduce heat loss by blood flow changes described above, and increase heat production, described below.

Shivering. If the environmental temperature is so cold that vasoconstriction can't solve your heat-loss problem, you'll start to shiver. Shivering is involuntary contraction of muscle fibers. Nearly all energy from shivering converts to heat. Average shivering boosts resting metabolism by three times, hard shivering up to four or five times, depending on the study cited. Thin people usually begin shivering in water one to two degrees warmer than better insulated people. A thin person who shivers hard may be able to keep as warm for a limited time as a fatter person who does not shiver. The temperature at which a person begins to shiver is called the critical shivering temperature. In water, critical shivering temperature is higher than in air because heat is lost more rapidly in water than in air, or to put it technically, because of the greater thermal conductivity of water.

Thin people usually begin shivering in water one to two degrees
warmer than better insulated people.

Shivering is so common that divers often accept it as inevitable. It is not a good idea to continue diving past the point of shivering. Shivering doesn't always mean you are hypothermic. It does mean it's safer to stop your dive.

Non-Shivering Thermogenesis. Your body can produce heat by complex chemical processes that don't involve shivering. Production, or genesis, of heat without shivering is called non-shivering thermogenesis.

Ways You Gain Heat

1. External Sources:	2. Generated From Within:
• Radiation	• Physical work
• Conduction	• Shivering
• Convection	• Non-shivering chemical mechanisms

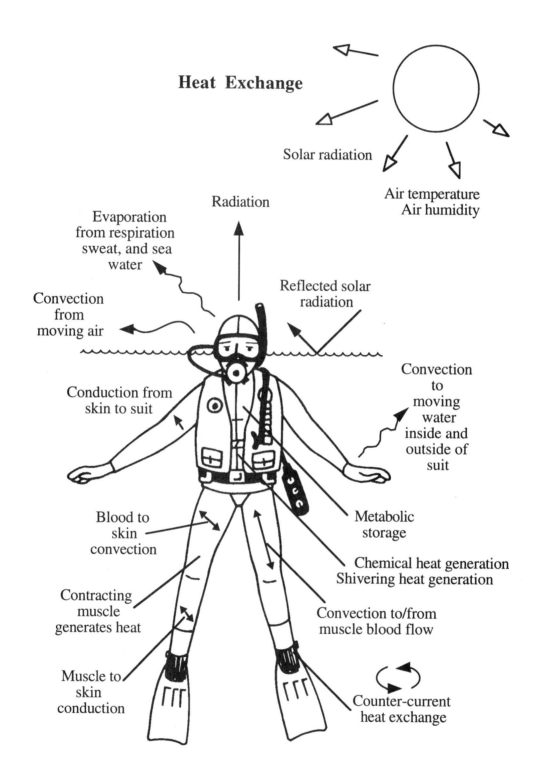

Figure 3.3. Your body has several mechanisms for heat loss, storage, and gain. You lose heat through evaporation, conduction, convection, and radiation. You gain heat from your environment, and by generating it through muscle work, shivering, and chemical heat production. Your clothing blocks both heat loss and gain.

SUMMARY

Your health in the cold depends on keeping your core within a set temperature range. Rate of core heat loss must be roughly the same as heat generation. There are several ways you lose heat, several ways you produce it, and several ways you keep the heat you produce. Some heat-conserving methods physically increase resistance to heat loss, such as layers of insulation and changes in blood flow. Your body boosts heat production chemically through increasing metabolism, and physically through shivering and exercise. Your regulating mechanism, in a part of the brain called the hypothalamus, is like a thermostat. It has a predetermined temperature setting. When cold receptors in your core and skin tell your thermostat you are getting below a certain temperature, the thermostat sends signals to reduce heat loss and increase heat production.

Heat Production   ⇄   Heat Conservation   ⇄   Heat Loss

Internal temperature regulation is a continually self-adjusting system. Nature provides you with several ways to keep your body within a narrow range of internal temperature regardless of the environment. Each person may be more efficient in some ways than others, according to their body chemistry. Each person will also need more or less of each heat exchange pathway, due to high and low abilities in other pathways. There are limits to ability to adapt to cold, explained in Parts II and III of this chapter.

CHAPTER 3
PART II

SUSCEPTIBILITY TO COLD

Just as the "dose" of nitrogen or oxygen, meaning partial pressure and time exposed, are main factors in decompression sickness and oxygen toxicity respectively, major factors in cold stress are temperature and length of exposure. As with dosage of any drug or substance, several interacting factors determine individual tolerance. No one variable such as gender or skin surface area makes anyone more susceptible to chilling or hypothermia than anyone else.

- What Is Hypothermia (and What Is It Not)?
- Body Size and Shape
- Age
- Behavior
- Medication
- Rest and Exercise
- Physical Fitness
- Protective Clothing
- Gender
- Acclimatization
- Other Influences

WHAT IS HYPOTHERMIA (AND WHAT IS IT NOT)?

Hypothermia means that the temperature of your insides called your core has dropped below 95°F (35°C). Sometimes it is subdivided into mild, moderate, and serious drops in body core temperature. Hypothermia from water immersion is sometimes called immersion hypothermia. Hypothermia is not a reflex and does not cause or result from the dive reflex, as sometimes stated by divers. Hypothermia is only one type of cold injury, distinct from injuries like frostbite, trench foot, or chilblain, and different from the effects of simple chilling, which is more common.

Hypothermia is not the same as just getting cold. Cold hands, feet, or skin does not mean you have hypothermia. Shivering and teeth chattering does not mean you have hypothermia. Feeling cold does not mean you have hypothermia. Someone who loses more heat than someone else is not necessarily more susceptible to hypothermia. Your hands can become too cold to do any useful work with no change in your core temperature. You can become uncomfortable, even incapacitated by cold without ever becoming hypothermic. Divers rarely get as far as clinical hypothermia from diving, but often get cold and uncomfortable enough to affect fun and safety.

Cold hands, feet, or skin does not mean you have hypothermia.

BODY SIZE AND SHAPE

Body size and shape contribute to susceptibility to cold, but do not determine it. Susceptibility remains highly individual.

Overall Size and Limb Length. A large person can produce and store more heat than a smaller person. Adaptations in body shape and size, hypothesized to aid survival as a species in cold climates, is summarized in Bergman's rule. Bergman's rule is a generalization that peoples originally native to cold climates are larger than those from warmer climates.

With large body size, arm and leg length often increase. More heat is lost through these areas of high surface-to-mass ratio, and comparatively little fat insulation. Another generalization, called Allen's rule, takes limb length into account. The short arms and legs of large people from cooler regions, for example Eskimos, helps reduce heat loss.

Surface Area-To-Mass Ratio. Warm blooded animals like us produce heat internally through metabolic processes, with heat production roughly proportional to body mass. On the other hand, radiation of heat from the body to the environment is in proportion to surface area. The ratio of external surface area to internal mass contributes to cooling ability.

Bodies, and body parts that have large surface area compared to their mass can lose more heat than those with smaller surface area-to-mass ratios. Car and home heat redistributors are built to have long thin shapes so their high surface area-to-mass ratio gives off, or radiates, lots of heat. Imaginatively, they are called radiators.

$$\frac{\text{surface area}}{\text{smaller mass}} = \text{higher ratio} \qquad \frac{\text{surface area}}{\text{larger mass}} = \text{lower ratio}$$

Spaghetti cools rapidly. Baked potatoes stay hot longer. Like spaghetti, your fingers and ears are long and thin with much exposed surface. Fingers and ears chill faster than your torso. Fingers have less total surface than your torso, but a higher *ratio*. Your torso, very much like a potato, has more internal mass compared to its outer surface of skin, giving it a lower ratio of surface area-to-mass, Figure 3.4.

You cut your food into small pieces, or pour soup into shallow bowls to increase the ratio so they cool faster. The large thin ears of elephants are crucial to cooling such a large, low-ratio animal in the heat. The high surface area-to-mass ratio of ears allows higher radiant heat loss.

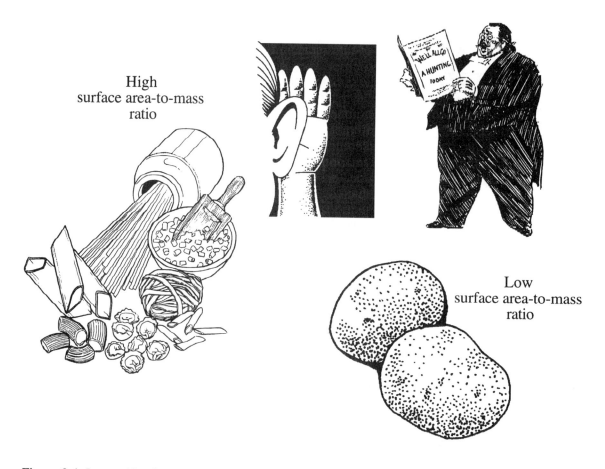

High
surface area-to-mass
ratio

Low
surface area-to-mass
ratio

Figure 3.4. Long, thin shapes like spaghetti, fingers, and ears have a high ratio of surface area to their mass. Your torso, like a potato, has more internal mass in relation to its surface covering, lowering the ratio. A surface area-to-mass ratio is different from total surface area.

Surface area-to-mass ratios of individual body parts are used in mathematical thermal models to estimate what final temperatures would be under specified conditions. Studies of total body surface-to-mass ratio among adult humans are not in agreement about contribution of the ratio to cooling. Although a higher ratio does allow more relative heat loss, it is not the main determinant of chilling. No single heat loss pathway creates global risk of chilling or hypothermia. In other words, someone with a larger ratio can lose more heat through that particular pathway yet still not be at greater risk of chilling, because of other heat-conserving and generating mechanisms. Moreover, a larger person has more total surface area and loses more total heat than a smaller person. For example, a large male has more total surface area, and so loses more total heat than a smaller man or woman, but is not more susceptible to chilling for that one reason. Chapter 4 tells more on gender and the surface area-to-mass ratio.

The surface area-to-mass quotient is a minor factor in humans,
except when comparing extremely small and large
people regardless of gender.

As demonstrated by elephant ears, the ratio has importance in the heat. Large people with lower ratios may overheat more readily than smaller high-ratio people. In the cold, the ratio seems to have greatest effect in fingers and ears compared to bodies, in jockeys compared to linebackers, in spaghetti compared to potatoes, and in children compared to adults. It contributes less among adults regardless of gender.

AGE

Young children are less able to thermoregulate in the cold than adults for a variety of reasons including size, active heat generation, vasomotor control, and other factors. Infants are at risk even though they have a higher capacity for non-shivering heat production than adults through a special heat-producing fat called brown fat.

Risk of hypothermia also generally increases with aging. In one study, older men were not as able to increase metabolic heat or constrict surface blood vessels to avoid heat loss as the younger men. In another study, older women matched younger women in their ability to maintain their core temperature during cold exposure. The researchers concluded that susceptibility to cold was due to changes in physical fitness and body composition that accompany aging, not only aging itself, and were factors that could possibly be altered to improve cold tolerance.

BEHAVIOR

A natural response to cold is behavior change. You can crouch down and huddle to reduce your exposed surface, and shield heat-producing areas. Another good maneuver is to remove yourself from cold conditions. A thermal stress workshop held at the Institute for Naval Medicine in England by the Diving Medical Advisory Committee discussed what they called the non-responder to cold. They stated, "It is still not known what the differences are between the man who responds to and complains of the cold, and another man who cools and is unaware that he is cooling. Presumably this latter type of diver is a potential hypothermic casualty." Regardless of size, age, or gender, those who get out of the water when cold reduce their susceptibility to chilling and hypothermia.

MEDICATION

Medications called beta blockers are commonly prescribed for migraine headache. They are also sometimes taken for high blood pressure, although other medications have gained greater acceptance as anti-hypertensives. People taking beta blockers sometimes report reduced cold tolerance. A possible reason is that beta blockers, particularly a class called non-selective beta blockers, were found in some studies to block non-shivering thermogenesis, which is one small means of heat production.

REST AND EXERCISE

When you are at rest in the cold, blood flow to your body surface and limbs decreases. The nearly bloodless zone of your shell widens, increasing insulation. Beneath that, your muscle layer adds a bit of insulation, and fat adds much insulation. During exercise the situation changes. Greater blood flow to the working arms and legs decreases peripheral insulation. Working muscles easily lose heat, shifting the job of insulation to fat and skin. It is true that exercise increases heat loss, but it is a very important point that it does not mean that you will cool. Exercise in cold water can generate enough heat to match or surpass the large thermal drain, depending on water temperature, work load, duration of exposure, and body composition.

Exercise seems to most help individuals with a low shivering response and those with high body fat. It is noteworthy that many studies showing the benefit of exercise to keep warm in cold water are of subjects exercising in cold water with no protective garments. Divers wearing exposure suits are more likely to benefit from the heat generation of exercise. In many cases, physical exertion in cold water intensifies cooling. But not all cases.

It is also possible to overheat while exercising in the water, as swimmers doing laps in warm pools and divers sweating into their masks can tell you. A recent Navy study looked at over-insulated divers swimming in cold water and found they needed a bit of heat extraction to prevent overheating. Military operations in the Persian Gulf experimented with ice vests to prevent overheating during strenuous maneuvers in the warm water.

Contrary to popular belief, you won't always get colder by exercising in cold water. Both heat loss and heat production increase. It depends which prevails.

PHYSICAL FITNESS

The relation between fitness and cold tolerance is not as marked as the definite advantage of the fit to tolerate heat. Even so, structural and metabolic changes occurring with exercise training appear to keep you warmer in the cold. A fit person may tolerate a lower body temperature than an unfit person before onset of shivering and can generate more heat through shivering. Increased muscle mass through resistance exercise increases heat production and storage. Physical fitness allows you to exercise at a higher intensity to generate heat. Thermal tolerance would, for those reasons, improve with physical fitness, although cold tolerance better increases with exercise in cold conditions than from exercise alone.

Thermal tolerance can improve with physical fitness.

PROTECTIVE CLOTHING

Clothing studies yield interesting results. Subjects' core temperatures are sometimes lower with protective garments than without. One study on Korean diving women found that wearing gloves did not add protection to wet suits in mildly cold water.

Lack of input from cold receptors in their hands, decreased their body's ability to make blood flow changes necessary for cold protection. Sensory information from cold receptors in the extremities seems of high importance in thermoregulation.

Still, protective clothing is important, and makes a life-and-death difference in extreme cold air and water. Protective clothing protects you from losing more heat than you can replace. In 1941, the now universal concept of a standard insulating unit of clothing was introduced, called the "clo." One clo is the amount of insulation keeping you comfortable at rest, in a room at 70°F (15°C), relative humidity less than 50%, and air movement less than 20 feet per minute. A man's suit is about one clo. As temperature falls, you need garments with higher clo value. To sleep comfortably in freezing temperature (32°F, 0°C), needed clo is about seven. This is the origin of the "three dog night." Dog fur is about 5.5 clo per dog. In warmer temperatures, and when generating heat through exercise, protective suits of lower clo value will do. For moderate work in freezing air you need three clo. For heavy work, about one will do. Air trapping makes a fabric effective, a fact formally recorded least as far back as 1620 by English philosopher and essayist Francis Bacon. Several factors beside clo determine a garment's ability to protect you from cold: Wicking moisture away from your body, moisture trapping and condensation of water vapor beneath the outer layer, resiliency of the fibers to retain loft needed for air trapping, surface area of the fibers, the fabric's heat capacity and thermal conduction, whether the fibers reflect back heat, their bulk and weight, if they are waterproof, if they will crack in severe cold, and other considerations. Body areas covered by the fabric vary greatly in skin temperature and heat flow. Hands are difficult to insulate heavily, yet not lose dexterity to bulkiness. New garment design of variable clo is promising. Thermal garment development for extreme exposures is a highly specialized field.

GENDER

There is no convincing evidence that women are more susceptible to hypothermia than men, as commonly stated by divers. Some studies show women may be less susceptible. Women may generate less total heat than men depending on work load, fitness, body size, and other variables, but have greater ability, on average, to limit heat loss. Men, on average, usually lose more total heat from higher skin temperatures due to smaller vasoconstrictor response, and from their larger total skin surface area, but counter with increased heat production from typically greater mass and metabolism (Chapter 4).

Evidence is strong that women protect their core temperature
in the cold as well or more than men.

ACCLIMATIZATION

Cold acclimatization is a well-documented process of gradually increasing your resistance to cold injury through regular cold exposure. Following the recommendation of the International Union of Physiological Sciences, the term acclimatization is distinguished from acclimation. Acclimatization means change from seasonal or geographical exposure; acclimation is change produced in a laboratory.

Major examples of geographic acclimatization to cold are the indigenous people of the African Kalahari, the Australian desert, and Tierra del Fuego in Southern Chile. Many sleep outdoors nearly naked in freezing temperatures. Seasonal acclimatization occurs in people working outdoors year round and fishermen who dunk their hands in cold water all winter to tend their nets. Divers continuing to work late into the winter season, or year round in cold waters, gradually increase their cold tolerance. Extent varies among individuals and with exposure.

Cold acclimatization involves at least three adaptations. Cold-acclimatized people begin shivering at lower body temperatures, because they generate more heat without shivering. Cold adjustment may involve both increased and decreased skin temperatures, depending on circumstances. In some cases, skin blood flow increases to keep extremities warm and to resist cold injury. In other cases it decreases to reduce heat loss. For example, skin temperatures of Australian Aborigines were lower while sleeping than those of the unacclimatized European investigators. A third hallmark of cold-acclimatized people is improved ability to sleep in the cold.

When chronic exposure ends, you gradually lose cold adaptation. When acclimatized Korean divers switched from bathing suits to wet suits, their thermal advantage decreased. Loss of acclimatization was also documented in the Ama divers of Japan when they began wearing cotton suit insulation and wet suits.

OTHER INFLUENCES

Cold tolerance decreases with dehydration, lack of sleep, and food deprivation. This stress response is covered in Part III of this chapter – Effects of Diving in the Cold.

Factors in Susceptibility to Cold

- Water and air temperature
- Duration of exposure

- Skin temperature
- Body composition

- Very young and very old age
- Certain medications

- Protective garments
- Physical work load

- Body size
- State of acclimatization

- Fatigue
- Hydration

- Nutritional status

SUMMARY

As obvious as it sounds, you can get cold when diving in cold water. Several interacting and competing heat gain and heat loss mechanisms determine if you will get cold, and by how much.

Major determinants of chilling are water temperature and duration of exposure. Results of studies of susceptibility to cold immersion vary with water temperature, duration of immersion, protective garments, work load, body composition, and other factors. Losing heat, by itself, does not mean that you are chilling. When exercising in cold water, both heat loss and heat production increase. Whether you get cold or warm depends which you have more of.

Thermal scientists can put all the figures for heat generation, heat loss, and resistance to heat loss, from the body and from the environment, into mathematical models to estimate what final temperature might be. It is complicated to cull out responsible variables, and more involved than just saying young or old, or big or small people have any one characteristic and therefore greater susceptibility.

CHAPTER 3
PART III

EFFECTS OF DIVING IN THE COLD

Getting into cold water triggers changes in several body systems. Information from temperature receptors, called thermoreceptors, come from your skin, and then from the brain as cooler blood reaches it. Although hypothermia is not a common problem in recreational scuba diving, becoming cold and uncomfortable is very common. Long before hypothermia, the effects of cold on your body cause problems ranging from inconvenient to hazardous.

- Respiratory Effects
- Vascular Effects
- Manual Impairment
- Mental Function
- Cardiovascular Effects
- Metabolic Effects
- Renal Effects
- Thermostat Effects
- Nitrogen Effects
- Preventing Cold Injury

RESPIRATORY EFFECTS

Cold water makes you gasp. The gasp reaction is not limited to immersion; it can occur with cold showers and even ice cubes down your back. In cold immersion, gasping at rates of up to 60 to 70 breaths per minute can continue up to a minute or two. This rapid breathing is out of proportion to need. A variety of chemical responses result that decrease your ability to control the beginning of your dive safely. The gasp response is one of several good reasons to get into cold water slowly and keep your regulator in your mouth on entry.

VASCULAR EFFECTS

Vasoconstriction. As soon as skin temperature begins to drop, your body's first protective response is to greatly constrict superficial blood vessels of your limbs, and slightly constrict those of your torso. Reduced blood flow resulting from this vasoconstriction reduces body heat loss by increasing the thickness of your peripheral tissue insulation, or shell, and decreasing skin temperature. Low skin temperature reduces the gradient for heat loss between skin and the environment. Blood vessels don't constrict in the skin of your head, leaving it a site of higher heat loss.

Vasodilation. Prolonged vasoconstriction during cold exposures can cause cold injury to your extremities. In response, when skin temperature falls below approximately 40°-50°F (4°-10°C), limb vessels enlarge briefly a few times a minute to try to bring blood back to your surface for warmth. That is why you can have rosy cheeks in the cold, even though the skin surface ordinarily vasoconstricts from cold.

Alternating cold-induced vasodilation and vasoconstriction is called the "Hunting Reflex of Lewis." The reflex was named for its characteristic of "hunting" for a temperature equilibrium point. It is not always successful finding it. Occasionally people have been found frozen to death and naked, a phenomenon called paradoxical undressing. One explanation is that due to the hunting reflex, in an extreme form, they felt so warm that in their cold disorientation they removed their clothing.

Severe conditions of cold, lack of food, sleep deprivation, and stress are common in two circumstances: warfare and dive trips. Such conditions increase circulating levels of nervous system chemicals called catecholamines (cat-eh-COAL'-uh-meens). The major stress catecholamine is epinephrine (eh-pin-NEF'-rin), also called adrenaline. Epinephrine levels rise in your body as a stress response, constricting blood vessels. This is different from another catecholamine called norepinephrine (nor-eh-pin-NEF'-rin) or noradrenaline, that your body produces for normal, everyday vasoconstriction. The epinephrine stress response is sometimes enough to obliterate the Hunting Reflex. With extended cold exposure, a blunted response increases risk of cold injury to the extremities.

Severe conditions of cold, lack of food, sleep deprivation, and stress are common in two circumstances: warfare and dive trips.

MANUAL IMPAIRMENT

Poor control of the hands and feet can occur with progressive cold, and may continue to the point where the dive ends in rescue.

Tactile Ability. Your sense of touch decreases in the cold. Protective gloves or mitts add clumsiness. When fingers or toes get cold enough, they hurt. Continued long enough, for example 50°F (10°C) for more than one or two hours, numbness and tingling may occur that persists for days.

Strength and Motor Function. Studies and field reports document that, with inadequate garment protection, divers lose hand grip strength, general strength, and motor skill as body temperature decreases. Limb muscles lose ability to perform coordinated movement. Loss of motor and sensory function increases the prospect of death by drowning, even before core body temperature falls to hypothermic levels.

Without good thermal protection, loss of motor and sensory
function increases risk of death by drowning, even before you
become hypothermic.

MENTAL FUNCTION

Staying in the cold for too long can affect intellectual function. Although
manifestations may seem humorous, they signal chilling to the point of danger.
Ending the cold exposure does not automatically end the risk. Any diver leaving the
water with changes in mental function should be medically evaluated.

CARDIOVASCULAR EFFECTS

Irregular Heart Beats. Irregular heart beats, called arrhythmias, ordinarily occur now
and then without you feeling them or knowing about them. Arrhythmias usually
cause you no harm. They occur more often as you get older. They also occur more
often with immersion in cold water. Immersion and cold both increase the amount
of blood returning to your heart, called venous return. Increased venous return
distends the heart and reflexively slows heart rate. High distention and very slow
heart rate increase tendency to irregular beats. In some divers, low heart rate and
abnormal heart rhythms may increase risk of blackout or death.

Dive Reflex. Immersion in cold water typically reduces heart rate and decreases blood
flow to your arms and legs, in a collection of effects called the dive reflex. As
described above, the combination of low heart rate and increased incidence of
arrhythmias from cold immersion may result in problems. The dive reflex does not
reduce your oxygen demand. Oxygen consumption increases with cold immersion
(Chapter 2 Part I).

Cardiovascular Endurance. When your core temperature drops, your ability to
exercise decreases and fatigue begins sooner.

METABOLIC EFFECTS

Cold immersion immediately increases metabolism, as evidenced by increased
oxygen consumption. Metabolism increases to deal with the work of staying warm
in the cold.

RENAL EFFECTS

Cold and immersion combine to increase urine production. Urinary fluid loss,
called diuresis, over long periods of time with insufficient replacement, can lead to
dehydration, thought to increase risk of decompression sickness (Chapter 2 Part II,
Diuresis, and Chapter 7 Part IV, Fluid Replacement).

THERMOSTAT EFFECTS

Dropping skin and core temperatures signal your body to increase heat production. Your body makes heat mechanically by shivering and through chemical reactions, described in Part I of this chapter. Your heat set-point is regulated by a structure in your brain called the hypothalamus, which functions like a thermostat. If your core temperature falls too low, your hypothalamus gets too cold to function properly. When this regulating mechanism fails, shivering and non-shivering heat production decline, and your body temperature falls unchecked. There is real danger of serious cold injury at this point.

FATIGUE

Your core temperature remains more or less constant as long as the heat your body produces equals the heat you lose. In the cold, chilling may occur rapidly or slowly. Consequences of rapid chilling are easily observable. Slow chilling, more common in warm water diving, usually robs heat and calories too slowly to detect easily. Heat is not the same thing as temperature. Your body can lose great amounts of heat with little change in temperature. Skin temperature does not drop far, and shivering may not occur, but heat is relentlessly pulled from your core. This phenomenon is sometimes called warm water hypothermia.

Your body works hard to keep up with heat loss. Although you do not directly sense it, this work requires your body to expend energy, as does swimming or other muscular exertion. The work of heat generation can eventually lead to fatigue. In cooler water, muscle tension and joint viscosity increase when your body chills. The increased work of moving chilled muscles and joints combined with the work of keeping warm adds to fatigue. Cooling-induced fatigue can be a problem with diving for repeated and prolonged periods without a wet suit in warm water, or with a wet suit in cooler water.

NITROGEN EFFECTS

Decompression. Cold exposure causes cardiovascular changes that decrease your body's ability to both absorb and eliminate nitrogen. Being uniformly cold throughout your dive may not increase risk of decompression sickness. One study found fewer Doppler detectable bubbles in divers who were cold than warm at depth. Richard Long, who developed the commercial version of the hot-water suit, noticed that decompression sickness was more likely in divers in hot-water suits than in divers who were colder while wearing wet suits.

Starting a dive warm then cooling may be a problem. If you begin a dive while warm you could absorb more nitrogen than in a cooler state. If you chill, common toward the end of a dive, eliminating that additional nitrogen gas burden slows. There are studies concluding that incidence of decompression sickness rises in divers who chill during or after decompression (Chapter 5 Part I).

Narcosis. Cold increases risk of impairment from inert gas narcosis. Unlike some experiences with warm water narcosis, narcosis in the cold may be unpleasant. Narcosis may also blunt the perception of cold. A diver with narcosis may not feel the need to get out of the water as soon, increasing chance of chilling.

Effects of Cold Water Immersion

- Gasping with sudden immersion

- Vasoconstriction

- Decreased tactile ability in chilled hands

- Decreased motor ability with continued exposure

- Decreased mental functioning - in extreme cases

- Increased incidence of arrhythmias

- The dive reflex – Chapter 2

- Increased oxygen consumption to deal with the work of being cold

- Diuresis – Chapter 2

- Shivering and non-shivering heat production

- Fatigue after long exposures

- Changes in decompression dynamics

- Altered effects of narcosis

PREVENTING COLD INJURY

Diving safely in the cold is a matter of not losing more heat than you produce. Divers rarely get clinical hypothermia from diving, but often get cold and uncomfortable, which can affect fun and safety. You can do several things to conserve heat while diving in cool and cold water.

One important way to conserve heat is to wear good thermal protection. Various animals dive in Arctic waters using both wet suit and dry suit technology. The fur of seals and polar bears, for example, is an effective wet suit. It adds exterior insulation to their thick fat layer by trapping a two to ten millimeter water layer near their skin. The feather pelt of penguins, on the other hand, works like a dry suit, maintaining an insulating layer of air. Humans who have no feathers or fur and who dive in cold water should wear exposure suits that include head covering.

Some divers ask if pouring warm water in your wet suit or warming up between dives in a heated car or boat cabin will cause you to vasodilate and sweat, thereby making you colder than before. These practices are not harmful. The additional heat gained is important for rewarming. You will be warmer than before and will build back a heat reserve. Rewarming is an important part of cold water diving. It is also not true that you should avoid wearing a coat indoors even if you are cold, on the assumption that you will be colder once outside. The heat you gain is beneficial and gives you that much more to spend in the cold. Even if you become warm enough to sweat, you will not lose more heat than you gained. You will generally be warmer than when you started. One study of exercise before immersion that is sometimes misinterpreted, showed lower temperature after immersion. The exercise was long and near exhaustive, and the temperature difference was tiny. Regaining needed heat after dives by rewarming should not be neglected.

Simple, but sometimes overlooked tactics for staying warm include wearing good thermal protection. Keep stress responses low by getting rest, having fun, and continuing dive training to reduce the strain of unfamiliar diving situations. Increase your capacity for heat production and conservation with regular aerobic and weight-lifting workouts. Stay hydrated. Dehydration reduces cold tolerance. Don't skip meals. You need the calories to stay warm.

Plan for cold water diving with checks of weather and site conditions. Allow wider safety margins as the temperature falls. At the dive site, pre-wet your face and hands to begin a peripheral vasoconstriction effect. Get in slowly, not all at once. Staged immersion can reduce the gasp response and its associated problems and is safer for your heart. If you get cold, end your dive. Continue your protection from cold exposure after you get out of the water. Convection from even a relatively warm wind can sometimes cool you rapidly. Dry off, change into dry clothes, and move to a warm location.

- Wear good exposure garments, suitable for conditions

- Get the weather report and make site condition checks

- Allow wider diving safety margins with colder conditions

- Stay well nourished, rested, and hydrated

- Pre-wet your face and hands

- Get in slowly

- After diving, dry off, get changed, and get out of the cold

- Rewarm well between dives

- Keep in good muscular and aerobic shape to increase heat-conserving and heat-producing systems

- If you are cold, do something about it

SUMMARY

Cold has several effects on the diver, ranging from inconvenient to lethal. Cold immersion affects many of your body systems as they make adjustments to increase heat production and decrease heat loss. Extreme cold exposures overwhelm these protective systems, with harmful effects. If you are cold, do something about it. Safety in the cold requires action and thought by the diver before, during, and after diving. You can dive safely in cold water when you properly prepare.

CHAPTER 3
PART *IV*

DIVING IN THE HEAT

Who will be cooler on a hot day, someone with or without a shirt on? Does a diver who sweats more than another diver have the advantage in the heat? Can you sweat underwater? What do divers need to know about diving safely in hot conditions? This chapter deals with overheating. As with cold, where many factors determine if you will chill, no single heat loss pathway, such as how much you sweat, determines if you will overheat. Many interacting heat gain and loss mechanisms contribute to your temperature at rest and when exercising in the heat.

- Environmental Variables
- Human Variables
- Shirts or Skins?
- Preventing Heat Injury

Long ago the Greek philosopher Aristotle thought the function of the brain was not of reason, but cooling; a mere human air conditioning unit for the blood. Today we know of several heat loss pathways, and, with any luck, use the brain for other functions.

As described in Part I of this chapter, there are several ways you generate heat inside you and gain more heat from your surroundings. You have some body structures that allow heat loss, and other body structures that prevent it. Your clothing and dive suits prevent heat loss, and also block heat gain from the environment around you. Moreover, each of these separate heat gains and losses occurs in several ways. Put those many pluses and minuses together, and whether you overheat or not depends on how much of each you have. As with cold, thermal scientists can plug all the variables into heat transfer equations to predict final temperature at several body sites.

ENVIRONMENTAL VARIABLES

The amount of heat you lose through each of your heat gain and loss pathways, described in Part I of this chapter, changes with temperature, humidity, whether you're underwater or topside, the speed of the surrounding water or air, your clothing, how hard you're working, your physical fitness, and your skin temperature, which in turn depends on many variables. How your body maintains internal temperature, given all these variables, is an interesting story.

If you can't lose heat one way, your body increases heat loss in other ways. At room temperature, if you were seated at rest and naked, you would lose most of your body heat, about 67%, by radiating it directly off your skin, plus a bit more through conduction to the air and to your chair. You would only lose 23% or so from evaporation through sweating and breathing. But how long do you sit naked at room temperature? With summer air temperatures in the mid 80's (about 30°C), your ability to radiate heat decreases. Your body adjusts by increasing heat loss through other means, in this case conduction and convection.

Temperatures above 95°F (35°C) make it too hard for you to lose heat through convection, and just about impossible through radiation. With air temperature higher than skin temperature, the heat gradient reverses, and you wind up gaining heat through that pathway. Evaporation of sweat becomes the major avenue for heat exit. Increased sweating keeps your skin cool, but only if your surroundings are dry. Add high humidity and you can't evaporate sweat, particularly when little air passes over your skin. Heat is only lost when sweat evaporates. Although your body has tried its best, your heat tolerance will finally go kaput. Then you go around saying, "It's not the heat, it's the humidity." Adding exercise in these varying environmental conditions further changes the relative contributions of each heat loss pathway.

Your body has several ways to gain and lose heat. It continually adjusts each to maintain internal temperature. When one way becomes blocked by environmental conditions, others increase or decrease automatically — up to a point.

On the other hand, if conditions increase one heat loss avenue and you need to conserve heat, your other heat loss mechanisms helpfully decrease. As an example, although you lose little heat through respiration, if breathing dry scuba air increases your respiratory evaporative and convective heat loss, other heat loss avenues quiet down to try to even things out.

When things can't even out, you have net heat gain or loss from the body with either overheating or chilling. Both heat loss and heat production increase during exercise in the water. It all depends whether you have more heat loss or gain.

HUMAN VARIABLES

Physical Fitness. Exercising in the heat has been described as probably the single greatest stress ever imposed on the human cardiovascular system. With increased physical fitness, your body makes several adaptations to tolerate activity in the heat. Some of many adaptations are increased total blood volume, increased water content, and changes in sweating.

Blood supply to your heart and limb muscles is important for exercise. Shunting blood to your skin is important for cooling. Because there is only a finite amount of blood to go around, competition problems can develop. The fitter diver has more blood volume and can pump more blood with each beat. That adaptation means you can better supply blood simultaneously to your muscles for exercise and your skin for cooling.

The better shape you are in, the more you sweat and the fewer electrolytes exit with sweat. Sweating also distributes more to the limbs, furthering cooling from these high heat loss areas. With increased fluids to go around for cooling and seating, a fit person's core temperature will not rise as high at the same exercise intensity as an out-of-shape person. The out-of-shape person has less cooling capacity, and decreased ability to exercise safely in the heat.

If you get out of shape, you lose your adaptations. Aerobic fitness is one of the most important factors in improving heat tolerance (Chapter 6).

Hydration. Dehydration dramatically reduces your ability to endure heat. Total body fluid volume is important to heat tolerance, as described earlier in the section on fitness. Military studies of forced marches made an interesting discovery. With no water, core temperature rose dangerously during the march. With water allowed as wanted, core temperature did not rise as high, but still rose. By weighing the marchers at intervals and replacing water for amount lost, core temperature did not rise.

Work since then has verified the importance of fluid replacement in heat tolerance during exercise. Sweating rate decreases with dehydration. When body water reserves are low, your body decreases loss (Chapter 7).

Age. As with cold exposure, young children are less able to thermoregulate in the heat than adults, for a variety of reasons: Sweating ability, circulating blood volume, the relatively higher heat load they generate doing the same work as an older person, and other factors. They are at greater risk of overheating.

With aging, heat tolerance also decreases for many reasons: Decreased sweating, decreased circulating blood volume, and general thermoregulatory decline. Changes in physical fitness that accompany aging seem to be closely linked with heat tolerance. Older people can dramatically improve heat tolerance with regular exercise.

Acclimatization. Just as with cold exposure, your body gradually adapts to heat. With heat exposure at the start of summer, or when traveling to a warmer climate for a dive trip, your body begins making several changes.

Your plasma volume increases, improving blood distribution to your skin for cooling and your muscles for activity. Increased plasma volume increases your sweating ability. The extra liquid volume is also a heat sink that can absorb more heat without increase in your body temperature. With heat acclimatization, sweating starts earlier, at a higher rate, with better electrolyte conservation. Your body also makes more of several protective proteins, called heat-shock proteins. Heat-shock proteins increase your tolerance to further heat exposure. Many plants, animals, and bacteria make heat-shock proteins when exposed to heat that is elevated, but not lethal.

Heat adaptation occurs quickly with the most dramatic changes in the first 4-5 days. Acclimatization is almost complete in one to two weeks of continuous exposure to exercise in the heat. Acclimatization does not occur if you spend your summers in air-conditioned environments. You rapidly lose heat acclimatization with lack of exposure.

Body Size. As described in the sections on cold, the larger person has more mass to generate and store heat. Since heat dissipation does not increase proportionally to size, large, round people are often able to produce more heat than they can get rid of.

Differences in body size and dimensions, discussed in Part II, account for two body types contributing to more efficiently keeping cool in the heat, all other factors held equal. They are small body size, and thin, taller people with long, slender limbs.

Gender. All information to date indicates that gender matters little compared to state of hydration, age, physical fitness, and how accustomed you are to heat, both at rest and during exercise. Women are not generally at greater risk of heat injury than men, as often stated by divers. Larger men seem to be more prone to overheating than smaller men and most women (Chapter 4).

Sweating. Heat loss through sweating depends on three main things, which vary with conditions. The first is rate of evaporation, which depends on humidity and amount of air passing over the skin. The second is rate of sweating, which changes with emotional state, age, race, hydration, physical fitness, and how accustomed you are to the heat. Third is the mineral concentration of sweat. Mineral content changes the amount of heat that sweat can take with it upon evaporation. This amount is called the latent heat of evaporation, or heat of transformation.

You have two kinds of sweat glands, apocrine and eccrine. Your apocrine sweat glands are emotionally activated. They are on the forehead, groin, armpits, hands, feet, and upper lip, and form the cold sweat of fear, and nervous sweaty hands and feet. They are also the smelly sweat glands. Your eccrine sweat glands are heat activated, and important in regulating body temperature. Eccrine sweat glands are all over your body and produce clear, watery, odorless sweat.

Babies are covered with apocrine glands, giving them their distinctive smell. After infancy, the apocrine glands become inactive until puberty, when you become smelly once again. For this reason children don't have sweat odor. If they are smelly, it is for other reasons. Men and women have the same number of sweat glands, contrary to popular myth, explained further in Chapter 4.

Sweating includes noticeable beads of sweat and insensible sweating, which does not mean it is not a sensible way to sweat, but loss imperceptible to the eye. In general, innate differences in sweating among people matter little compared to major heat-tolerance factors such as state of hydration and cardiovascular fitness.

SHIRTS OR SKINS?

Who will be hotter standing out in the sun, shirts or skins? It's skins. If you have no clothes on you will absorb all the radiant heat of the sun that falls on you. If you have clothes on, the clothes block about half the heat gain.

If anyone offers to take clothing off because of the heat, now you can dazzle them with a little science. Tell them they'll be cooler with their clothes on.

Human Variables In Response to Heat

- **Physical Fitness**. Aerobic fitness is one of the most important factors in heat tolerance.

- **Hydration**. Dehydration dramatically reduces your ability to endure heat.

- **Age**. Young children are less able to thermoregulate in the heat than adults. Older people can, with regular exercise, delay and reduce loss of heat tolerance associated with aging.

- **Acclimatization.** With exposure, your body gradually adapts to heat through several changes.

- **Body Size**. Large, round people are often able to produce more heat than they can get rid of.

- **Gender**. Gender does not seem to be a big factor, however large people, particularly large, round males, have a tendency to overheat.

- **Sweating.** Many variables affect sweating: Emotion, age, race, hydration, gender, fitness, and acclimatization.

PREVENTING HEAT INJURY

Your health in the heat depends on protecting you from more heat than you can get rid of. Dogs pant to cool themselves. Pigs cover themselves in cool mud. What can you do?

- **Water**. Fluid replacement is crucial to heat tolerance. Drink water and other fluids often. Drink more than you think you need. If you are overheating on dive boats, cool yourself by getting into the water, or if not possible to get into the water, use a hose or shower. Consider coolers of water and juice as standard equipment for all your dives (Chapter 7 Part IV, Fluid Replacement).

- **Dress**. Stay lightly clothed when exposed to direct sunlight. Wear a hat. For increased evaporative cooling, wet your shirt and hat, wring them out, then put them back on.

- **Get In Shape**. Your heat tolerance while exercising is probably determined more by your aerobic fitness than any other variable (Chapter 6, Fitness).

- **Acclimatize**. Increase your exposure to heat. Be safe and gradual, but the way to make your body adapt to heat is to expose it to heat.

- **Rest**. Take rests and reduce work rate and intensity in the heat. Take it easy until you are more in shape for the activity and more used to the heat.

• **Prepare For Conditions**. Get the weather report. Pack suitable clothes and more things to drink than you think you'll need. Pack appropriate shade items like hats and tents. Before you go, check the dive boat or shore operation for shade conditions, availability of drinks, refrigeration for drinks, and shower or hose facilities for cooling off. Plan less strenuous activities until you have gotten into shape for more.

SUMMARY

Just as with cold, it is fairly obvious to say that if you are out in the heat, you can get hot. Several interacting and competing heat gain and loss mechanisms determine how well you will fare. Susceptibility to heat stress varies with ambient temperature, wind and water speed, humidity, clothing, work load, body composition, age, state of hydration, cardiovascular fitness and many other factors. People at greatest risk of overheating are those who are obese, out of shape, and dehydrated.

To increase your tolerance to the heat, improve your cardiovascular condition and general fitness level, work up to exercise in the heat, and drink extra fluids.

Separating responsible variables is complicated, and more involved than just stating that someone with a specific characteristic such as high sweating ability will have more heat dissipation. Nature provides you several ways to keep your body in a healthy range of internal temperature, regardless of the environment. Each person may be more efficient in some ways than others, according to their body chemistry. If you are overheating in your wetsuit or drysuit before, during, or after a dive, do something about it. You can dive safely in hot weather when you prepare properly.

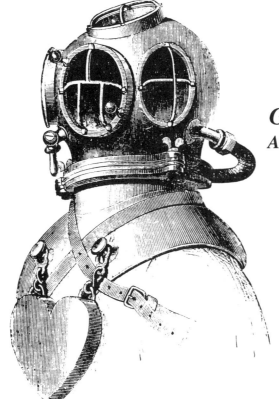

CHAPTER 4

GENDER FACTS AND FOLKLORE

Divers often make much of gender difference in diving. Overemphasis of small, and in some cases, nonfactual differences is common.

British diving physician Dr. Maurice Cross states: "From a diving point of view, I have never seen any convincing evidence that there is any gender difference between boys and girls in diving once commonsensical physiology is taken into account ... I don't think that there is a difference between the ordinary male and female diver but the pregnant female diver is clearly something different for a number of reasons." According to diving physician and Green Beret Lt. Col. R. Kelly Hill, M.D., "The only real difference between men and women divers is that during pregnancy women shouldn't dive - everything else is trivia and misinformation."

To dispel common myths, and to provide facts to take the place of misinformation, this chapter explores common facts and folklore about women and men divers.

- Issues Specific To Men
- Issues Specific To Women
- Issues Affecting Both
- The Folklore

CHAPTER 4
PART I

ISSUES SPECIFIC TO MEN

- Penile and Testicular Implants
- Infertility
- Offspring Gender
- Hair Restoration

PENILE AND TESTICULAR IMPLANTS

A portion of men divers and fliers have penile and/or testicular implants. Silicone testicular implant prosthetics are used for cosmetic restoration after testicular cancer, a leading cancer of young men. Five year survival of testicular cancer has increased to around 90%, up from only 63% in the 1960's. Testicular implants are also used to cosmetically restore shape after severe trauma and undescended testicle called cryptorchidism (cript-OR'-kid-izm), from the Latin words 'crypt' meaning hidden, and 'orchis' meaning testicle. Various penile implants of silicon, silicone-gel, and saline-hydraulic, also called inflatables, are used in reconstruction after injury, or more commonly, to restore erectile function after spinal cord injury, severe pelvic disease, and prostate or colon cancer surgery.

Because of questions of flight readiness of a pilot with a testicular implant, the German Air Force subjected a gel filled "test object of testicle-like shape" to extremes of pressure change in simulated altitude. They found no change in volume or shape. The researchers concluded that implants of this material, including mammary implants, would not be affected.

During penile prosthesis implantation surgery, small amounts of air sometimes remain trapped in saline-hydraulic prostheses. A US Air Force study subjected three such devices, with varying amounts of trapped air, to pressure reductions at altitude. They reported no leaks of air or fluid from increased volume upon pressure reduction, and that the prostheses worked normally post-test. In an unpublished study, the USAF repeated the altitude study in a hyperbaric chamber, also with no problems on ascent.

What Men Divers Can Do: Penile and testicular implants do not seem to pose a problem with alteration in size from pressure change. Some of the conclusions are based on altitude data, not diving where additional gas may be absorbed, and pressure change is often greater. Apocryphal stories of implants swelling to gargantuan proportions, or exploding with air travel or ascent from a dive are the stuff of tabloids, not reality.

INFERTILITY

Cold water and hot water both may reduce male fertility. The testicles reside near the body surface, subject to temperature variation. Women's reproductive anatomy is more protected. In Western society, infertility is estimated to affect 15% of marriages. Studies implicate a "male factor" in one-third to one-half of these cases depending on source cited. So-called "hostile environments" from tight shorts, constant bicycle riding, and chronic hot or cold exposure have been named as contributors.

What Men Divers Can Do: Men in treatment for infertility might look into the small possibility of thermal effects from chronic hot or cold water exposure. Men should not rely on hot or cold water exposure during diving for contraception. Effects on fertility are not guaranteed either way.

OFFSPRING GENDER

Anecdotal reports persist that male jet fighter pilots and military divers father more girls than boys due to some aspect of their careers. Various surveys done so far have not supported or refuted this assertion. If it is the case that more daughters are born to wives of these men, it is not known if the observed difference is due to pressure changes, other co-occurring conditions, or pure chance.

Work by Marguerite St. Leger Dowse and colleagues, with the Diving Diseases Research Center (DDRC) in England, found no difference from the expected proportion of gender offspring among males who fathered children during their diving career. They did find that women divers, gave birth to a higher rate of girl babies (non-diving father), but cautioned that at this point in the data gathering, the work is not definitive, with still too small a sample size, and too many other factors and unknowns that can affect outcome.

What Men Divers Can Do: Folklore for thousands of years has reputed varied techniques and practices to predetermine offspring gender. As far as we know, diving does not seem to be one of them. The surest way at present, involves medical intervention. The male contribution to conception is placed in a test tube and spun in a centrifuge. Cells bearing the gender-determining X (female) and Y (male) separate to an extent by motility. Even this method is not guaranteed.

HAIR RESTORATION

Balding is not unique to men although hair loss and restoration are more common in men than women. One medication used to attempt to stimulate hair regrowth is minoxidil. Minoxidil is originally a blood-pressure medication. When taken internally for high blood pressure, it could have effects during diving. When used for hair loss, it is applied topically and has no known ill effects during diving, however it has not yet been formally investigated.

Hair implantation and scalp reduction are surgical procedures. After a healing period of a few weeks, there seem to be no problems related to diving. The cosmetic effects are not always as appealing underwater as above. Some larger hair implant plugs can look like "doll hair" underwater.

What Men Divers Can Do: Topical hair growth stimulators and surgical hair restoration procedures do not seem, as far as we know, to be a concern to diving health. After transplant surgery, be patient with healing before swimming or diving. Newer hair transplant techniques using grafts, which contain fewer hairs per site than plugs, and micro transplants of one or two hairs at a time for hairlines, look more natural above and below the water.

CHAPTER *4*
PART *II*

ISSUES SPECIFIC TO WOMEN

- Pregnancy
- Oral Contraceptives
- Breast Implants

PREGNANCY

Diving while pregnant is difficult to study in humans. Much is unknown. There are many reports of diving during pregnancy with no known effect on the woman or the fetus. There are a few reports of birth defects. Risks, as identified by animal studies, may be associated with the hyperbaric environment of diving or treatment for decompression illness. However, hyperbaric chamber treatment for carbon monoxide poisoning is not ruled out during pregnancy, and there do not seem to be reported problems. In Europe, diving is not ruled out during pregnancy.

What Women Divers Can Do: Because of lack of good data, rather than any good evidence, the most common recommendation is not to dive during pregnancy.

ORAL CONTRACEPTIVES

Much discussion in the past surrounded theoretical risks of decompression sickness with oral contraceptive use. There is no substantiating evidence of greater risk. Moreover, incidence of death from pregnancy and childbirth is 3-8 per 100,000 in the Western nations, higher after age 35, and tremendously higher in many other areas of the world. Incidence of DCS is miniscule in comparison.

What Women Divers Can Do: There is no demonstrated influence of the pill on diving. Observe ordinary dive safety.

BREAST IMPLANTS

Silicone, and now more commonly, saline implants are used for augmentation and for reconstruction after radical breast cancer surgery. (Primarily a procedure undergone by females, males also receive these implants to enhance appearance of chest and other muscles.) To address the possibility of gas uptake or other change from pressure differences, Dr. Richard Vann at Duke University subjected three types of mammary implants to various chamber profiles simulating recreational and saturation dives. Small volume changes occurred after ascent in silicon gel devices, and smaller changes in saline devices. The difference was attributed to lower nitrogen solubility in saline than gel. The greatest, although still small change, was in gel-and-saline devices, attributed to the gel acting as a reservoir which diffused to the saline. It was noted that in all cases, changes were larger than those that would occur in the body under actual conditions, and would be unlikely to cause damage to the implant or surrounding body tissue. A caution was made against the unlikely worst-case situation of saturation diving followed by air travel in a craft that completely loses cabin pressure.

As reported in the previous section on issues for men divers, the German Air Force identified no change in volume or shape of a gel-filled "test object of testicle-like shape" that they studied under extreme pressure changes in simulated altitude. The researchers concluded that implants of this material, including mammary implants, would not be affected.

In commenting on unconfirmed tabloid "reports" of injury from implants following diving or flying, Dr. Peter Wilmshurst, medical advisor to the British Sub-Aqua Club, reminds that skin and subcutaneous tissue overlying the chest is flexible, changing much more during menstrual cycles, pregnancy, and breast feeding than possible from decompression. In addition, remember how much the skin and tissues of your chest wall stretch during breathing. Very small volume changes of implants would not likely result in trauma.

What Women Divers Can Do: Breast implants do not seem to pose a problem to diving from gas absorption, or change in size with pressure change. As with testicular and penile implants for men, apocryphal stories of the devices swelling or exploding with air travel or ascent from a dive are the stuff of tabloids, not reality.

According to diving physician and Green Beret Lt. Col. R. Kelly Hill, M.D., "The only real difference between men and women divers is that during pregnancy women shouldn't dive – everything else is trivia and misinformation."

CHAPTER 4
PART III

ISSUES AFFECTING BOTH
WOMEN AND MEN

Most physiologic issues affect both women and men divers. Although ordinarily there is not much to say about these issues as related to gender, they are included to dispel misconceptions. Remember that any gender predisposition in these cases is often overshadowed by behavior or other individual characteristics.

- Work Load
- Diving Accidents
- Cardiovascular Health
- Spontaneous Pneumothorax
- Flexibility
- Joint Structure and Injury
- Diver's Acne
- Back Pain
- Overweight
- Eating Disorders
- Anabolic Steroids and Steroid Substitutes
- Air Consumption
- Slipping Weight Belt
- Hernia

WORK LOAD

It is often stated that women, typically smaller with less musculature and aerobic capacity than men, would work closer to their maximum capacity while doing the same activity, thereby increasing risk of exhaustion, or just not be able to do as much. If that were so, then Arnold Schwarzenegger would beat Olympic swimming gold medalist Janet Evans in a swimming race. Or any man would race ahead of any woman, clearly not the case. In mixed-gender swimming and running races, after the first few elite males cross the finish, the rest of the entire race, to the last stragglers, is checkered with females and males of all shapes, sizes, and abilities.

Your ability to do physical tasks depends on your level of conditioning, work load, type of work, how efficiently you exercise while carrying out the activity, and whether the work is external like carrying weights, or internal like carrying yourself around, which varies with your weight. While walking up a hill, for example, a heavy man may work harder and closer to his maximum than a light woman of similar fitness, and depending on work load, even of lesser fitness. Internal work like gymnastics usually favors the smaller, lighter person. In external work, a larger person and a person with high muscular fitness usually has an advantage, male or female. In the shot put, for example, athletes who do well are usually large. Men and women span a spectrum of abilities in both types of sports.

What about aerobic capacity? VO_{2max}, which is the maximum amount of oxygen your system can extract and use to do exercise, and a top indicator of aerobic capacity, peaks in boys aged 12 to 15, and girls 9 to 14. Obviously, there is more to performance than just aerobic capacity. Men divers, though they might possess higher aerobic capacity than some women, may have poor finning skills or high body fat, requiring higher aerobic capacity to do the same scuba activity. They may present a larger frontal area to the water, which increases resistance to forward movement, and raises aerobic demand. Work by Dr. David Pendergast at Buffalo, determined that the oxygen cost for women in a finning task was lower than that of men because of their better lower body buoyancy, which improves horizontal trim. There are people with lower aerobic capacities that can work at higher percentages of their maximum, with less lactic acid accumulation and other markers of high work load. That means that they can run or swim at a faster pace, and endure longer than someone else who has a higher VO_{2max}.

Not all scuba tasks are aerobic, making aerobic fitness less pertinent for some tasks. Short, intense activity is not aerobic, but anaerobic. Aerobic capacity does not determine performance in an activity like power finning for short distances through surf.

Among elite athletes, the performance gap is narrowing with better training opportunities for women. Dr. Christine Wells, exercise physiologist and gender researcher at Arizona State University stated, "It's amazing how closely matched our abilities are, given our basic biology."

All the details may sound confusing, but the bottom line is that physical fitness, efficiency, and practice in the skill overshadow gender. The overlap in fitness is high between males and females. Fitness and skill levels attainable through exercise by females can fall within the wide range of male values.

What Divers Can Do: All divers can increase diving safety by increasing physical fitness (Chapter 6), concentrating on specific scuba skills like fin kicking.

It is potentially dangerous to exclude men from safety statements. A common statement is that women are smaller and weaker, and should not be pushed by male divers and instructors into situations beyond their capacity. Remember that no smaller, weaker, or out-of-shape diver should have their safety jeopardized by any male or female instructor or dive buddy in better shape.

It has been stated that women, typically smaller with less musculature and aerobic capacity than men, work closer to their maximum capacity while doing the same activity, thereby increasing risk of exhaustion. Were that so then Arnold Schwarzenegger would beat Olympic gold medalist Janet Evans in swimming.

DIVING ACCIDENTS

Diving accident treatment facilities and accident tracking centers report more cases of decompression sickness among men than women, but there are more men diving. When adjusted for relative numbers, there appears to be approximately the same rate of decompression sickness among men and women. According to records of the Divers Alert Network, more men are involved in fatal accidents, even when corrected for relative numbers diving. This may relate more to risky diving practice than physiology. As with lung cancer, which relates to smoking practice rather than physiologic gender susceptibility, women are catching up.

What Divers Can Do: Heed caution, remember your loved ones. Don't drink and dive, smoke and dive, or take judgment-affecting substances and dive. Avoid fatigue which leads to errors in judgment. Remember that risk does not always equal bravery. Don't be pressured into anything against your better judgment by a dive buddy or instructor. Prepare well for dives with skill practice, and appropriate working equipment.

CARDIOVASCULAR HEALTH

Cardiovascular disease, including stroke and heart attack, is the number one killer of both female and male divers, as it is in the general population. Cardiovascular disease increases risk of illness or sudden death during diving. It lowers your physical capacity to deal with exertion and cold, and increases the tendency to abnormal heart beats called arrhythmias.

Clogged and injured blood vessels do not restrict themselves just to the arteries of your heart. Your brain also depends on unimpeded blood flow. Reduced blood flow to your brain can unfavorably change your mental processes. "Hardening of the arteries" sometimes explains a person's senile behavior. Another body site affected by change in blood supply concerns men. An often ignored signal of dangerously narrowed arteries, warning of heart attack and stroke, is decrease in erectile function.

Males develop cardiovascular disease, on average, about ten years younger than their female counterparts. Most men dying a sudden death during physical activity have been found to have underlying heart disease. Men usually display greater blood pressure and other cardiovascular responses to cold water immersion than women. Men also have increased tendency to irregular beats. As with shoveling snow, the combination of work and cold during diving can be potentially lethal.

What Divers Can Do: Most cardiovascular disease has a large nutrition and fitness component. See your physician for a program to cut dietary fat and get in good physical shape. Don't smoke. When diving, wet face and hands before getting into the water. Get in slowly, and begin activity in an easy manner. Swim often to acclimatize to cold and to aquatic exercise.

Remember that cardiovascular disease is the number one disease of men and women, not just men. Don't dismiss symptoms of heart attack in a woman as indigestion on the false assumption that women don't get heart attacks. Get regular cardiovascular checkups, and consider getting an exercise stress test.

SPONTANEOUS PNEUMOTHORAX

Spontaneous pneumothorax is an injury where a lung collapses suddenly for no outwardly apparent reason. It occurs most often in young males in their 20's and 30's who smoke, sometimes when they are doing nothing more than sitting in a chair. Openings on the lung surface may come from a weakened area that ruptures. Often the weakness is congenital, meaning it has been present since birth. A history of spontaneous pneumothorax is usually considered a contraindication to diving, as there is possibility of recurrence. Pneumothorax occurring during diving can be fatal (Chapter 5, Part II - Lung Injuries).

What Divers Can Do: If you're a smoker, quit. Get regular checkups. If you have a history of spontaneous pneumothorax, it's recommended that you don't dive.

FLEXIBILITY AND JOINT INJURY

Flexibility is important to reduce injuries. A tight-jointed diver may be predisposed to muscle pulls and strains. A diver with tight back muscles is back pain waiting to happen. Although men generally have less natural flexibility than women, men can attain healthy flexibility with regular stretching. A less common phenomenon is joints that are too loose, more likely in women than men. Such joints may not seat well, increasing wear and tear if excess laxity is not offset by supporting musculature. This seems to be a less common problem than being too tight, and can be corrected with specific exercises. It is not true that musculature or exercise reduce flexibility. Lack of stretching reduces flexibility.

What Divers Can Do: Reduce your injury potential by stretching. Stretch often. Like gains from other exercise, flexibility is easily lost. Keep joints strong with exercise. Chapter 6 explains healthy stretching and exercise practices.

JOINT STRUCTURE AND INJURY

Regular exercise to get in shape for diving and other activities is beneficial and becoming more popular. A common misconception concerning gender and joint injury is that women's typically wider hip, and larger angle at the knee joint predispose to injury from regular exercise. Many studies do find higher incidence of lower body joint injury from exercise in women than men, but it seems that the underlying factor is not gender.

Lt. Col. Bruce H. Jones, M.D., Chief of the Occupational Medicine Division of the US Army Research Institute of Environmental Medicine, reported on data from army recruits. He found that those of lower physical fitness had consistently higher injury rate. When men and women of equal aerobic fitness were compared, their rate of injury was similar. More confirming data came from a 13-year study by Stephen G. Rice, M.D., of 60,000 high school athletes involved in 18 sports. Dr. Rice concluded: "What we may have here is not a gender issue, but instead a classic combination of training error and physical fitness."

What Divers Can Do: Women should not be dissuaded from regular exercise on the grounds of anatomic predisposition to injury. If anything, a vicious cycle of inactivity and injury grows. Both women and men divers need regular physical exercise for general health, diving health, and injury prevention. See your physician for a program that is right for you. Become more active slowly and carefully, working within your safety and comfort zone to make activity a lifetime habit, rather than a chore to endure and avoid if possible (Chapter 6).

Lt. Col. Bruce H. Jones, M.D., of the US Army Research Institute, found a similar rate of injury in men and women of equal aerobic fitness. From a 13-year study of 60,000 high school athletes in 18 sports, Stephen G. Rice, M.D. concluded "What we may have here is not a gender issue, but instead a classic combination of training error and physical fitness."

DIVER'S ACNE

Acne is an inflammation of sebaceous glands and hair follicles of the skin, usually of the face, shoulders, and back. Irritation from close-fitting diving suits, hoods, and equipment straps seems to contribute to increased occurrence of acne of the back and shoulders among divers. Although not limited to men divers, diver's acne is more often reported among men. Sebaceous glands secrete sebum, a semi-fluid oily secretion. Men's skin is, on average, naturally oilier owing to more sebaceous gland activity, which in turn, seems to be hormonally controlled. This type of acne is also reported among weight lifters and other athletes who often press sweaty backs against weight lifting benches and mats. Less commonly, a skin rash from the bacteria responsible for swimmer's ear may occur (Chapter 5 Part V, Swimmer's Ear).

What Divers Can Do: Keep your skin clean, wash with antibacterial soap. If you have a beard, don't forget to soap your beard. Don't use harsh cloths or abrading buffs. They seem to irritate and cause further problems. See a good dermatologist for persistent cases. When diving, adjust your equipment for optimal fit. Between dives rinse off, dry out, and take your gear and suits off, where feasible.

BACK PAIN

Back pain afflicts approximately 8 of 10 people at some point in their lives, and is the second leading cause of work absenteeism, after the common cold. According to some estimates, men suffer back pain up to three times more often than women. One factor may be the chronic load of carrying around their larger shoulders, bigger backs, occasional beer guts, and longer, larger torsos relative to their height than women. Women typically keep more of their weight lower and biomechanically safer. Onset of back pain can ruin a day's diving, then curtail activities for weeks, sometimes longer.

What Divers Can Do: Like lung disease that finally appears from years of smoking, sudden back pain usually comes from years of abuse. Wear and tear from your body weight alone by poor sitting, standing, and bending habits can injure your back over time as badly as a single accident. Sit, stand, and bend keeping the normal inward curve of your lower back. Tight, weak, torso and leg muscles are the major contributors to back pain. You can reverse and prevent back pain with good back habits and specific exercises. A few main examples follow:

Your abdominal muscles support your back from the front, like guy wires. Exercises like 'crunches' work the abdominal muscles. But remember that abdominal exercises give only part of the support your back needs.

You need to also work the back muscles to complete the ring of support. Exercise your upper back muscles by lying face down, and gently raising your upper body from the floor without using your arms. Work up to several sets of ten repetitions. For the lower back, lie face down, keep knees straight, and lift both legs or one leg at a time, whichever is more comfortable. Work over time to increase the number.

For flexibility, lie face down and arch your back by raising your head and torso from the floor, pushing gently up to your elbows. Then lie on your back, and stretch one leg at a time by holding it straight in the air and pulling it gently toward you. A variation of this stretch, where the bent knee is pressed to the chest, produced an injury reported in the March 1993 *New England Journal of Medicine.* A compression injury named "stretcher's scrotum" occurred when a man performing the stretch wore restrictive gym shorts, squeezing the testes between the bent leg and the body. The Journal cautioned that practitioners prescribing such stretches for back pain should recommend that males wear loose, stretchable pants. See your physician before attempting any back exercises and for a back exercise program that suits your own back health.

Sudden onset of back pain is often attributed to a single lifting or bending event, when usually results from years of bad back habits. Wear and tear from your body weight alone by tight, weak muscles, and poor sitting, standing, and bending habits can injure your back over time as badly as a single accident.

OVERWEIGHT

Body fat benefits diving several ways, described in Chapter 6. Too much, however, is unhealthy in general and for diving. It is estimated that slightly over 40% of American men are overweight compared to just under 30% of American women. Paradoxically, up to one-half of American women but only one-fourth of American men are estimated to be on a weight-reduction program at any point in time. The disparity often results in a phenomenon called "The Flintstones," where couples consist of an overweight man and slimmer woman.

Problems of overweight include the well-known relationships to heart disease, stroke, cancer, osteoarthritis, and gall bladder trouble. Adult onset diabetes deteriorates blood vessels, sometimes ending in blindness and loss of legs from gangrene. Seventy five percent of adult onset diabetes cases in men result from obesity.

Then there are problems no one tells you about. Fat is a key reason men snore. Increasing evidence suggests that serious snoring, and the related disorder of sleep apnea, where the snorer stops breathing during sleep, are both associated with stroke, cardiac irregularities, and not enough oxygen to the brain. Not enough oxygen to the blood vessels results in growth of fatty deposits. Other long-term harmful effects from these sleep disorders are more subtle but equally dangerous, like habitual daytime sleepiness related to high risk of serious automobile accidents. Losing weight is a first line of treatment.

A man just 20% overweight is twice as likely as a man of normal weight to die before age 50 from a weight-related disease, which would put the kibosh on his diving. That's a man who should weigh close to 160 pounds (73 kg) who weighs 192 pounds (87 kg) or a man who should weigh about 180 coming in over 216 pounds (82 kg and 98 kg).

Then there's the scary stuff. "Cognitive decline" was linked to circulatory disorders resulting from obesity in a Cornell Medical College study published in the February 1992 *Clinical Geriatric Medicine.* Data reported in the September 1992 journal *Hypertension,* indicated that men with long-term high blood pressure lost tissue of the left hemisphere of the brain, compared to men with normal blood pressure. A high percentage of high blood pressure cases link to overweight, even without high salt intake. The researchers suspect the specific areas of brain tissue loss affects memory, language, and "finding your way around." None of the above-mentioned problems go well with diving.

What Divers Can Do: Dieting is not the answer, as explained in Chapter 7. Regular exercise that you enjoy increases your general and diving health. Cutting saturated fats and increasing healthy food habits lets you eat without starving yourself. See your physician for a program you can live with.

EATING DISORDERS

Although common to think of eating disorders as women starving themselves, eating problems affect men, too. Males may attempt drastic weight restriction measures to make weight for wrestling, boxing, light weight crew, to be jockeys or coxswains, and for other sports where high body weight impairs performance, such as distance running and gymnastics.

Males not involved in sports may restrict food to unhealthy extents for the same reasons as females - in the belief that low body weight is esteemed, in a heightened focus on physical appearance, or for biochemical reasons that govern eating behaviors. Many do not know it is unhealthy.

Eating disorders are not always as obvious as low body weight. People with eating disorders may have normal or above normal weight. Hidden problems for both men and women are malnutrition, dental and electrolyte disturbance from frequent intentional vomiting, reduced bone density and increased risk of osteoporosis, and impaired reproductive function. Eating disorders are unhealthy for diving. They may lead to dehydration, poor tolerance to heat and cold, low exercise capacity, and general poor health.

What Divers Can Do: As with overweight, anyone with eating disorders should see their physician for a nutrition and exercise program they can be happy with. Eating disorders do not appear to be all psychologically based. Certain medications, a sensible exercise program, frequent small high-complex carbohydrate meals, and good hydration often help.

ANABOLIC STEROIDS AND STEROID SUBSTITUTES

The other side of seeking smaller body size through food avoidance is seeking larger than average size, more common among males than females. This is usually done with exercise, but sometimes aided through chemistry.

Not all steroids are anabolic, for example the steroid anti-inflammatories like cortisone and prednisone. The word "anabolic" means promoting tissue growth. Steroid anti-inflammatories do not do that. Vitamin D is another steroid that is not anabolic.

Anabolic steroids help increase muscle size. They may be injected or produced naturally in your body. Physical and emotional side effects of excess anabolic steroids are common. Most are incompatible with scuba diving: high blood pressure, elevated "bad" cholesterol (LDL), liver and kidney damage, greater risk of heart and vascular disease, volatile aggressive "roid" rages, and reckless uncontrolled behaviors.

Growth hormone, abbreviated GH, is sometimes used together with, or in place of steroids, because it is (so far) undetectable in drug tests. GH in adults may irreversibly increase growth of the jaw, forehead, hands, and feet. Trouble with GH arises for divers from increased risk of diabetes, high blood pressure, and heart trouble.

What Divers Can Do: Large muscle mass gains don't routinely occur without intense strength training. If you want to release growth hormones and anabolic steroids in your body in a controlled, natural, safe, and inexpensive manner without side effects, vigorous exercise does exactly that.

AIR CONSUMPTION

Higher air consumption, sometimes two or more times higher, is common in males, particularly large males, making them more likely to run out of air on the same profile as their female dive buddy, all other things kept the same.

Lung capacity is not the only determinant of air consumption. Out-of-shape divers may breathe more heavily at the same work load. They use tank air more quickly than more in-shape divers of similar lung capacity. However a diver, even if out of shape, may also be efficient at a particular scuba skill, reducing demand on their air consumption. As mentioned above in the section on work load, Dr. David Pendergast determined that women's better horizontal trim, due to more evenly distributed buoyancy, reduced their oxygen cost compared to men in the same fin swimming task.

Conversely, divers sometimes ask whether high physical fitness that improves oxygen consumption will increase air consumption. The answer has several parts, but the bottom line is that the usual effect of improved physical fitness is lower air consumption at the same work load. The extra oxygen that an in-shape person can extract is from the same volume of air. Increased fitness allows greater work loads, which may, on the other hand, increase air consumption. Obviously, like most things there are several contributors. In general, air consumption usually is higher in the nervous new diver, divers with large lungs, and during high work loads.

What Divers Can Do: If you empty a tank quickly, remember to monitor your air closely. With increased diving skill, air consumption usually decreases to various extents. Low air consumption is not always equal to high skill or comfort level, or high physical fitness. It may mean skip-breathing, a pattern of breathing more slowly, more deeply, and stopping longer than usual at the beginning and end of each breath. Skip-breathing is covered in Chapter 5 Part IV. Don't skip-breathe to reduce air consumption. If you use up your air quickly for whatever reasons, go ahead and use it. Just remember to come up before you use it all.

If you use up your air quickly, go ahead and use it.
Just remember to come up before you use it all.

SLIPPING WEIGHT BELT

Although not common, a weight belt can remain buckled, yet slip down and off the body of a vertical diver. Sudden weight belt loss can lead to uncontrolled ascent, particularly while wearing a wet suit or dry suit. This is mostly a problem of men and children divers with little difference between waist and hip circumference, and particularly if waist measurement exceeds that of the hip.

What Divers Can Do: If your weight belt slips often, consider an integrated buoyancy compensator and weight belt design. Do not tie on your weight belt, use a commercial shoulder weight strap, or make your weights difficult to ditch in an emergency.

HERNIA

A hernia, or rupture, is a weakness allowing an organ or other body structure to protrude through the tissue wall that normally contains it. Of several kinds of hernias, more than 75% occur in the groin (inguinal hernia). Umbilical hernias poke through your navel. Femoral hernias occur at the top of the thigh. Hernias are far more common in men than women because the inguinal canal is weak in males where the testicles descended from their abdominal position prenatally. One of every eight men will suffer a hernia in his lifetime, more commonly over age 40. Hernias are recognized by a soft lump under the skin that may go away when lying face up and return upon standing. They may cause pain when lifting, coughing, straining, or otherwise increasing internal abdominal pressure, as during a Valsalva maneuver. Obesity also contributes. Swallowed air at depth may distend the bowel on ascent. Lifting heavy gear may also aggravate a hernia. A hernia is not considered dangerous unless it becomes tightly constricted, cutting off blood supply, or a loop of intestine gets pushed through the opening and trapped.

What Divers Can Do: In the early stages, a hernia can be pushed back into place. Many people live uneventfully with hernias, although they often enlarge if not surgically repaired. Hernia repair is one of the most common surgeries in the United States with more than 600,000 procedures annually. Most hernia repair can now be done laparoscopically through tiny incisions, minimizing anesthesia, pain, and recovery time.

CHAPTER 4
PART IV

THE FOLKLORE

- Decompression Sickness (DCS)
- Hypothermia
- Hyperthermia
- Dehydration
- Drag
- PMS
- Sharks

DECOMPRESSION SICKNESS (DCS)

Most studies find no gender difference in DCS risk in diving or other hyperbaric exposures. Early studies that showed difference compared out-of-shape women with in-shape men, and studied too few women to draw sure conclusions. The often quoted Bangasser study showing higher DCS incidence among women was a questionnaire. Questionnaires have the problem of inherent bias toward findings because of reliance on voluntary participation – those who have had DCS will more often respond than those who have not, and women are known to be more likely to admit DCS. Marguerite St. Leger Dowse and colleagues at the Diving Diseases Research Center (DDRC) in England, looked at incidence rate. Rather than compare just crude data, as others had, they looked at co-varying circumstances, and found higher incidence among less experienced divers. A higher proportion of women divers have fewer years of diving experience, as women are proportionally newer to the sport. The difference may lie, not in physiologic susceptibility, but diving practice and experience.

Most studies of bubbles believed to cause DCS, as determined by Doppler ultrasound testing, indicate no gender difference in the number, magnitude, or duration of bubbles after identical profiles. Two show a difference – a 1985 report to the European Undersea Biomedical Society documented fewer bubbles in women than men, and another, the Doppler monitoring during the DSAT Recreational Dive Planner testing trials showed no difference in Phase I, but in the Phase IIb multiday series, "The number of dive sets (days) in which men had detectable bubbles was greater than that of women."

It's often stated by divers that women have more fat than men and therefore greater risk of decompression sickness. That statement is arguable at several levels. First, a 120 pound woman with 20% fat carries 24 pounds of fat. A 180 pound man with only 15% fat tops that with 27 pounds of fat. A 200 pound man with only 15% fat carries 30 pounds of fat. It is probably safe to say that many 200 pound male divers have more than 15% fat. The typically larger male often has more fat than an average female. Next, some researchers maintain there is no link between DCS risk and body fat. Finally, as mentioned before in the section on Diving Accidents, there seems to be no difference in real-life decompression sickness incidents between males and females in the diving population.

It seems likely that any difference in risk that may exist between men and women would be far smaller than the variability of risk among men or among women, or even from dive to dive in the same person.

What Divers Can Do: Risk of DCS does not appear to be gender related. Assumption of reduced risk for being male should not be relied on. Keep in good physical shape and avoid high body fat in general. Being an out-of-shape diver regardless of gender seems to increase risk. Honor the three major risk factors – depth, time, and ascent rate.

There is no conclusive difference in physical susceptibility to DCS between men and women. Risk seems to vary more among men as a group, than compared to women.

HYPOTHERMIA

Men have not been found to have less risk of hypothermia than women, as often thought. Extensive cold research in military and private sector laboratories finds no general evidence of greater risk to women's core temperature, from even extended and extreme cold exposure.

Both women and men have several mechanisms to maintain core body heat. Women preserve their core temperature with more conservation mechanisms. Men tend to lose more heat and produce more to match loss. A few examples follow. While the many particulars may seem confusing, the bottom line seems to be that men and women both protect their core temperature:

- Studies of body surface insulation find generally lower values in men. Men store less fat under the skin, giving their surface layer less insulating value. They generate more heat to match loss.

- Studies of heat generation typically find less heat generation among women. Their usually high conservation ability means less loss and therefore less need to raise metabolism to generate heat.

- A lesser known yet important insulation mechanism is the thickness of your shell. Your shell is your superficial zone including skin and subskin tissue. Shell thickness changes with amount of blood flowing through it, varying the insulation. Decreases in peripheral blood flow, called vasoconstriction, in response to cold thicken your shell. Men maintain high blood flow in their shell because of smaller vasoconstrictor response to cold than women. Consequently, men usually maintain less shell insulation. For more on shell, see Chapter 3 Part I.

- With less fat and shell insulation, men usually maintain higher skin temperatures. In a cold environment, a higher gradient exists between men's warm skin and the environment. That's called a high shell-to-environment gradient. Heat travels along gradients from high to low causing men with higher skin temperatures to lose more heat in the cold. An analogy is if you stand outside your house in cold weather, touch the outside wall and find it warm, you would notice the expensive loss of heat. Studies showing lower skin temperatures in women are often misinterpreted. Lower temperatures were of surface skin, lowering the shell-to-environment gradient, thereby reducing heat loss. They were not deep skin temperatures or, more important, core temperatures.

- Blood vessels of the head do not constrict in response to cold. Consequently the head is a high heat loss zone. Bald men lack the insulation imparted by hair. Without natural head covering they are usually subject to slightly more heat loss.

- Large men lose more total heat in the cold through their larger total surface area. To match loss, they also must generate more heat.

- Men usually display greater blood pressure and other cardiovascular responses than women to cooling, which may increase risk of cardiovascular illness during exertion in the cold.

Many variables working together and against each other make gender difficult to separate out. When exercising at the same absolute intensity, a smaller woman will gain body heat faster than a larger man because of smaller body mass to warm. In studies where women and men with similar subcutaneous fat thicknesses were compared in cold water, the women lost more heat than the men, but raised their metabolic rate to maintain core temperature without ill effect. Normally women have substantially higher skinfold thicknesses, decreasing need for metabolic increases. Studies showing higher heat loss in women of similar skinfold thickness as men are sometimes misinterpreted. Heat generation also increased to match loss. Heat loss by itself did not put the women experimental subjects at risk. Moreover in real life, women average higher subcutaneous thickness than men. One field survey of hypothermia incidents on land found fewer cases, by percent, among women. They concluded that women are less susceptible than men to hypothermia due to better insulation. Women also seem to be more likely and willing to get out of the cold.

It is commonly stated by divers that since women have a larger surface area-to-mass ratio than men, they are at greater risk of hypothermia. This is arguable at several levels. The surface area-to-mass quotient is not determined specifically by gender, and varies little among adults unless you compare extremely small and large people irrespective of gender. A tall, thin man's ratio might exceed that of a shorter, heavy woman. Short, thin men have high ratios compared to large men. Moreover, the surface area-to-mass ratio is not the main determinant of chilling.

Many variables determine heat loss, heat conservation, and heat production. No single heat loss pathway creates global risk of cold injury, and is generally counterbalanced by other factors. Other factors include body composition, fitness, hydration, age, distribution of body heat to the surface area, the amount of surface area in contact with the cold air or water, and others. Chapter 3 Part II further explains surface area-to-mass ratio.

Divers sometimes ask if, given that women have more curves than men, would they therefore have increased surface area to mass ratio to lose heat, and higher susceptibility to chilling? Although large variations in overall body shape and size affect surface area-to-mass ratio, extra curves, usually well insulated, make a minuscule difference. Then too, men's bodies are full of curves, from muscles to other normal structures. Further, as explained in Chapter 3, total body ratio differences are minor compared to ratios of individual body parts.

Men's genitals don't fare well in the cold for similar reasons as fingers and ears. "Frostbite Shorts," under various names, is a documented cold injury. Underwear for men runners and hikers is available with insulated, wind-proof front panels to protect this susceptible area.

What Divers Can Do: Keep body parts with high heat loss covered. Dress for conditions. If you get cold easily, take extra precautions. Get in good physical shape, including weight lifting for increased heat production and storage. If you are cold, do something about it. Don't tough it out.

There is no convincing evidence that men are at less risk of hypothermia than women, as often thought.

HYPERTHERMIA

In physics class you learn that a large pot of water takes longer to boil than a small one, and requires more heat energy to bring it to a boil. Unfortunately, the simple extrapolation that a man will not overheat as easily as a woman because he is larger ignores several physiologic processes.

Heat production increases with body mass. As people get bigger, the discrepancy grows between the amount of heat they produce and the amount they lose in the heat.

Men usually produce more heat than women but dissipate it less efficiently in hot weather. A man's customarily smaller surface area-to-mass ratio than women's can't radiate away as much heat relative to production. At the same time their usually larger total surface area provides more surface to absorb the heat of the summer sun. Men's skin temperature is often higher than that of many women, reducing the shell-to-environment gradient in hot weather. A low gradient impedes heat loss.

Large men seem to be more prone to heat injury than women, the reverse of common contention among divers. A paper in the 1990 *Medicine and Science in Sports and Exercise* indicated exercise-induced heatstroke is more common in males than females. Motivation to push to limits along with physiologic factors might contribute to this, according to a 1993 review of the phenomenon in the *Journal of Strength and Conditioning Research.*

Less serious than heat stroke is simple overheating which is uncomfortable, reduces exercise capacity, and may dehydrate through high sweating, all conditions unfavorable to the diver. On average, large men seem more predisposed than smaller men and women; of course, susceptibility varies.

Large size predisposes to heat buildup in hot conditions, but it does not seem to be as important as physical fitness in susceptibility to heat problems. An out-of-shape woman working at the same intensity as a more in-shape man would also have high core and skin temperatures. If ambient temperature is high, the low skin-to-environment gradient would also be a problem to the woman.

Men and women have the same number of sweat glands, contrary to popular myth. Although, in general, men begin sweating at lower body temperatures than women, that does not necessarily put women at higher risk of overheating, as sometimes thought. If you sweat more than can be evaporated, the extra sweating confers no cooling advantage. Other heat dissipation pathways compensate for lower sweating rate in women. Moreover, once a sweating threshold is passed, males and females seem to sweat at the same rate.

The many variables involved in studying heat tolerance at rest and during exercise make gender distinctions difficult to assess. As a generality, the people most prone to overheating seem to be large people, particularly large men.

What Divers Can Do: Keep your fat weight low and get in good physical shape. Both increase heat tolerance. Hydration is a major factor in heat tolerance (Chapter 7 Part IV). When active in the heat, drink extra fluids, reduce your work load, and take breaks in a cool area. If you are overheating on a dive boat, get in the water or hose yourself down (Chapter 3 Part IV).

Evidence does not support the common assertion that women are more susceptible to hyperthermia than men. Large men seem to be more prone to heat injury than women.

DEHYDRATION

Thermal researcher C.H. Wyndham described men as "wasteful, prolific sweaters" in a paper in the *Journal of Applied Physiology* comparing male and female heat adjustments. That much seems to be true. However, it's myth that men have more sweat glands than women. Men often begin sweating at a lower body temperature than women, so lose more fluid by volume and percent through sweating than women. Some studies found that after a threshold is reached, women and men sweat equal volumes.

In studies of marathon runners, men lose a higher percent of their body weight in sweat than women. With prolonged and profuse sweating, combined with men's usually higher water requirement due to their usually larger size, men may incur higher risk of dehydration and electrolyte loss than women.

What Divers Can Do: Be aware of the phenomenon and drink extra fluids, particularly in the heat. Except with running marathons or exercising long hours in the heat without stopping to eat, electrolyte loss is not usually a problem to men or women. Most meals restore all the electrolytes you need. Remember to stop to eat and drink or use sport drinks, which contrary to popular dive rumor, do not dehydrate you (Chapter 7, Part IV). Remember to pack food and plenty to drink for dive trips.

It's myth that men have more sweat glands than women.

DRAG

Although some divers ask if women's breasts affect their horizontal "trim" underwater, it is not the case. Scientific techniques that analyze center of gravity and buoyancy reveal that men seem to have a greater predisposition to streamline problems caused by poor trim.

Men usually carry more fat on their upper bodies compared to women, who have fat distributed on both upper and lower body. Men's longer, leaner legs are more likely to sink, causing increased drag in the water. An interesting study by Pendergast on competition swimmers found male swimmers to have a poorer comparative power output than female swimmers due to buoyancy distribution. The males' less horizontal position increased drag.

What Divers Can Do: Proper weighting and kicking techniques seem to be more important than gender in determining diving trim. Experiment with different weight distribution of your belt and belt placement.

Practice kicking in a pool to develop a long, loose, effective kick. Keep your feet loose, without curling your toes. Keep ankles floppy, not stiff.

Although some divers ask if women's breasts cause horizontal 'trim' problems, scientific analysis indicates it is not the case. Men more frequently have 'trim' problems from their longer, leaner legs.

PMS

Concerning published statements that PMS would "enhance tendency to hostility" and "difficulties" with buddies, there is quantitatively no more of a tendency than inherent in the average male throughout the month. It may be safe to say that tendency to aggression or altercation may be more representative of the male than female.

SHARKS

Divers sometimes ask if menstrual blood attracts sharks. This has not been found to be the case. Neither does menstrual blood attract grizzly bears during camping trips, cause wine to sour as stated in ancient religious writings, or cause wings to snap off airplanes, as pilots insisted in the 1920's. Conversely, in an as yet unexplained phenomenon, Dr. Carl Edmonds found that Australia's shark attack tracking system reports nine times more shark attacks on men, even though there was an even number of male and female swimmers. The term man-eating shark, for now, remains.

CONCLUSION

Anyone who goes scuba diving brings different combinations of body attributes and skills to the sport. Great overlap in abilities exists between male and female divers. Common attempts to attribute specific characteristics such as susceptibility to overheating or hypothermia as gender generalities should be questioned skeptically. Predisposition of one gender to a particular problem is often inconsequential relative to other factors. Compared to the major factors of physical fitness, experience, and skill, gender merits little attention and does not seem to be important in diving.

CHAPTER 5

DIVING INJURIES

Diving is a relatively safe activity compared to many other active pastimes. Injuries occur when diving, as they do in any aspect of life. Some are the usual bumps and scrapes of living. Others are specific to diving. This chapter tells their interesting stories, prevention, and what to do if they occur.

- Lung Injuries
- Decompression Sickness
- Oxygen Toxicity
- Diving Headaches
- Swimmer's Ear
- Marine Stings

CHAPTER 5
PART I

LUNG INJURIES

You can injure your lungs in diving accidents and from non-diving activities. Lung injury may increase your chance of further injury when scuba diving. Diving lung injuries range from mild to fatal.

- Breath-Hold Injury
- Pneumothorax
- Bronchitis
- Emphysema
- Asthma
- Pneumonia
- Preventing Diving Lung Injury

BREATH-HOLD INJURY

On ascent, pressure drops, allowing air in your lungs to expand. If you won't let expanding air out the way it came in, it may make its own hole to try to get back out. This is called a lung overexpansion injury. Overexpansion injury from diving is in the category of pulmonary barotrauma, the prefix "baro-" referring to pressure. A sometimes descriptive acronym for the alternate term of **p**ulmonary **o**ver**p**ressure **s**yndrome is POPS.

Breath holding on ascent is the most common cause of lung overexpansion. Air may leak through without definable lung injury, or in extreme cases, may rupture the lung wall causing lung problems from mild injury to complete collapse.

Escaped air may enter your arteries, the blood vessels that carry blood to everywhere in your body (Figure 5.1). It is not usually one bubble that makes problems, but many. If these bubbles, called air emboli, get to a vessel too small to pass through, they get stuck. Sometimes serious problems occur from bubbles that obstruct blood vessels in important places like your heart and brain. You may have long-term problems in the body areas served by the injured brain cells. You may have trouble walking if the injured area was a motor area. You may not remember well or have other mental changes if the bubbles destroy a cognitive center. It depends on area involved. There is no way to predict which area will be damaged. The usual acronym for arterial **g**as **e**mbolism is AGE. A **c**erebral (brain) **a**rterial **g**as **e**mbolism is abbreviated CAGE.

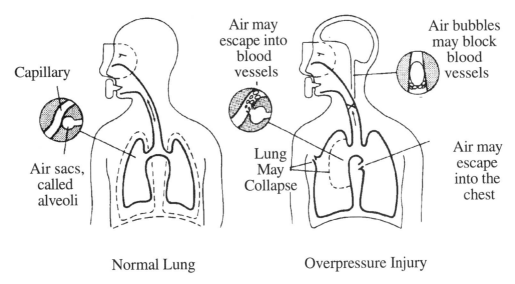

Capillary

Air sacs,
called
alveoli

Air may
escape into
blood
vessels

Lung
May
Collapse

Air bubbles
may block
blood
vessels

Air may
escape
into the
chest

Normal Lung

Overpressure Injury

Figure 5.1. Air escaping through lung wall into circulation may get into the chest cavity and collapse the lung, or enter the circulation and from there lodge in the heart or brain.

Anything interfering with uninterrupted air passage through lung airways may lead to lung overpressurization and air embolism: congestion or constriction from respiratory illness, and lung weakness or scarring from injury or previous lung surgery.

PNEUMOTHORAX

Pneumothorax occurs when air gets into a section of your chest cavity outside the lungs. *Pneumo* is a Greek word meaning air. *Thorax* is your chest cavity. The space between the lining of the lungs and the chest wall, called the pleural space, is normally airtight. Air and fluid accumulating in the pleural space surrounding your lungs can collapse your lung on the affected side. Air entering your circulation becomes an air embolism. Pneumothorax can occur from a diving overexpansion injury, although it is rare. Non-diving events can also cause pneumothorax.

Traumatic Pneumothorax. If an object like a bullet, knife, or broken rib pierces your chest wall, air rushes in from outside. Pneumothorax from such accidents is called traumatic pneumothorax. A diving overexpansion injury, whether by breath holding or air trapping from lung scarring, may also cause a traumatic pneumothorax.

Spontaneous Pneumothorax. Pneumothorax occurring suddenly without any obvious injury is called spontaneous pneumothorax. Weakened areas on the lung surface may just give up and rupture. Often the weakness is congenital, meaning it has been present since birth. Spontaneous pneumothorax stereotypically occurs in young males in their 20's and 30's who smoke, sometimes when they are doing nothing more than sitting in a chair.

Tension Pneumothorax. An occasional serious complication of traumatic or spontaneous pneumothorax is a tension pneumothorax. In tension pneumothorax, the pleural tear acts as a one-way valve. Air forced into the pleural space progressively compresses the heart, decreasing its ability to function, and compresses the other lung. If a pneumothorax occurred while diving, the change in pressure on ascent could produce a tension pneumothorax, which can kill you in a hurry.

Can Someone With A History Of Pneumothorax Go Diving? There are people with a history of pneumothorax who continue diving. Do they risk collapsing their lung again underwater, a potentially grave injury? What is their chance of embolism through the injury site?

Dr. Jim Clark, diving physician of the University of Pennsylvania Institute for Environmental Medicine, and Past President of the Undersea and Hyperbaric Medical Society, rules out diving ever again after spontaneous pneumothorax: "With spontaneous pneumothorax, you don't know cause. There may have been an abnormal predisposition for spontaneous pneumothorax to occur in the first place and subsequently recur.

"Trauma-induced pneumothorax is a tougher call, however. The chance of diving injury after traumatic pneumothorax depends on the degree of lung weakening and scarring from the trauma. There are potentially dire consequences of gas embolism through the weakness. But at least with traumatic pneumothorax you know the cause and potential for healing. What you don't know is if the injury site is weak or how well it healed. There are no tests for that. To exactly know that requires an open chest procedure like an autopsy, but of course I'm being facetious, and even then you can't tell. If there is scarring it will show on an x-ray. You need a clear x-ray and good exercise tolerance to be considered for diving again."

Dr. Fred Bove, diving physician, Chief Cardiologist at Temple Hospital and Medical school, and Past President of the Undersea and Hyperbaric Medical Society, comments on relative risk of traumatic pneumothorax and overexpansion pneumothorax:

"Pneumothorax caused by injury to the chest wall does not carry the same risk of recurrence as pneumothorax from an overexpansion injury caused by air trapping. With traumatic pneumothorax, there was no trapping before and no blebs. Adhesions, which are scar tissue sticking to another surface, are not as much a problem. There is the unproven claim that adhesions in the pleura can cause lung shear (differential in lung expansion) that could tear a lung with subsequent embolism.

"It's different if the pneumothorax was caused by a major traumatic injury. The chest x-ray will show the damage: significant anatomy change like distortion or missing ribs, evidence of partial collapse that never re-expanded, pleural thickening, calcium around the pleura, or leftover inflammation. But if the x-ray is normal the chances are low for inducing another pneumothorax through diving. It's different in each case. You need case-by-case physician assessment."

BRONCHITIS

Drs. Clark and Bove agree that chronic bronchitis is a diving contraindication. By definition, "chronic" means lung changes and anatomic damage. The person would be prone to diving overpressure injury and possibly pneumothorax because of obstructing damage, or lung wall weakness. An isolated episode of viral bronchitis is believed to be another story. Just about everyone has had a chest cold. They recommend waiting 3-4 weeks before diving until completely resolved, and you're no longer infectious.

EMPHYSEMA

Dr. Lawrence Martin, Chief of Pulmonary and Critical Care Medicine at Mt. Sinai, Cleveland, adds emphysema in the category of chronic lung disease contraindicated for diving. He states, "Chronic obstructive pulmonary disease (COPD) is the umbrella term for both chronic bronchitis and emphysema, two conditions that are almost always due to long-term cigarette smoking... Unlike asthmatics, where the air flow obstruction is episodic and largely unpredictable, patients with COPD have permanent air flow obstruction. Anyone with COPD should not dive."

ASTHMA

Asthma is a chronic respiratory disease. It is characterized by sudden, recurring attacks of constricted breathing passages, called bronchoconstriction. Some diving medicine authorities advise against ever diving with active asthma. They feel that the chronic obstructive nature of asthma increases risk of problems, although it is not known to what extent. Bronchoconstriction at depth may lead to lung overpressure injury on ascent. Asthma symptoms at the surface may reduce exercise tolerance and ability to complete the dive safely. This only has to happen once in a diving career to be a problem.

Recently there has been reason to rethink the blanket disqualification. For those with allergic asthma, there are fewer substances to be allergic to, called allergens, around the water environment. According to diving physician Maurice Cross, "Many asthmatics have perfectly good diving careers, particularly the allergic asthmatic. However, when asthmatics get into trouble, the risk of problems is high." According to Dr. Lawrence Martin, "Asthma is a highly variable condition. Each person with a "history of asthma" who wishes to dive should be evaluated on an individual basis by someone knowledgeable about diving. If lung function and chest x-ray are normal and there is no chronic need for medication, there should be no medical prohibition – provided the person is aware of the theoretical risks of diving, and diving with any manifestation of asthma that may arise. This statement implies informed consent on the part of the potential diver, and eschews any statement such as "it is safe" or "it is unsafe" for the person to dive. In fact, there are inherent risks to diving, and an asthma attack could, of course, increase those risks."

PNEUMONIA

After pneumonia see your diving physician. You will need a physical evaluation and chest x-ray to be sure your lungs are clear with no areas of increased density or inflammation.

PREVENTING DIVING LUNG INJURY

- See a diving physician after medical conditions involving your lungs before you go diving again.

- If you smoke, quit.

- Breathe normally during diving.

- Avoid breath-holding ascents

- Avoid inhaling to total capacity while underwater.

- If something frightens you underwater, don't rapidly ascend holding your breath. According to diving physician and researcher Dr. Philip James, of Dundee, Scotland: "Keep breathing, it's good for you."

CHAPTER 5
PART II

DECOMPRESSION SICKNESS

As the problem that most limits duration and depth of all recreational, technical, military, commercial, and scientific diving, a section on diving injuries would seem remiss without mention of decompression sickness (DCS).

As the malady with the most elusive nature, topics like specific mechanisms, exact causes, definitive treatments, even how bubbles form and affect the body are not really known. This section attempts to encapsulate current thinking.

- How Decompression Sickness Occurs
- Where Are The Bubbles?
- Mechanical Effects Of DCS
- Biochemical Effects Of DCS
- Where Do Bubbles Hurt You?
- Is It DCS or AGE?
- Factors Affecting Risk of Decompression Sickness
- Bubbles Not All Bad?
- Preventing Decompression Sickness

HOW DECOMPRESSION SICKNESS OCCURS

Chapter 1 gives the basics of how nitrogen enters and leaves your body with and without forming the gas bubbles associated with decompression sickness (DCS). Mechanisms of gas transit and bubble formation are not well understood. Describing what is known in nontechnical language requires oversimplification and omission. An interesting paradox results. Top decompression scientists will tell you they don't know how decompression sickness occurs, whereas a basic diver will usually be glad to tell you exactly how. With that in mind, a brief review:

When you go diving, nitrogen in the air that you breathe from your tank or other air supply passes from your lungs to blood vessels in your lungs, changing from gaseous to dissolved form. Dissolved nitrogen travels with your blood to your body tissues. Increased pressure with increased depth dissolves more nitrogen in your blood, then everywhere else in your body. On ascent, the extra nitrogen begins coming back out of you. The nitrogen passes back into your bloodstream from the tissues still in a dissolved state, then travels to your lungs where you breathe it out again as a gas.

At least that's what we hope happens. If you come up too fast, nitrogen can't stay dissolved. It begins to become a gas again before you can breathe it out. This gas forms small bubbles in your body that are mostly nitrogen, and partly oxygen and carbon dioxide.

Many questions remain about bubbles. How do they cause the varied problems of decompression sickness? What happens when they form? Sometimes bubbles are painless, called silent bubbles. Other times they hurt, cripple, or kill. Why? How? Where do they start? Where do they go? No one knows for certain. Some possibilities follow.

WHERE ARE THE BUBBLES?

Bubbles form after many dives, even those within limits of decompression tables and computers. It's probably not true that bubbles form after every dive. Not all dives produce conditions sufficient for bubbles to stick around, much less form. Bubbles may travel through the blood to new locations, or just grow in one place, or both. Most of the time you are not aware of these bubbles. Other times, pain or loss of body function make you very aware.

Bubbles in the Venous Side. Bubbles may get stuck where they form, causing pain and damage. They may also form without symptoms in the veins that return blood to the right side of your heart. From there the heart pumps them with the blood to the lungs which filter most bubbles out. In this case, harm is limited to some temporary damage to the cell lining of your venous system. What bubbles probably don't do is pass from body tissues into veins, unless the veins are already torn. Bubbles, even though tiny, are too big to physically pass through blood vessel walls. They may redissolve for passage through vessel walls then reform into bubbles, but can't drain into intact vessels.

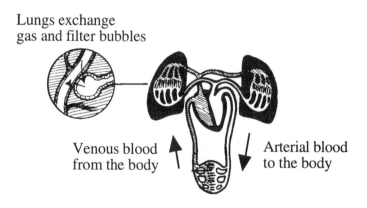

Lungs exchange gas and filter bubbles

Venous blood from the body

Arterial blood to the body

Figure 5.2. Blood returns from your body through veins to the right side of your heart, which pumps it to your lungs. Your lungs send filtered, oxygenated blood to the left heart, which pumps it to everywhere in your body through the arterial system. Bubbles are one of many things that lungs can filter.

Bubbles in the Arterial Side. Bubbles in your veins (venous gas emboli) return with blood from all over your body, to the right side of your heart, then to your lungs, Figure 5.2. Your lungs can get rid of bubbles by filtering them out. Like your nose and upper respiratory passages that trap and filter out dust, particles, and some bacteria, your lungs are a constant filter of all kinds of organic and inorganic particles that sweep through them all the time. In one experiment, the lungs effectively filtered out small glass beads injected into the blood stream. Lungs are also efficient filters of gas bubbles after diving. Such filtering keeps bubbles, in most cases, from going back to your heart and being pumped from there in the arterial blood to your body. That would hopefully be the end of bubbles there. Too many bubbles overwhelm your lungs' ability to filter them. Bubbles then return with the blood from the lungs to the left side of the heart. From there they get pumped into your arteries. Arteries are blood vessels conducting blood from your heart to everywhere in your body. You can see how arterial bubbles could be serious.

Another way bubbles cross over to your arterial circulation is through defects in the heart. One receiving recent attention is the patent foramen ovale (for-RAY'-men oh-VAHL'-ay). In Latin, foramen means opening, and ovalis means oval. A foramen ovale is an oval opening in the partition between the right and left upper chambers of the heart, present in a fetus before birth. A flap usually closes over it soon after birth. A patent (PAY'-tent) foramen ovale (PFO) remains open after infancy, or opens if pressure rises sufficiently, so that some blood passes from the right side of the heart directly to the left, bypassing the lungs. Little or no blood may go through the shunt under ordinary conditions. A large amount may pass through during a maneuver commonly, though technically incorrectly, called the Valsalva maneuver – see the glossary for explanation. The Valsalva consists of forcibly exhaling against a closed nose and mouth that divers sometimes use to "pop" their ears, some with more vigor than others. It is estimated, depending on the diagnostic procedure used, that from 10% to 30% of adults retain some degree of patency. Although demonstrated that bubbles pass into arterial circulation through a PFO, it is not known how much this patency contributes to decompression sickness. Some work indicates it may increase severity of a DCS hit but may not increase likelihood of occurrence.

Other shunts may open in the lung itself if you have too many bubbles, allowing bubbles to cross to the arterial side, particularly with high blood pressure. Another possibility, though difficult to demonstrate for trans-lung bubble passage, is if the bubbles are too small to filter. Small bubbles may pass to the arterial side then pick up more gas and grow to damaging size during a repetitive dive. Problems that bubbles cause seem to be from both their mechanical and biochemical effects, and from the interaction of mechanical and chemical effects.

MECHANICAL EFFECTS OF DCS

Bubbles compress blood and lymph vessels from the outside, and obstruct from within. Small blood vessels and adjacent tissues get squashed, sometimes torn from bubbles forming near them. Fluids and lymph may get backed up from obstruction, accumulating where they should not be. Decrease in blood supply from all the interference is called ischemia (pronounced is-KEE'-me-uh). Pain and loss of function follow ischemia. If you examine the word ischemia you can find the word hemia, whose Greek root haima means blood. Other words from this root are hemorrhage, hemophilia, hemoglobin, even hemorrhoid.

Bubbles may also compress nerves. Nerves, particularly central nervous system nerves, don't like being pushed around. A small compression quickly impairs function. This nerve compression may be behind symptoms of decompression illness that occur soon after the dive. Loss of function from physical nerve compression can occur much faster than loss of function from impeded blood flow, or the chemical effects that accompany bubble trouble.

BIOCHEMICAL EFFECTS OF DCS

Bubbles are more than small mechanical presences. They interact with your body's ready defenses against foreign invaders. White blood cells called leukocytes, and blood clotting cells called platelets, clump together (aggregate) and adhere to bubbles and the blood vessel lining. Platelets are small blood components shaped like flat little plates. Platelets aggregate and stick to each other and to other things, which is the basis of their role in normal blood clotting. The biochemical mechanisms behind why leukocytes and platelets adhere to microbubbles at the bubble-blood interface are unclear. It may just be that the body sees nitrogen microbubbles as invaders to aggregate around and adhere to. That's their job. Other electrochemical forces may congregate little globs of free fats in the blood into blockages called fat emboli. Several biochemical pathways such as coagulation and an enzymatic breakdown process called fibrinolysis also get busy on bubbles.

Another biochemical response to bubbles is an interesting cascade of immune reactions called complement activation. Complement is a complex system involving some 20 proteins floating in your blood serum that can assemble themselves on foreign bodies to destroy them. Dr. David Hsu, of U. Pittsburgh's Medical School vividly describes three actions of the complement system: "It sends out a delicious odor to attract special engulfing cells called phagocytes to dine. These cells can cause your brain to turn up the thermostat, giving you a fever. Then it pokes forks in the meal, the better to dine. It also rallies its disassembled pieces floating around in your bloodstream into a battering ram that knocks a hole in the thing and phffft! The battering ram is called the membrane attack complex, or MAC attack." Less commonly, the complement is called alexin, from a Greek word meaning "to ward off." What the complement cascade means to diving and microbubbles is not really known. For more on complement, see the glossary.

All the various biochemical reactions may circulate throughout your system to take place far from the original site of bubbles. All add to existing mechanical problems of obstructed blood flow, edema, and possibly toxic oxygen free radicals, discussed later in the section on oxygen toxicity.

Extreme fatigue following dives is generally accepted to represent one of the variants of DCS. One rationale for the mechanism is bubble overload in the lungs. Venous blood containing tiny blockading bubbles (venous gas emboli) returns to the right side of your heart, which pumps it to your lungs. The mechanical presence of high bubble load causes the lungs to release a potent class of chemicals into the pulmonary circulation. The resulting fatigue, called inappropriate fatigue, is different from just being tired after a dive. Those who have had it describe an overwhelming, heavy, bone-weary fatigue.

WHERE DO BUBBLES HURT YOU?

What About Joint Spaces? The joints are common sites of decompression pain. The joints have many components. One is the joint space. A frequently asked question is whether bubble formation in the joint space is the cause of joint pain. With joint surgery called arthroscopy, air bubbles may be left behind, and you can inject gas directly into the joint space. Neither is known to produce pain, so bubbles in the joint space itself are not likely as a big source of decompression pain.

What About Tendons and Ligaments? Tendons and ligaments are components of a joint. Tendons attach muscles to bone on either side of a joint. Ligaments attach the bones of a joint to each other. Are bubbles forming in tendons and ligaments around the joint the source of joint decompression pain?

Although bubbles form in tendons and ligaments, they are not easy places for bubbles to form. Their anatomic make up is more watery than fatty. Blood flow is low and intermittent. There won't be many molecules of gas available to form bubbles. They are also poorly compliant, which means their inherent resistance to stretch and their tough fibrous structure oppose bubbles formation and growth. Conversely, this lack of compliance to stretch increases the possibility of impingement, and subsequent pain. Tendons and ligaments are well innervated. Mechanical impingement of nerve by bubbles would rapidly cause joint pain. Because this type of local joint pain is rapidly reversible with recompression, it is theorized that the source of pain is more likely to be bubbles than chemical activation of complement and local inflammation.

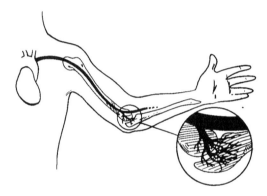

Figure 5.3. Bubbles may occur around joints.

What About Nerves? Nerve tissue is directly involved in certain decompression sickness cases. Pain and loss of function occur quickly from mechanical nerve compression, described earlier in Mechanical Effects. Pain can be at the site or refer to other body parts. In serious cases of decompression injury, bubbles can mechanically injure the spinal cord in several ways. Bubbles physically disrupt the nerve cells called neurons, but not enough neurons may be involved to account for loss of function. Another possibility is that because of a fairly tight membrane surrounding the spinal cord, expanding gas bubbles inside the membrane compress the spinal cord, promoting ischemia. Then again, there may not be enough gas to raise cord pressure sufficiently to account for ischemia.

Another way bubbles may affect the nervous system is to tear blood vessels. Small vessels in the spinal cord don't have much supporting connective tissue as does the rest of the body. These small vessels may tear and bleed, a serious problem in the central nervous system. One intriguing problem with bleeding is that blood contains iron, a potent promoter of certain types of toxic oxygen reactions. Iron in the body is usually found in a form tightly bound with a protein, as in hemoglobin. When it becomes available in unbound form it turns on harmful oxygen reactions (Oxygen Toxicity, Part III in this chapter). It is possible that this type of hemorrhagic injury is part of the delayed problems that go along with spinal cord hits.

Other chemical changes may damage the fatty covering over nerves called myelin, and change the ability of vasculature to function around nerves. Vessel changes may allow fluid shifts, which may explain some symptoms of shock in DCS.

What About Bone Marrow? Bone marrow is a relatively fatty tissue. It is possible that bubbles form in bone marrow. Bubbles may easily grow, as there are many molecules of gas there to make bubbles. Bubbles growing inside a confined space like bone marrow raises the pressure. Ischemia may result, but this possibility is currently a big unknown.

What About Skin? Some use the term "skin bends" to mean itchy skin common after a chamber dive, but rare after in-water dives. It is probably due to gas diffusion through the skin. Another phenomenon is a characteristic red mottled rash anywhere on the body, most commonly on the torso. Experiments on animals find bubbles in the skin when this kind of skin bends occurs, and that body chemicals that influence blood vessel dilation and constriction may be involved, but the connection is not well defined.

What About Your Brain? There is much discussion about whether and when bubbles affect the arterial circulation of the brain. Small amounts of bubbles seem to block vessels only fleetingly (minutes), then the vessels dilate and bubbles move on, perhaps leaving some damage to the inside of the vessels. Several events may follow large amounts of bubbles reaching the arterial circulation of the brain. In the first few minutes, bubble blockade reduces blood flow, resulting in loss of function. Brain vessels react to this embolic event by dilating, allowing bubbles to move on. Bubbles traveling through the brain circulation may strip the thin layer of flat cells lining the blood vessels, called endothelial cells, leaving injured endothelium and bare patches. The body sends white cells to help, which stick to the areas causing more narrowing, more decrease in cerebral blood flow, and more loss of function.

Vasodilation dies down in a reactive phase over the next 45 minutes to a few hours. Leukocytes and platelets, described before in Biochemical Effects, accumulate and aggregate, along with all the other biochemical events that follow bubbles. Autopsies of the brain after this find inflamed areas with tiny red spots of bleeding called punctate hemorrhages. In severe cases, brain blood vessels are found filled with bubbles of air.

Researchers Dr. Brian Hills and Dr. Philip James, among others, found increase in permeability of the blood-brain barrier from bubbles. The blood-brain barrier is an important brain defense that allows some things through brain capillaries, and prevents others. They found that bubbles rapidly impair the blood-brain barrier's way of dealing with protein, resulting in fluid accumulation called edema. They state that this and related phenomena may explain symptoms of DCS that are not well explained by bubbles just occluding the vessels.

IS IT DCS OR AGE?

Arterial decompression bubbles can produce serious disability. Symptoms are often hard to tell from those following a lung overexpansion injury, because both have arterial bubbles called arterial gas emboli (AGE). In lung overexpansion, air escapes through the lung wall into circulation if expanding air can't leave the lung during ascent. AGE was explained in Lung Injuries, Part I of this chapter.

There may be no clinical evidence of lung damage from lung overexpansion injury, so lung x-rays will not always help tell AGE from arterialized DCS bubbles. Onset time of symptoms may give more information. The time course of air embolism symptoms from lung overexpansion is usually short — immediately or within minutes after surfacing. Decompression sickness usually develops after a dive, sometimes up to several hours later. Bubbles take time to develop and more time to appear in the arteries. Dive profile is also revealing. A short dive, well within the tables, but with rapid ascent, may be evidence in favor of lung overexpansion injury causing AGE. Then again, rapid ascent also can trigger decompression bubbles. This is not an easy field.

The bubble problems of air embolism and decompression sickness are grouped by some researchers into the single category of decompression illness (DCI). There is no need for the diver to spend time diagnosing which is which, often impossible anyway. Start the diver on 100% oxygen by mask. Contact the local emergency system, and transport to a facility with a hyperbaric chamber that treats diving injuries. To learn ways to prevent and treat dive accidents contact the Divers Alert Network. To learn the location of chambers in your dive area contact the Undersea and Hyperbaric Medical Society for their UHMS Chamber Directory.

FACTORS AFFECTING RISK OF DECOMPRESSION SICKNESS

Major determinants of your risk of DCS are depth, time at depth, multiple ascent and descents, and ascent rate. Lesser factors have been explored. DCS susceptibility is not well understood, leaving these variables open to sometimes wild conjecture. Although factors behind individual variability in risk of DCS are not pinned down, it is no mystery that individual variation exists. Just as the same dose of medication varies in action on different people, divers react differently to similar doses of nitrogen. People's bodies vary in how they absorb, use, and eliminate any drug or substance because of differences in activity of their cardiovascular, enzymatic, metabolic, and other systems. Infants and elderly take longer to metabolize drugs, for example. Many things interact to change individual response to a given dose of nitrogen during diving. A few of many possibilities follow.

Dehydration. Dehydration is commonly accepted as important to DCS susceptibility. It's not really known how. Possibilities are increased blood viscosity and decreased tissue perfusion, which would limit gas elimination (Fluid Replacement, Chapter 7 Part IV).

Cold and Warmth. Cold decreases your body's ability to take up and give off nitrogen. Being uniformly cold throughout your dive seems to decrease decompression risk. It seems to make a difference if being cold occurs during gas uptake or release portion of the dive. A diver starting a dive warm absorbs more nitrogen at depth than a cooler diver. If the warm diver then chills, common toward the end of a dive, eliminating the additional nitrogen gas burden slows, increasing risk (Effects of Cold, Chapter 3 Part III).

Another factor sometimes discussed by divers is that slightly more gas dissolves in a liquid as temperature of the liquid drops. Recreational divers have questioned if this increased solubility increases uptake and risk of decompression sickness. It is not likely that this is the reason behind increased risk from cold in some circumstances. Increase in dissolved gas is small, and while gas solubility increases as temperature drops, diffusion decreases directly as temperature drops, because thermal motion of molecules that determines diffusion decreases with cold. Any effect of increased solubility is likely to be small compared to the greater effect of cold to decrease circulation and nitrogen exchange.

Previous Bends. It is not firmly established whether having had a decompression "hit" makes you more susceptible to another. If you have an underlying condition that led to the first incident, you may be more susceptible than someone else to subsequent ones, but perhaps not because of the hit itself. Of course there is argument about this. If injury from DCS changes tissue structure, it might change the workings of your body involved in gas transit and bubble formation. Another possibility is that a bends incident may be more severe in an already-damaged area because there is less margin to tolerate damage and less ability for compensation. There are also anecdotal reports of repeat temporary joint pain with ascent from diving to the surface, or from the surface to altitude during air travel. It's not known if this is from underlying susceptibility or from previous injury.

Ascent Rate. Slow ascent rate can make the difference between having time to offgas nitrogen through exhalation, and allowing bubbles to form in your body before you can breathe them out. Safety stops act to slow your ascent, and also make the difference between having time to offgas nitrogen before it evolves into bubbles, or allowing your body to fill with inert gas grenades. An interesting hypothesis involving slow ascent rate to reduce risk of DCS comes from Dr. Peter Bennett of Duke University. He proposes that lung overexpansion from rapid ascent occurs much more frequently than is now appreciated, producing arterial gas emboli, discussed previously in the section, Is It DCS Or AGE?

Aging. Risk of DCS seems to rise with age, but we don't know why for sure. Some theories involve increasingly irregular joint surfaces with aging, making conditions better for bubble formation. Other theories invoke circulatory changes and changes in fitness and body composition. Many dive authorities recommend increasing conservatism by reducing bottom time as years pass.

Body Fat. Fat is known to take on more nitrogen than other body constituents, but it is not known if fat contributes directly or indirectly, or at all. It may be that fatter subjects in studies of risk were in poorer physical condition, had higher incidence of fatty blood vessels that compromise circulation, or were older. Some clinicians treating decompression accidents, from the early days of the tunnel and caisson workers to present day scuba divers, find more DCS cases in the overweight, out-of-shape diver. Others state that they can find no relation. Moreover, it seems almost to be the norm for divers to be overweight, in general.

Gender. Although popular to assume that risk differs enough to matter between men and women, evidence so far does not seem to bear this out (Chapter 4, Gender Facts and Folklore).

Multiple Exposure. Repeated diving has the distinction of seeming to both raise and lower DCS risk. Some sort of acclimation or accommodation effect appears to occur with multiple dives. At the same time, the multi-day repetitive dives that are popular in dive vacations correlate with higher probability of a DCS incident as the number of dives increases during the week. Early diving researcher Haldane recognized the effect among newly exposed caisson workers and recommended part-time exposures to start.

Exercise. Effects of exercise on risk are not well understood. The nature, intensity, and timing during both the dive and decompression portion of the dive seem to affect risk.

Exercise during a dive increases nitrogen uptake. Exercise also warms you, further increasing uptake. One United States Navy experiment indicated that more decompression was needed after exercise at depth. On the other hand, exercise during decompression seems to be a stimulus for gas release. Exercise during the decompression stop increased offgassing, reducing decompression time. This study was not of a typical recreational diving profile, and should not be duplicated to try to modify your own risk.

It is possible, but not confirmed, that mild movements during the decompression phase of diving may be beneficial, but that vigorous exercise after diving may relate to some DCS problems.

Fatigue. The Divers Alert Network Accident Report for 1992 lists fatigue and overexertion as common factors in many decompression sickness accidents. It's not known if fatigue changes decompression dynamics, or as in any sport, decreases judgment, affecting risk accordingly.

Diver Creativity. Divers are often creative with dive rules and guidelines, producing conditions that interfere with orderly nitrogen transport. In other words they don't use the tables and computers properly.

BUBBLES NOT ALL BAD?

An intriguing possibility is that bubbles, in certain situations and quantities, are helpful. Work by Dr. Eric Kindwall, Dr. Ed Lanphier, and others explored the idea that small bubbles can transport gas more efficiently than can gas in solution. That means that bubbles can remove extra nitrogen coming out of solution, then travel with blood to the lungs which filter them and remove them from further circulation. A certain amount of bubbles, too small to do harm, may remove nitrogen faster and more efficiently than if no bubbles had formed. Bubbles that are too many and too large, however, result in decompression sickness.

PREVENTING DECOMPRESSION SICKNESS

Due to many unknowns in decompression science, some authorities have gone so far as to say the only sure way to prevent decompression sickness is to stay on land and hope a low pressure system doesn't pass suddenly overhead. If you choose to dive, just as with any other dose-related activity like taking pharmaceuticals, drinking alcohol, and sun tanning, you can make general guidelines to avoid injury:

• Major factors influencing your risk of DCS are depth, time at depth, and ascent rate.

• Keep your ascent rate slow and controlled. The new US Navy tables slow ascent rate from 60 feet per minute (about 20 meters per minute) to 30 feet per minute (about 10 meters per minute). For perspective and practice, pace that off – it's slow.

- Make safety stops.

- Back off the limits of your tables or computer more with each birthday.

- Be in good physical shape, well hydrated, and well trained. Avoid things that negatively affect judgment, skills, or physical condition such as alcohol, drugs, and fatigue.

- Carefully read the instructions that came with your computer or dive tables and follow them. To quote Dr. Tom Neuman, "It doesn't matter which tables you don't use."

SUMMARY

Nobody knows for certain exactly when, how, or where decompression sickness happens. Effects of bubbles in the body seem to be both mechanical and chemical. Bubbles mechanically blockade flow of blood and oxygen, and may squeeze nerves, causing pain and loss of function. Bubbles also activate your body's chemical defenses to invaders. Effects occur in many areas of the body.

Major determinants of your risk of decompression sickness are depth, time at depth, multiple ascent and descents, and ascent rate. Other factors affecting risk are dehydration, chilling toward the end of a dive, and improperly using your decompression table or computer. Possible factors include aging and too much exercise post dive. Evidence does not support gender as a factor. Unknowns include body fat and previous bends.

Divers often concentrate on wanting to know if different pharmaceuticals, or exercises that change blood flow, or if small differences in body fat or physical condition will reduce their risk of a decompression problem. Instead, a more effective way to reduce decompression risk is to concentrate on the main determinants of susceptibility – depth, time, multiple ascents and descents, and ascent rate.

CHAPTER 5
PART III

OXYGEN TOXICITY

Oxygen is toxic to all living things. In many animals including humans, several hours exposure to oxygen at moderately higher pressure than you ordinarily breathe, leads to the painful breathing, fluid in the lungs, and lung damage of pulmonary oxygen toxicity. Breathing oxygen at extremely raised pressure brings trouble more quickly, affecting your central nervous system but not your lungs. Several problems occur, including convulsion without warning. Convulsions while diving without a mouthpiece retainer, full face mask, or helmet could be fatal by drowning. Why should long, low exposure hurt your lungs and not much else? Why does shorter, higher pressure not hurt your lungs, but make so much trouble elsewhere? How can you prevent it?

- Defenses Against Oxygen
- Free Radicals
- Pulmonary O_2 Toxicity
- Central Nervous System (CNS) O_2 Toxicity
- An Intriguing Twist
- When Is O_2 Toxic?
- Susceptibility
- Treatment
- Prevention

In primordial times, there was no oxygen in the thin atmosphere around Earth. Later, oxygen was a toxic gas released by early cyanobacteria and other creatures swimming in the global bathtub. Many living things died out when oxygen first became widespread. Others developed varied strategies to defend against too much oxygen. Those that didn't, such as certain bacteria called anaerobes, live only in oxygen-free environments. Some anaerobes live peaceably in our gut. Others menace us with botulism and gas gangrene. Because oxygen is toxic to them, we can treat problems like gas gangrene using hyperbaric chamber exposure to high oxygen. Whether living things are anaerobic or use oxygen, too much oxygen is toxic, from plants, to insects, to fish, birds, bacteria, and divers.

DEFENSES AGAINST OXYGEN

When you dive, you can be exposed to higher levels of oxygen than normal. When you go to altitude, the percentage of oxygen in the air is still 21%, but pressure is lower so there are less oxygen molecules for your body to use. Your body does various things to deal with both conditions so the amount of oxygen your body gets varies little, even with variations in external pressure as wide as half normal pressure at altitude, to many times normal at depth.

Vasoconstriction. One way your body controls oxygen delivery is the small blood vessels. Oxygen is a vasoconstrictor. With high oxygen levels, small blood vessels constrict, reducing amount delivered around vascular beds.

Hemoglobin-Oxygen Buffer. Another fascinating mechanism is what physiology books call the hemoglobin-oxygen buffer system. Hemoglobin has another duty beside carrying around oxygen and blindly dumping it on your cells. Hemoglobin tightly regulates the pressure of oxygen it releases to the body. With low surrounding oxygen partial pressure, as at altitude, hemoglobin releases more than usual. With high levels of oxygen, hemoglobin releases less. Within limits, though you breathe higher or lower than normal pressure oxygen, hemoglobin still delivers oxygen to your body tissues at almost normal pressure. Your lungs get exposed to too much oxygen, but the rest of your body doesn't.

Breathing oxygen at different pressures is a major, important diversion from Henry's Law, the physical principle that the amount of gas dissolving in a liquid increases as the partial pressure of the gas increases (Chapter 1). During diving, nitrogen tensions increase your body, more or less according to Henry's Law. But although increased pressure with depth dissolves more oxygen in your blood, the hemoglobin-oxygen system prevents it all from being delivered to your cells. Oxygen tensions throughout your body vary little during external pressure changes, within the range from almost half normal pressure at moderate altitudes, to many times normal at depth. Above and below that range, your body can't compensate, Figure 5.4. Physical chemist Dr. David Hsu, put it colorfully: "The difference between other gases like nitrogen and a gas like oxygen is that oxygen has a special carrier, hemoglobin, that feeds the hungry but not the rich. It's like having a cart of oxygen molecules trundling along, and if somebody needs a molecule, she gets one, but if she has too many already, none is given her. A just system!"

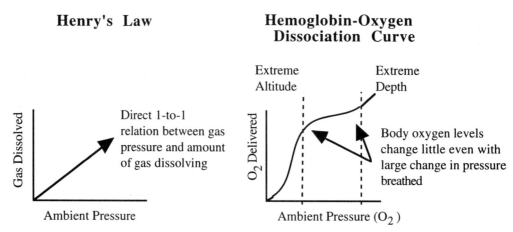

Figure 5.4. As ambient pressure changes, nitrogen tensions in your body change more or less according to Henry's Law, but oxygen tensions vary little, within limits. With too little oxygen pressure, you can't extract enough to live. With too much, oxygen toxicity develops.

Enzymes. Your body has several body enzyme systems to remove special molecules called oxygen free radicals that form under several conditions, particularly high oxygen pressures. Other chemicals repair damage in your body caused by oxygen free radicals, up to a point. Eating these enzymes will not benefit you because digestion breaks them apart, discussed later in Preventing Oxygen Toxicity.

FREE RADICALS

Oxygen toxicity is an intriguing and complicated phenomenon. Not fully understood, and having many contributors, it is generally accepted to involve oxygen free radicals.

What Are Free Radicals? Free radicals are atoms or molecules that exist temporarily with at least one unpaired electron. Being unpaired often makes them reactive and eager either to acquire another electron or lose the unpaired one. They are called free radicals, because they exist free from their usual state for a short time (very short – fractions of seconds).

The oxygen we breathe is regular molecular oxygen. It often, particularly under high oxygen pressure, accepts an extra electron and converts into one of several forms of oxygen called oxygen radicals. Oxygen free radicals are one kind of many free radicals. Although not all radicals are unstable, oxygen free radicals are unstable, making them reactive. Oxygen radicals are hungry for another electron to "eat." They grab one from another molecule, rendering that molecule temporarily radical, which quickly goes on to bite an electron from another molecule, and so on, like a destructive game of tag.

Fire is one of many reactions propagated by free radicals. Experimental analysis suggests that the deep color of the soil of Mars is iron that was highly oxidized by free radicals. One of the most important of several oxygen free radicals is called superoxide (O_2^-), a good name for a "super" oxygen molecule. Another important player in oxygen toxicity, produced by radicals, although not itself a free radical, is hydrogen peroxide. This is the same hydrogen peroxide that disinfects cuts and ramp-launched the German V-1 flying bomb.

What Do Free Radicals Do? Like many reactive and unstable things, oxygen free radicals cause damage. Sometimes this damage is helpful to you. Naturally occurring hydrogen peroxide and superoxide in your body rapidly kill bacteria, part of how your immune system deals with infectious disease. Other radicals appear to be obligatory for normal muscle contraction.

Sometimes the damage harms you. Free radicals grab electrons from hemoglobin and cell membranes, damaging them. Autoimmune disease, a process where your body mistakenly attacks its own cells, may be an example. Although poorly understood, part of the problem is believed to involve production of too much hydrogen peroxide in the body, damaging cells. Superoxides may contribute to other illnesses like heart attack, cancer, stroke, and emphysema. Radicals are an intriguing topic in the study of joints, particularly in arthritis research.

Free radicals are believed responsible for beneficial effects in the body such as muscle contraction and immune response, and detrimental actions of some disease processes and oxygen toxicity.

When Do Free Radicals Form? Small amounts of oxygen free radicals form in your body all the time during metabolism of the oxygen you breathe to produce energy. More free radicals form during the increased metabolism of exercise, and with exposure to smog, and high oxygen environments. Repeated grinding of protein, as with cutting and filing fingernails generates some free radicals. The tar in each puff of cigarette smoke has about 10^{14} free radicals (one hundred million million), and the gas phase has about 10^{15} (one thousand million million) per puff.

Your body has many different mechanisms to get rid of the various free radicals that form, so radicals have little ill effect unless there are too many. One thing your body does is make several enzymes that rapidly scavenge radicals. The enzyme family that removes superoxide is superoxide dismutase (SOD). SOD converts superoxide into hydrogen peroxide. The enzymes catalase and peroxidase convert hydrogen peroxide to water. A treatment of autoimmune disease currently under study involves use of your own immune system's catalase enzyme. It is hypothesized that without these naturally occurring scavenger enzymes in your body, even the normal oxygen level of breathing air around us would be toxic.

Different organisms developed different strategies to protect against too much oxygen. We constrict blood vessels to reduce oxygen supply, and have hemoglobin to regulate delivery. Our bodies produce enzymes to inactivate oxygen free radicals. It's probable that without these enzymes, even the normal oxygen level of breathing air around us would be toxic.

PULMONARY O$_2$ TOXICITY

When there is too much oxygen for your body to defend against, you can suffer the toxic effects of oxygen. Breathing moderate pressure oxygen for a long time directly exposes your lungs, and the two branches of your windpipe leading to your lungs called bronchi (BRON'-kai), to higher than average oxygen pressure, damaging the tissues.

Pulmonary oxygen toxicity wouldn't readily occur in recreational scuba diving. It occurs after long exposure to oxygen, as during extra-long treatments in a hyperbaric chamber (six or more hours above the equivalent of 50 or 60% oxygen, $PO_2 = 0.5$ or 0.6, compared to the normal land pressure of 0.21, see Chapter 1, Partial Pressure). Pulmonary oxygen toxicity is also called oxygen poisoning or the Lorrain Smith effect, after Lorrain J. Smith, the first to study it, describing it in 1899.

CENTRAL NERVOUS SYSTEM (CNS) O₂ TOXICITY

With breathing too high oxygen pressure, your hemoglobin-oxygen buffer fails. Oxygen pressure soars in tissues. One hypothesis is that overly high oxygen pressure allows free radicals to swamp your enzyme systems for removing them. Free radicals go floating around in the blood, hoping for electrons. One place, among many, that they find them is in lipids (fats) and proteins that are critical to making up every cell membrane. Free radicals damage the lipid membrane in a process called lipid peroxidation. Damaged (peroxidized) lipids then grab electrons and hurt the next lipid molecule. Oxygen free radicals have impairing effects, particularly on nerve cells. That's why most of the impaired function from this type of oxygen toxicity occurs in the central nervous system, before enough time passes to affect the lung. Oxygen free radicals also inactivate several enzymes regulating body processes, attack the hemoglobin in red blood cells, and damage the lining of blood vessels in spots. White blood cells called neutrophils rush to defend the vessels, and stick to the stripped areas. This "help" often makes things worse by causing mechanical obstruction, further damage to the lining, and occlusion of the vessel. CNS toxicity is also called the Paul Bert effect, after the physiologist who first described its effects in 1878.

Pulmonary oxygen toxicity takes a long time to develop, and affects your lungs and breathing passages. Central nervous system oxygen toxicity comes on quickly and affects the nervous system, before enough time passes to affect the lung.

AN INTRIGUING TWIST

Paradoxically, trouble can occur when giving oxygen to treat an injury from not enough oxygen. In a heart attack, areas of the heart shut off from oxygen begin to die. In crush injury to a limb, you may lose function or even the limb from lack of oxygen-carrying blood flow. When blood flow, called perfusion, is restored, oxygen flows back into the area and with it, the free radicals and cascade of oxygen free radical damage. Then you're off and running on what's called a reperfusion injury. Much interesting work in high pressure oxygen science deals with trying to understand and avoid the paradox of the reperfusion injury.

WHEN IS O₂ TOXIC?

There is no one depth where oxygen becomes toxic. CNS O₂ toxicity can occur during a dive if you dive too deep, or too long for the amount of oxygen in your breathing mixture. In other words it depends on the percentage oxygen in your breathing mixture, depth, and exposure time. It is beyond the scope of this section to detail the many mixes and their applications. This overview gives a basic understanding about oxygen in diving. If you choose, you can learn the many details in mixed gas training classes.

Recreational Air Diving. Recreational diving usually uses regular air with 21% oxygen. Oxygen toxicity is not expected during recreational diving while breathing air. Pulmonary toxicity would take longer to develop than recreational divers ever dive. The depth range on air where CNS toxicity becomes an issue is far deeper than the 130-foot limit for recreational diving suggested by many dive training organizations. That limit for recreational air diving, often not considered a limit at all, exists for reasons other than oxygen toxicity. Reasons usually center on nitrogen narcosis, decompression sickness, tradition, experience of the diver, and other factors. Like many issues in diving, these reasons are the subject of spirited debate, which there is no need to go into here.

Deep and Technical Diving. It is becoming more common for private citizens to conduct dives for personal enjoyment at depths and requiring equipment and breathing mixtures previously used only in military, scientific, or commercial settings. Much discussion in the diving community continues about what defines the deep diver and what is a technical diver. Regardless of definition, whether you dive deep or on mixes with more oxygen than air, CNS O_2 toxicity is a possibility.

Both maximum partial pressure of oxygen (PO_2) and time at depth are considerations. As explained in Chapter 1, a common unit of partial pressure of oxygen is the atmosphere absolute (ATA or atm abs). See Chapter 1 Units of Partial Pressure). To avoid CNS toxicity, the current recommendation regarding PO_2 is to stay below 1.6 ATA for short dives in easy conditions, and below 1.4 in harsher, more typical conditions. Some people state that between 1.45 and 1.6 ATA is a "caution zone." Others recommend against divers exceeding 1.45 ATA in general, and cutting back further with conditions. Another consideration is time. Lower PO_2 allows more time exposed. For example, maximum time allowed at 1.6 ATA is 45 minutes. Longer dives require planning for lower PO_2. Hyperbaric chamber treatments expose patients to higher PO_2, but patients are at rest in a dry environment, reducing risk. Maximum PO_2 is subject to much discussion among scientists and deep divers, with claims and counterclaims about divers exceeding or observing each suggested limit with or without incident.

Limits divers choose are partly based on rough subjective measures, such as if the water is cold, whether there will be strenuous exercise, and how much risk of convulsion they are willing to accept. A less subjective variable is exposure time. Serious CNS trouble may start quickly at high PO_2, while you may tolerate lower PO_2 for longer periods. Onset time of oxygen toxicity symptoms is variable among divers and in the same diver, so conservatism reduces risk. There are tables of PO_2 exposure limits for diving. Limits over several days of exposure are lower per day than for a single exposure, because oxygen damage can be cumulative. Damage (up to a point) reverses with removal from exposure. Examples are time between dives, and with switching to lower FO_2 (fraction or %) mixtures in a procedure called "air breaks."

Oxygen toxicity threshold varies from diver to diver, and in the same diver from day to day. Conservatism reduces risk.

The depth where you will reach your decided maximum PO_2 depends on the amount of oxygen in your breathing mix. For perspective, PO_2 of air at the surface is 0.21 ATA (21% at 1 atmosphere). Going underwater to 33 feet breathing air, doubles partial pressure to 0.42 (0.21 times two atmospheres). At 66 feet, or triple the pressure, PO_2 is 0.63 ATA. At 99 feet it's 0.83 ATA (Chapter 1, Partial Pressure).

Diving with higher percentage oxygen mixes, or going deeper further raises PO_2. Two common Enriched Air Nitrox (EAN) also called Oxygen Enriched Air (OEA) mixes contain a higher percentage of oxygen than the 21% in regular air. Their depth limits due to risk of oxygen toxicity are shallower than for air. Breathing 100% oxygen reduces depth maximum still further. Table 5.1 lists depths at which you will reach various PO_2 using four different breathing mixtures. It is not a list of depths to dive.

Table 5.1. Depths (fsw) at which four partial pressures of oxygen (PO_2) will be reached using different mixes.

Mix	PO_2 (ATA or atm abs)			
	1.2	1.4	1.6	2.0
Air 21%	156	187	218	281.3
NOAA Nitrox I 32%	91	111	132	173.2
NOAA Nitrox II 36%	77	95	114	150.3
100% Oxygen	6.6	13.2	19.8	33

SUSCEPTIBILITY TO OXYGEN TOXICITY

Susceptibility To Oxygen Toxicity Increases With:

- Depth
- Partial pressure of oxygen (PO_2)

- Length of exposure
- Cold conditions

- Exercise
- Carbon dioxide retention

- Previous history of seizure
- Gas analysis errors

- Various drugs
- Factors unknown

- Factors increasing metabolism and/or lowering seizure threshold, possibly fever, steroids, and hyperthyroidism

---

Oxygen toxicity varies among people and in the same person from exposure to exposure. As with decompression sickness, but with greater variability, main factors in risk are your depth, pressure of the target gas you breathe, in this case O_2, and length of exposure. Susceptibility often increases with cold conditions. Interestingly, under experimental conditions, clinical hypothermia has been found to delay onset or decrease severity. Hypothermia is not recommended for divers, and more practically, chilling, which is different from hypothermia, described in

Chapter 3, seems to increase risk. Susceptibility increases with factors that raise blood flow to the brain, like hard exercise and carbon dioxide retention, and factors increasing metabolism. Animal studies have identified increased risk from various central nervous system stimulants like amphetamines. Although not yet formally tested on humans, it would make sense for divers to avoid amphetamines or drugs with actions like amphetamines. Oxygen convulsions have occurred after accidental exposure to high PO_2 by breathing a mix with higher oxygen content than thought, due to analysis errors or accidentally switching at depth to a special tank with high oxygen reserved for a shallow decompression stop (Chapter 1 Part V, Gas Switching).

TREATING OXYGEN TOXICITY

Unlike decompression sickness, which has been called the "pay upon leaving" disease because symptoms usually begin after surfacing, CNS O_2 toxicity occurs during a dive. Numbness, visual changes, and tingling in extremities are warnings for the lucky. They reverse with ascending to lower PO_2. Convulsions may come on with little, if any, warning. If you survive the convulsion, no specific treatment is usually called for, except to surface and be evaluated medically.

Oxygen Treatment Misconception. It is not true that the extra oxygen you breath with oxygen-enriched mixes makes you ineligible for hyperbaric oxygen treatment in case of a decompression accident. As explained in Chapter 1, you may accumulate similar doses of oxygen while breathing regular air at a deeper depth, as with higher oxygen percentage in shallower water. Divers breathing regular air at deeper depths may expose themselves to the same amount of oxygen, and are treated if necessary. Consider this: you would be given oxygen on the way to the chamber, standard treatment for decompression sickness.

PREVENTING OXYGEN TOXICITY

Some time ago a sham product to prevent oxygen toxicity was promoted to divers. Because it was already well established that the superoxide radical is involved in oxygen toxicity, and the enzyme removing superoxide is superoxide dismutase (SOD), the sham involved selling pills containing the antioxidant SOD, claiming it would reduce or prevent oxygen toxicity. This does not work. All enzymes are proteins. If you eat enzymes, including SOD, they will be digested before they can pass through your intestine. Digestion breaks down proteins and other nutrients to components until they are small enough to pass through your intestinal wall. That's the job of digestion. Broken down SOD will not reassemble into SOD on the other side of the intestine, so eating SOD will not raise your body levels of SOD. Eating ordinary enzymes, except those that aid digestion, is a useless and expensive snack.

As is often the case with sham cures offered in pill form, there were many research studies that seemed to back up the claim. Obviously, studies exist showing SOD reduces free radical formation. None of these studies involved eating the SOD. Research is looking into injectable forms, other nervous system agents, and other antioxidants. Vitamin E is a known antioxidant. It is lipid soluble and protects cell membranes, which have a major lipid component, against daily oxygen free radical activity. Vitamin C is a water soluble antioxidant, having protective effects in blood and the fluid inside and outside of cells. Vitamins E and C also work together in their free radical inactivation work. The way Vitamin E inactivates radicals is to accept the extra electron from radicals, becoming itself radical. Vitamin C is next in the cascade, taking the electron to restore Vitamin E. However, and this is an important distinction, taking more Vitamins E and C has not been shown to increase their usual effects on radicals in the body. If you are vitamin deficient, they may show effect, but not if you are vitamin sufficient. They should not be used in a mistaken assumption of reducing susceptibility to oxygen toxicity. As an interesting aside, remember that radicals are not all bad. They perform critically important functions in your body. You may not want to push your resting levels down, even if it were possible to do so by eating antioxidants. If SOD levels rose in the cells that fight infection, like neutrophils and monocytes, you will be seriously at risk of catastrophic infections because then these cells wouldn't have the free radicals they need to kill invaders. As of this writing, there is no pharmaceutical for divers to prevent O_2 toxicity. You will, for now, have to observe the rules of safe diving with oxygen.

Get training before diving with gas mixtures other than air or at deep depths. Several organizations provide training and certification for deep and mixed gas diving. Training involves learning about the dose of oxygen you get with varying breathing mixtures and depths, about the pros and cons of each gas mixture for each depth range, and the equipment you will need. Bacteria called *E. coli* that live in your intestinal tract, will swim away from areas of too high oxygen to protect themselves. You can swim away from too much oxygen too, by honoring depth-time projected maximums for each gas you dive with. Shorten exposure or conduct your dive at shallower depth if conditions of hard exercise, cold, or other susceptibility factors arise. Know your gas mix. Know the special equipment and procedures required for different gas mixes. Know before you go.

- Honor depth-time maximums for each gas mixture

- Reduce your PO_2 limits for cold, exertion, fatigue, other non-optimum conditions

- Know your gas mix

- Get training

SUMMARY

Oxygen, in varying amounts, is toxic to living things. All creatures must either live in an oxygen-free environment, or have ways to defend against too much oxygen. Humans vasoconstrict blood vessels, and regulate oxygen release from hemoglobin. Hemoglobin releases more oxygen to body tissues when supply is low, as at altitude, and restricts release when supply is higher than needed. Delivery to the body remains in normal ranges, within limits. Several body enzyme systems remove extra oxygen free radicals that form under several conditions, particularly high oxygen pressures. Other chemicals repair damage in your body caused by oxygen free radicals, up to a point.

Problems from oxygen occur from too much oxygen for too long, and, interestingly, after restoration of blood flow (perfusion) from a previously starved area, such as areas of the heart after a heart attack, or a limb after a crush injury.

When perfusion is restored, oxygen flows back into the area, sometimes causing reperfusion injury.

Pulmonary toxicity (Lorrain Smith Effect) can occur with several hours exposure to oxygen about 2 1/2 times higher pressure than we are used to on land (PO_2 above 0.5 or so, compared to normal of 0.21). Effects of CNS toxicity (Paul Bert Effect) are rapid. Once high pressure oxygen (varying around 7 times normal and above) overwhelms your mechanisms against it, oxygen concentration soars quickly. You don't have time for pulmonary toxicity to develop because you are in serious trouble already.

No drug, food, or pharmaceutical available to divers increases tolerance to high oxygen pressure. Eating antioxidants in hope of reducing the oxidative damage of free radicals does not work. Antioxidants are either destroyed during digestion, as with superoxide dismutase (SOD) and catalase, or do not seem to increase their usual effects on radicals in the body unless you are deficient, as with Vitamins E and C. That is a good thing, as free radicals are necessary in your body. You would have trouble moving or fighting infection without them.

The amount of oxygen that triggers CNS oxygen toxicity varies person to person, and day to day in the same person. This often frustrates divers who want a single number answer. No number can describe the complex, changing environment that is your body. There are generalizations to minimize risk of oxygen toxicity: Observe depth and PO_2 guidelines. Reduce PO_2 for long dives and dives where you will be cold, fatigued, or exercising. Keep fit, well nourished, and hydrated – that's just common sense. Get good training for diving with mixes other than air and for high PO_2 air diving. Follow your training.

CHAPTER 5
PART *IV*

DIVING HEADACHES

Fact and fiction surround the different headaches sometimes associated with diving. This section is not a medical diagnosis, but a look at possible mechanisms. See your diving doc if you get diving headaches.

- Does Diving Cure a Headache?
- Does Diving Cure a Hangover?
- Does Diving Cause a Headache?
- Preventing Headaches

DOES DIVING CURE A HEADACHE?

Divers sometimes say that diving cured their headache. Is there a factual basis for that idea?

One of the mechanisms proposed for at least one stage of migraine and cluster headache is enlarged and inflamed brain blood vessels. Accepted treatments reduce the size of the enlarged blood vessels using drugs, ice hats, or oxygen. When you breathe high pressure oxygen, your body constricts brain blood vessels to prevent your brain from suffering the ill effects of too much oxygen. Breathing 100% oxygen on land has been known to help relieve some cases of migraine and cluster headache, but there are very little good data on this. Breathing oxygen at higher than usual pressures in a hyperbaric chamber is also under study. Is it possible that in specific cases, the higher-than-normal oxygen pressure during diving has some effect on migraine and cluster headaches? No one can really say that it was the dive, without measuring all the blood gas variables at the time. It could just as easily be the soothing effect of cold water, or time passing, or any other reason.

DOES DIVING CURE A HANGOVER?

A popular misconception is that diving cures an alcohol hangover. It doesn't. This myth is dangerous.

Possible origins for this myth are that the cool water, and maybe the higher oxygen pressure during diving, might alleviate certain migraine or cluster headaches sometimes occurring as part of the hangover. Migraine and cluster headaches are different from alcohol hangovers but may occur with a hangover, because they can both result from drinking alcohol. Alcoholic drinks are among the several substances that enlarge blood vessels, and can trigger or aggravate cluster headaches. Several classic foods trigger migraine headache, including chocolate, aged cheese, nuts, red wine, and beer. The resulting headache may not bloom until the next morning, along with a hangover. Cold water and oxygen have no known effect on a hangover, but may relieve the migraine or cluster headache that was confused with, or appeared concurrently with, the hangover headache.

Oxygen's lack of effectiveness against hangover is so well established scientifically that oxygen is used as a placebo in studies of alcohol withdrawal treatments. There are stories of divers draining a dive boat's first aid oxygen tanks to relieve their hangover. Although their headache eventually goes away, the oxygen didn't do it.

Don't use diving as hangover treatment. The diving medical community and plain common sense discourage diving after a bender or if you are experiencing any effects of alcohol.

DOES DIVING CAUSE A HEADACHE?

Oxygen. Blood vessels of some people are more reactive than others to oxygen. It's theoretically possible to get a rebound vasodilation headache after coming off oxygen. One possibility is when the partial pressure of oxygen in ordinary air decreases on ascent. Another is after breathing high concentration oxygen on decompression stops. This does not seem to be common, given the large number of people who breathe 100% oxygen for various reasons, all without headache. Without more information it's impossible to say that the increased oxygen pressure causes a headache during or after diving.

Carbon Dioxide. It's often stated by divers that various activities build carbon dioxide (CO_2) in the body, and that CO_2 buildup triggers headaches, possibly from its effect to dilate brain blood vessels. Divers often attribute just about any headache following diving to carbon dioxide retention. How much of this is true? How do divers get too much CO_2? First let's clear up two ways you don't get too much CO_2.

It is not true that since exercise produces carbon dioxide, your CO_2 levels rise automatically with exercise. Under normal circumstances, your breathing rate increases by many times during exercise to "blow off" extra CO_2, and your blood has powerful buffers to control CO_2 level. Although you produce more carbon dioxide with exercise, body levels do not ordinarily rise. You also do not produce more CO_2 merely by being under pressure at depth. Unlike nitrogen and oxygen, which you get from your breathing supply, the partial pressure of CO_2 (PCO_2) in your body does not increase merely by going to depth. In fact, because you breathe in more nitrogen and oxygen, the same production of CO_2 represents less of your total alveolar air at depth.

How can you get too much carbon dioxide? Dr. Ed Lanphier, long time, major researcher in this area says, "When I was at the USN Experimental Diving Unit in the 1950's, we encountered divers who did not increase their breathing enough to keep CO_2 at a normal level during exercise. We came to call them CO_2 retainers, and others like them have been described since. Almost all were experienced hard-hat divers or had other reasons for repeated elevation of their arterial PCO_2 like repeated deep breath-hold diving. However, there are a few individuals (we don't know just how few) who retain CO_2 with no suggestion that this is an adaptive response. Such people could be at unexpected risk of such things as CO_2 blackout, unusual degrees of nitrogen narcosis, or susceptibility to oxygen toxicity. We found no easy, reliable method of identifying 'retainers' in advance; but unusually low air-use rates and repeated dive-related headaches would arouse our suspicions."

With specialized diving equipment, CO_2 may build in the large dead space of rebreathers, helmets, and full face masks. At depths of hundreds of feet, increased density of the breathing gas increases work of breathing to the point where it reduces ability to do work, and increases carbon dioxide buildup. At shallower depths, faulty CO_2 scrubbers in rebreather units have led to high CO_2. During World War II, British divers using oxygen rebreathers were passing out without warning. The term "shallow water blackout" was used in 1944 by Barlow and MacIntosh for blackout suspected, and later confirmed, from too high CO_2 levels (hypercapnia). Oxygen rebreathers could only be used in shallow water because of the high oxygen content. Most of the cases weren't deep enough to have been O_2 toxicity, which had previously been the prime suspect. The problem subsided after improving carbon dioxide absorption canisters. Although the term already had an established meaning, it was later applied to unconsciousness from too low oxygen (hypoxia) in breath-hold diving, especially following excessive hyperventilation.

In recreational diving, there aren't clear studies to say if carbon dioxide retention happens, although some of the same conditions that lead to buildup seem to occur. When CO_2 begins to build, you ordinarily increase how fast you breathe, so CO_2 levels normalize. Divers who do not increase ventilation rate could retain CO_2, as described above by Dr. Lanphier, particularly at high work loads. Studies show some people just seem to be less sensitive, in general, to the CO_2 stimulus to breathe more, whether it is an adaptive response to exposure or not. High partial pressure of oxygen at depth seems to slow respiratory rate. Too tight wet suits and gear may restrict breathing. Heavy underwater exercise using a hard breathing regulator may present enough breathing resistance to build CO_2. Some divers deliberately skip breathe to make a tank of air last longer. Skip breathing is a pattern of breathing more slowly, more deeply, and stopping longer than usual at the beginning and end of each breath, but there is some question how much skip breathing is needed before CO_2 rises.

Your body can compensate nicely for all these problems, but only up to a point. Then CO_2 would build. For divers who remain unaware of it at levels where other people become uncomfortable, increase breathing rate to blow off the extra CO_2, or terminate exposure, studies have identified increased risk of oxygen convulsions, nitrogen narcosis, and underwater unconsciousness. Studies mention that when these problems have occurred, there sometimes was dizziness, but often no warning. A few mention headache when the experimental subject regained consciousness or finished the underwater test. Others mention headache in susceptible people during exposure.

At the other end of the spectrum, it is fairly easy to lower CO_2 levels. Some divers begin to breathe too deeply and quickly for any number of reasons including fear and excitement. Such breathing quickly lowers body carbon dioxide levels, sometimes enough to cause limb tingling, dizziness, lightheadedness, headache, or other odd sensations. If you are seated in a safe place on land, you can try this by taking many deep, quick breaths. Be careful not to fall over.

Common Possibilities. Many conditions common in diving, beside oxygen and carbon dioxide, can trigger headaches.

Cold water can make your head hurt. Salt water up the nose can make your head hurt. Tight hoods or neck seals can cause a headache, as can a tight mask producing a condition sometimes known as "maskus-too-tightis." Pressure-related sinus, tooth, mask and ear squeezes start some headaches. Forceful or unsuccessful ear-clearing technique can leave you with an achy head. Biting the regulator-mouthpiece too hard is common, particularly among newer divers, causing jaw fatigue and sometimes head pain. Someone with a dysfunction of the jaw joint, called the temporomandibular joint (TMJ), may become headachy from regulator mouthpiece biting. Occasionally you can have a poorly fitting mouthpiece that causes jaw misalignment and pain. Exertional headaches occur in some susceptible people from moderate to vigorous physical activity. Other people get headaches from not enough physical activity. Headache is a common flag of an uncommon problem – carbon monoxide poisoning from a bad tank of air. Carbon monoxide poisoning can be serious. Headache occurring after a dive is one possible symptom of decompression sickness. Swimming horizontally underwater while keeping the neck craned at sharp angles to look forward or upward, can give you a headache, particularly in heavy gear.

Other headaches are not caused by your dive, but occur coincidentally around the time of diving, including allergies, eyestrain, bright sunshine, hunger, thirst, and sinus trouble. Caffeine and caffeine withdrawal both can bring on a headache, which is a vicious cycle among some coffee and soda drinkers. People who get migraines often get them from classic food triggers – foods containing high amounts of chemical substances called tyramines: chocolate, red wine, beer, walnuts, peanuts, liver pâté, and aged cheeses like bleu cheese. A classic non-food trigger for migraine is altered sleep schedules, such as sleeping later than usual. Non-migraine headache is common after too much wine, whisky, brandy, and most rums, because they are high in a headache-causing substance called congeners (unlike vodkas). Processed meats, like hot dogs, contain nitrite compounds, which can dilate blood vessels in susceptible people, causing pounding head pain. Cigarette smoke and diesel fumes are hard to get away from on confined dive boats. Regular, long-term use of pain-suppressing drugs, both prescription and non-prescription, lower your own body's natural pain-suppression ability. Sudden withdrawal from these drugs can rebound you into a headache. Sometimes it's hard to tell just what started a headache.

Should You Dive? For maximum safety, postpone your dive if you have a headache. On the small chance that headache during a dive is a warning signal of serious problems on the way, end your dive.

PREVENTING HEADACHES

- If you are not a small person, yet your tank lasts longer than other people's, check yourself for skip breathing patterns.

- Relax and enjoy your dives with comfortable gear and body position, and not clenching the regulator mouthpiece.

- Make sure your air fills contain good air, with regular air quality testing at the compressed air source. At least one product, called CoCop, is available to test your own tank easily for carbon monoxide. For CoCop and other air quality information contact the Lawrence Factor Company (800) 338-5493, or (305) 557-7549 outside the US.

• Review your health, exercise level, and nutrition habits.

• If you have a history of headache, see your physician for assessment to identify what kind of headache you get and what usually triggers it. Then, as obvious as it sounds, work to avoid things that give you headaches. For more information about headache in general, call the National Headache Foundation's toll-free hot line (800) 843-2256.

CHAPTER 5
PART V

SWIMMER'S EAR

It's one of the most common ailments of swimmers and divers. It has many names: swimmer's ear, external ear infection, external otitis, secretary's ear, otomycosis, otalgia, and earache. Cotton swabs, ear plugs, and swim caps more often cause than prevent it. Divers suffer for days, even weeks, even though treatment and prevention are simple.

- What Is Swimmer's Ear?
- Symptoms
- Causes
- Treating Swimmer's Ear
- Preventing Swimmer's Ear

WHAT IS SWIMMER'S EAR?

Swimmer's ear is an infection of the external ear canal. The external ear is the part of the ear you can see, and includes the canal you can stick your finger into. The canal dead-ends with the water-tight ear drum, Figure 5.5. Swimmer's ear involves only the external ear, and is not related to middle ear problems caused by pressure changes during surface diving, congestion, and/or infections of the Eustachian tubes, sinuses, or middle ear spaces.

SYMPTOMS

Swimmer's ear usually begins suddenly. Itching and pain are the most common symptoms. Pain can be severe, and is most pronounced when you move your head or pull on your ear. Even chewing food can cause discomfort that radiates down your neck.

CAUSES

Giving Germs a Chance. The external auditory canal is approximately 1 inch (2.5 cm) long. The outermost $1/2$ inch contains hair cells and oil-producing glands called sebaceous glands. The pH is slightly acidic. Waxy secretions of the sebaceous glands mix with shed skin cells to make cerumen, which is earwax. Cerumen is a protective barrier against invasion by bacteria and fungus.

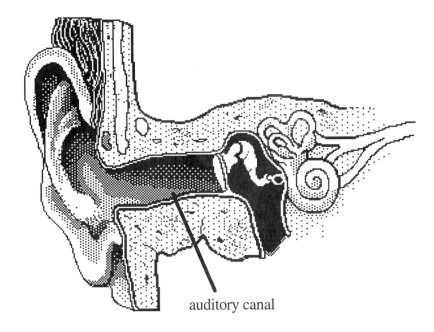

auditory canal

Figure 5.5. Swimmer's ear is an infection of the external ear canal, also called auditory canal. The external ear is the part of the ear you can see and stick your finger into. The canal dead-ends at the ear drum.

If you remove the cerumen by scratching, using cotton swabs, ear plugs, wax removing drops, or sometimes even hearing aids, you predispose the canal to infection by giving a foothold to bacteria and fungi (if bacteria and fungi had feet). Common bacterial intruders are *Pseudomonas aeruginosa*, proteus, and *Staphylococcus aureus*. Less frequently, any of a number of fungi, called tinea and otomycosis, similar to those causing athlete's foot, may be involved. When swimmer's ear itches, the scratching sets up a continuing cycle of scratching away needed cerumen, and entry for pathogens.

Bacteria live on your skin all the time. When you scratch away your protective cerumen, you give them a chance to become a problem.

Moisture. Bacteria and fungus thrive anywhere in the body that supports warm, moist, and dark conditions. When you allow moisture to settle in the ear canal after diving, showers, even sweating, some skin cells shed into the canal, shifting pH to the alkaline, and leaving debris that bacteria use as food. Water sloshing in and out of the external ear canal during swimming and diving helps remove debris. Swim caps and hoods sometimes contribute to swimmer's ear as they prevent sloshing, allow water entry, and enclose the ears in the warm, moist, dark environment inviting to bacterial and fungal growth. Clamping a phone receiver over a sweating ear for extended periods is also a culprit behind external ear infections, popularizing the name Secretary's Ear. Swimmer's ear is an important consideration for those who live and work in humid undersea habitats or spend lots of time in indoor pool environments or hyperbaric chambers.

Ear plugs are not used for scuba diving because of possible pressure injury, but they are often used for swimming in the mistaken belief they prevent swimmer's ear. Ear plugs prevent sloshing, irritate the canal, and are not watertight regardless of advertising claims. They trap moisture in the warm, dark, and moist space between the plug and the eardrum, and may be the cause of swimmer's ear in some cases. Swimmers often remove their ear plugs after swimming, using dripping fingers, then take a shower, so their ears get wet anyway.

Other. In rare instances, chronic swimmer's ear may be the first indication of bone spurs called hyperostoses, or very rarely, bony tumors called osteomas of the ear canal. Cause is unknown but it may be the body trying to close the ear canal as a defense against repeated exposures to very cold water.

Bacteria and fungus thrive anywhere in the body that supports warm, moist, and dark conditions. These conditions may occur in your external ear after diving, showers, sweating, with hearing aids, and clamping a phone receiver over your ear for extended periods.

TREATING SWIMMER'S EAR

Drops. Although swimmer's ear is painful, treatment is usually simple. One common, easy treatment is to pour ordinary white vinegar into your ears using a dropper or squeeze bottle. Turn your head to the side and fill each ear, one at a time. Wiggle the ear to spread the vinegar around the canal, then let drain. Some people use rubbing alcohol. Alcohol easily absorbs water, works to quickly calm swimmer's ear, then evaporates quickly. Since alcohol can sting an irritated ear and removes cerumen with prolonged use, avoid using alcohol for more than a few applications. Rapid cooling during evaporation of the alcohol may also cause brief mild dizziness. Dr. Fred Pullen, otolaryngologist, recommends against using hydrogen peroxide, except to remove impacted cerumen, because it breaks down to water, leaving the ear wet. Because swimmer's ear does not involve the middle ear, decongestants and antihistamines are not appropriate medicines.

Keep Dry. Keep your ears dry when you're out of the water. Some people have a structural variation in the auditory canal, like a bend, that reduces water drainage. If you do, pay extra attention to drying your ears after diving. Sometimes a hair dryer helps. Don't scratch away cerumen by putting things in your ear.

Pain Control. Swimmer's ear can be very painful. Aspirin or ibuprofen compounds like Advil® are useful for pain. Tylenol® (acetaminophen) doesn't have the inflammation fighting properties of aspirin or ibuprofen but use it for pain if your stomach doesn't tolerate aspirin.

Physician. If vinegar drops don't help within a day, or for constant infections, see a physician for prescription medicine. The physician can distinguish bacterial from fungal infection with cultures, and determine appropriate medication with susceptibility tests. Fungal infections won't respond to bactericides, and can be stubborn even with proper anti-fungal medication. Follow your physician's prescription faithfully and complete your entire course of medicine even after you feel better. Don't use prescription medication for prolonged periods as prevention.

Inadequate dose and extended use both teach offending germs to be resistant. Beware long-term use of topical steroids, which can chew up your skin. If your symptoms don't resolve within a day or two, or worsen, you may be sensitive or allergic to the medicine, or have the wrong medicine for your type of germ. Either way you need a change.

Should You Stop Swimming? Swimmer's ear does not automatically mean you must stop swimming or diving. Under ordinary living conditions, the ear can dry and heal well before heading back to the pool for the next weekend's dives. A few douses of vinegar between swims often works just fine.

At an ongoing dive site in humid conditions, a physician should decide if staying out of the water will help. When Dr. Caroline Fife was diving medical officer of research diving projects in Turkey, she found that prescribing Cortisporin (a preparation of antibiotic and hydrocortisone, an anti-inflammatory) at the first sign of trouble, with high dose oral antibiotic and a day or so out of the water, was often necessary to prevent further trouble.

For mild pain, use white vinegar.
If vinegar drops don't help within a day, for severe pain,
or for chronic infections, see a physician right away
for prescription medicine.

PREVENTING SWIMMER'S EAR

Preventing swimmer's ear is similar to treating it, just better.

- Dry your ears gently after diving.

- Don't irritate your ear canals or remove protective wax with ear plugs or cotton swabs.

- If you're subject to swimmer's ear, carry a squeeze bottle of homemade or prescription drops in your gear bag, and use before and after getting your ears wet.

CHAPTER 5
PART VI

MARINE STINGS

A common injury to divers is a marine bite or sting, usually unintentional by the underwater biter or stinger. Effects range from inconvenient itching, to uncomfortable pain, or occasionally to lethal systemic collapse. How these stings occur, the chemistry behind the bodily reaction, and how to treat and prevent future encounters is all a very interesting story.

- Poison and Venom
- Why Do They Sting Us?
- What Happens When They Sting Us?
- Treating Stings
- Preventing Stings

POISON AND VENOM

What's the difference between poisonous and venomous? Here's a hint. Puffer fish are poisonous but not venomous. Stonefish are venomous but not poisonous. Give up? Here's another hint. Have you ever heard of a venomous mushroom?

Probably not because a venomous creature has specialized anatomy to deliver the mixture of chemical compounds called venom. A poisonous beastie can only produce and store the stuff so it must be eaten to do any harm. Puffer fish, ocean sunfish, and porcupine fish contain a poison called tetrodotoxin, possibly produced by bacteria living inside them, that accumulates in tissues, particularly the gonads and liver. Although illness or death occasionally occur from eating them without careful preparation, divers handle them safely, frightening them into hapless basketballs for entertainment. Not so the stonefish, which is safe to eat but whose sting can kill.

WHY DO THEY STING US?

To answer that you have to look at the end that's doing the stinging. Stings can be for offense or defense. Offensive stinging is used to kill prey. The venom delivery system is near the mouth, as in the anemone and sea snake. Defensive venoms guard against attacks by predators and are located around the tail, as with the stingray, Figure 5.6. Since defensive venoms evolved as deterrents, they usually are less potent than the offensive sting. Fish don't bite us for fun. Venomous creatures are almost always slow pokes or fixed-to-the-bottom (*sessile*) animals.

They sting defensively if stepped on or cornered. Those who sting offensively for food usually want morsels smaller than they are.

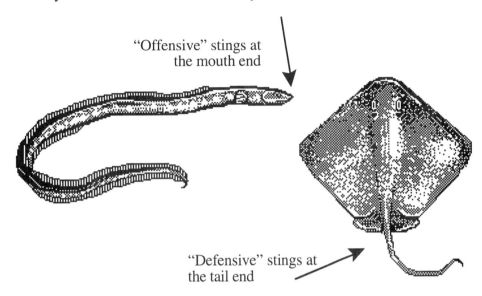

"Offensive" stings at
the mouth end

"Defensive" stings at
the tail end

Figure 5.6. Sea snake with "offensive" delivery system at the mouth compared to stingray with "defensive" delivery system at the base of the tail. Offensive stinging is used to catch prey. Defensive venoms guard against attacks by predators, and are located around the tail.

That's not to say offensive systems won't sting unintentionally. Jellyfish can swim weakly by jet propulsion but mostly drift around with current, tide, and wind. When a diver swims into jellyfish the stinging cells, called nematocysts, trigger automatically and continue to deliver venom until spent, as long as contact continues, even after the diver has left the water. When jellyfish wash ashore, the nematocysts can brave many hours drying in the sun and still fire upon contact.

WHAT HAPPENS WHEN THEY STING US?

Venoms are unstable mixtures of pieces of protein molecules called peptides and large protein molecules called enzymes. Enzymes are present in all living things. They control the speed of biochemical reactions that go on all the time in every cell. Foreign enzymes of a venom upset the human enzymes' ability to control reactions in the body. When the respiratory, nervous, or circulatory systems are affected, the consequences are severe.

Foreign proteins entering the body are called antigens. The body responds by producing its own proteins called antibodies to react specifically with the invading antigens. Powerful venoms overload the antigen-antibody reaction and affect the body's systems.

Reaction to a venom can be allergic, toxic, or sensitized. Allergic means that someone is hypersensitive to a substance that is harmless to others. Toxic is more universal. Sensitization is high susceptibility to a second sting at a later date from the first, when the first sting caused no serious symptoms. When the body is sensitive or allergic to a foreign substance it releases a substance called histamine. Histamine is present in all tissues of the body all the time and is a breakdown product of histidine, a common amino acid. Histamine works normally to dilate small blood vessels, including capillaries. When a reaction releases much histamine, blood vessels become more permeable. Fluids escaping from blood plasma cause swelling, a problem called extravasation. Blood vessel dilation increases local blood flow, causing warmth and redness. Pain is believed to come from the injury itself, from chemical substances released, and from local pressure of swollen tissue. These four characteristics, medically termed tumor (swelling), calor (warmth), rubor (redness), and dolor (pain) are the hallmarks of inflammation. A substance that blocks the inflammatory effects of histamine is called an antihistamine. Inflammation also attracts immune cells, which secrete free radicals to kill bacteria and other invaders. See the section on free radicals in Oxygen Toxicity Part III.

A substance that blocks the inflammatory effects of histamine
is an antihistamine.

TREATING STINGS

The most common stings are by coelenterates, pronounced cell-EN'-ter-ates. Coelenterates are the almost 10,000 species of invertebrates like jellyfish, anemones, the sea wasp, hydroids, and corals. Only a dozen or so of the more than 500 species of jellyfish are venomous, and of those, only a few have potent stings.

The term coelenterate means "hollow cavity" because these beasties are mostly a digestive passage and a way to get food into it. Their feeding mechanism consists of cooperating tentacles, liberally armed with nematocysts. More than thirty kinds of nematocyst exist, but two main types concern us. One is a cell with a miniature harpoon inside. A hair protruding from each nematocyst fires the stinger when touched. The other type clings to the skin by a sticky mucus, then deposits venom. Each can only fire once but there may be millions of nematocysts per tentacle.

Jellyfish. Composition of the tentacles of jellyfish, Portuguese man-of-war, and the sea wasp is very close to that of sea water, making them translucent and hard to see. Tentacles trail in the water in clusters from a few inches to 100 feet in length. Fish and divers swim into them and don't know it until a reaction begins soon after contact. Divers fare better than the fish, which are paralyzed, drawn into the mouth by the tentacles, and eaten. Reaction to coelenterate stings is dose dependent and varies a bit from person to person.

Initial response is pain or a prickly sensation, then an itchy rash, blistering, and swelling from histamine release. The characteristic welts left by the jellyfish called Lion's Mane are familiar to fans of Sir Arthur Conan Doyle, whose story *The Adventure of the Lion's Mane* recounts a man's death from an encounter with the creature. Man-of-war and Australia's box jellyfish (*Chironex fleckeri*) stings are serious. Pain can be severe enough to knock divers unconscious, causing them to drown. Effects range from nausea, fever, and delirium, to paralysis, respiratory difficulty, and death from cardiorespiratory collapse. Be prepared to inflate the person's buoyancy compensator, get them back to safety, and, for extreme cases, give artificial respiration or cardiopulmonary resuscitation.

Knowing which jellyfish caused the sting is difficult, but usually not necessary. Treatment is where argument begins. Most agree on plain white vinegar to stop the nematocysts.

Differentiating the species behind the sting is difficult. Luckily it isn't necessary. Treatment is where all the argument begins. Everyone agrees on preventing nematocysts left on the skin from discharging, but how? Rubbing with sand and pouring on fresh water or alcohol cause more discharge. Some commercial preparations for bites and stings reduce itching later but do nothing to reduce nematocyst activity. Meat tenderizer is popular in dive first aid kits for stings. It contains papain, a digestive enzyme, supposedly to digest the protein in the sting. Not all authorities are convinced it helps relieve stings, plus it sometimes causes problems. Some people are sensitive or allergic to the tenderizing enzyme, which would leave a rash of its own. If your skin is chewed up by the sting, the tenderizer may try to tenderize you, too. Does urinating on the wound do anything? Yes, it relieves the bladder. Depending on the diet, most urine is too close to neutral pH to have much effect. Fortunately, most agree on plain white vinegar to stop the nematocysts. Diving physician Paul Auerbach recommends the following for jellyfish stings once the diver is stabilized:

- Soak the injury in vinegar.

- Remove remaining tentacles with forceps, not your hands.

- Apply hydrocortisone lotion.

Hydroids and Fire Corals. Stinging hydroids look like fluffy plants but are animals like all coelenterates. Fire coral is not coral, but a stationary hydroid colony. Stinging corals have no tentacles but plenty of nematocysts that fire when bumped. Corals' hard external skeleton easily cuts bare skin, and the wound infects easily from bits of organic matter pushed under the skin. Hydroids and fire coral are more closely related to jellyfish than hard or soft corals. Treatment is standard coelenterate first-aid.

Sponges. Another coelenterate animal, sponges don't have nematocysts, but sharp spicules, which are small needle-like frameworks supporting the soft sponge. Spicules can puncture the skin making entry portals for venom and germs. Sponges may produce their own venom or get it from the bacteria, fungi, and algae that colonize them. First aid is the same as for jellyfish, except that instead of shaving, apply and pull off a strip of tape, which is more effective to remove spicules.

Venomous Fish. Of the more than 200 known species of venomous fish, four are most common: stingrays, lionfish, stonefish, and catfish. Stingrays deserve a close look.

Stingrays are venomous, and cause tissue damage with their sharp tail, which can hold from one to four spines. The jagged cut is prone to infection. The spine, located in the base of the tail, is covered with a membrane called an *integumentary sheathe* that tears to release venom from ventrolateral grooves. Venom releases as long as bits of the sheathe remain in the wound. A blue area often surrounds the wound due to vasoconstrictive action of the venom. Keep the lucky person quiet – activity circulates the venom. Place a constricting band, not a tourniquet, above the wound if it is on a limb and soak in as hot water as tolerable for thirty minutes to an hour. Venom proteins are unstable compounds and easily denatured. which means permanently changed in composition by heat. One possible source of fairly hot water, if you're on an outboard motorboat, is water used to cool the outboard motor. The motor takes in water below the water line, circulates it, then releases it in a stream called the tell-tale. It's called a tell-tale, because it lets you know that water is circulating, so cooling the motor. Don't get carried away with too hot water, which is water above 110°-113°F (45°C), or you'll treat a burn next.

Removing the barb is difficult. The retropointed barbs tear more on the way out. Remove any that you can remove comfortably, except from the chest or neck. Don't tape or sew the wound shut unless necessary to stop bleeding. See a doctor right away.

General Wound Care. Regardless of what got you, keep the wound clean and dry. Small stings can fester a long time in the high humidity of ocean areas. Paint the area with antibiotic cream, as venoms lower local tissue resistance to bacterial infection. Use anesthetic cream to reduce pain and hydrocortisone cream for itching. Divers with sensitivity or allergy should see their doctor for a prescription antihistamine for their dive first aid kit. A Red Cross first-aid class is a good way to prepare for wound care. Keep your tetanus shots current, too. Deep cuts may expose you to tetanus bacteria often living among marine organisms. Although rare, it is painful, and often fatal. Tetanus is also called lockjaw. It is easily preventable by immunization and periodic boosters.

PREVENTING STINGS

- When in doubt about marine life, don't touch. Better yet, don't touch anything Don't handle the reef, it destroys the reef.

- Listen to pre-dive environmental briefings.

- Keep hands out of rocky holes, somebody venomous may live there.

- When wading, shuffle feet on sandy bottoms to warn buried stingrays.

- A sponge won't jump off a rock and bite you, so take their picture; don't squeeze them. You'll be considerate to the reef and to your immune system.

Protective clothing thwarts most stings. There are exceptions: the spines of stonefish, stingrays, sea urchins, and some starfish can pierce protective clothing, and the nematocysts of the Man-of-war can pierce a rubber glove.

Australia's lifeguards used panty hose before the diveskin was invented, not surprisingly, in Australia. Many divers today use diveskins or light wet suits, which are also good against sunburn. Don't consider protective clothing license to drag your body all over the reef. That is ecological bad manners. It also stirs up stingy things that lodge on skin surfaces and under bathing suits and sting away. Don't torment the reef creatures. If you frighten them, they may defend themselves. And remember to watch the end that does the stinging.

CHAPTER 6

EXERCISE FOR DIVERS

Being in shape benefits your diving health in surprising ways. What does getting in shape mean? How can you get in shape without killing yourself? What can you do to specifically improve your diving fitness? How can you keep from losing the gains you made if you need to stop your regular program?

- Fat's Not All Bad
- Why Should Divers Get Fit?
- Aspects Of Fitness
- How To Get Fit
- Tailoring Fitness For Diving
- Getting Out Of Shape And How To Avoid It

CHAPTER *6*
PART *I*

FAT'S NOT ALL BAD

A quick look around most dive boats reveals that divers are not generally a skinny bunch. That's not entirely bad. Within a range, body fat is healthy and helps in different physical activities, including diving.

- When Fat Helps In Sports
- When Fat Hinders Sports
- What About Diving?

WHEN FAT HELPS IN SPORTS

Success in different sports depends on characteristic body sizes and compositions. Football linemen almost always have more than an average amount of fat compared to other athletes. Fat weight is an advantage to linemen for the added mass and padding for blocking ability. Increased muscle mass accompanies the extra fat weight to carry the whole package around.

Sumo wrestling is another sport where extra fat weight helps. Linemen and sumos don't have to run around much. It's not a big disadvantage to carry extra weight. Other examples of sports where the players have more fat than average for athletes are baseball, discus throwing, ice hockey, and swimming.

WHEN FAT HINDERS SPORTS

Extra fat weight is a burden to carry across distance or against gravity. The high calorie cost of transporting extra weight makes low body fat advantageous to running, gymnastics, and climbing. World class distance runners almost always have extremely low body fat. Runners and gymnasts, along with boxers and wrestlers, often adopt unhealthy dietary restrictions trying to keep their weight low enough to help them in their chosen sport.

WHAT ABOUT DIVING?

Fat helps selected aspects of diving. Cold immersion studies confirm a direct relation between body fat and keeping warm in cold water. You don't have to be obese for thermal benefit. Any amount of fat adds insulation. Because of the extra work of carrying around quite a lot of extra fat, an active heavy person generally develops extra muscle mass, furthering the thermal advantage in cold water, and usually increasing overall strength. Extra muscle comes in handy in external work like lifting things. You can consider the extra fat as a built-in daily weight-lifting regimen.

Fat increases buoyancy, adding safety and comfort to long swims. A little fat on your legs lets you float more horizontally, as you should for good trim in recreational diving. Skinny legs often sink, altering streamline. Fat pads the discomfort of carrying heavy equipment and cushions blows that might otherwise have more impact on internal organs. High body weight, whether from fat or lean, provides the loading your bones need to stay dense and strong. Obese people have low rates of osteoporosis.

Too much fat, on the other hand, has drawbacks in diving and in general health. Too much fat seems to be linked to cardiovascular, orthopedic, and endocrine problems. The same fat that keeps you warm in the cold makes you warm in hot weather, too. One predisposing factor to overheating is being large, round, and fat. Extra fat weight is more work to carry around. Extra weight makes carrying yourself around more work. The extra work is tough on the joints and sometimes beyond the ability of the out-of-shape heart to supply itself and the body with oxygen, or beyond the capacity of fat-narrowed blood vessels to conduct enough blood, putting the heart at risk.

SUMMARY

A certain amount of body fat helps several aspects of general living. For water sports like diving, body fat adds warmth, buoyancy, streamline, and padding for heavy equipment and sitting on dive boats.

The body is designed to hold dearly to its fat. What if you don't like the idea of holding dearly to your fat? Too much is not healthy. If you and your physician have determined you have more than enough of a good thing, what can you do about it? Being slim, by itself, does not mean being in shape for diving, or anything else physical. What else do you need to be physically fit for diving?

The following sections in this chapter cover the basics of varied aspects of fitness and getting in shape for diving.

CHAPTER 6
PART II

WHY SHOULD DIVERS GET FIT?

Being in good physical shape benefits many aspects of scuba diving that are not directly obvious. This is true even though diving may not always be a physically difficult activity.

- Increased Heat Tolerance
- Increased Cold Tolerance
- Better Health
- Diving Safety
- Injury Reduction
- Delayed Aging
- Positive Mood
- Fat Loss

INCREASED HEAT TOLERANCE

Exercise in the heat has been described as probably the single greatest stress ever imposed on the human cardiovascular system. Being in shape increases your ability to remain cool in conditions that would overheat an out-of-shape diver.

The in-shape cardiovascular system can carry away extra heat, and has grown more small blood vessels to do it. In-shape people sweat earlier, sweat more, and conserve more electrolytes during sweating than out-of-shape people. When you are in shape and accustomed to exercise in the heat, your core temperature does not rise as high while doing the same workload. More than any other factor, physical fitness reduces susceptibility to overheating (Chapter 3 Part IV, Diving In The Heat).

INCREASED COLD TOLERANCE

Physical fitness improves tolerance to exercise in cold environments, although to a lesser extent than for heat tolerance. Increased muscle mass through resistance exercise increases heat production and storage. A fit person can generate more heat through shivering and physical exercise. Exercising in the cold is a more effective way to tolerate cold conditions than cold exposure without exercise.

BETTER HEALTH

Evidence continues to build that an active lifestyle makes major positive changes in your health and well being. Common Western ills, such as heart and blood-vessel disease, obesity, and certain musculoskeletal problems, are known as "hypokinetic" diseases (*hypo* means less than or not enough, and *kinetic* means activity). Hypokinetic Disease is a fancy term for illness related to, or even caused by, being sedentary and out of shape.

Epidemiologic studies suggest that regular exercise lowers colon and reproductive tract cancer risk in men and women, and breast cancers in women. Resistance exercise thickens bones, important to all divers since osteoporosis, discussed in the next chapter, affects both men and women. Cardiovascular fitness through aerobic exercise reduces your risk of early death from vascular disease, heart disease, and high blood pressure, all major killers of both men and women. Sudden death from heart attack is also more common in an out-of-shape person who exerts past capacity, than in those who regularly exercise.

Being in shape is speculated to decrease risk of decompression sickness through circulatory advantages, although the mechanisms and certainty of relation to risk are unclear. Although not firmly established, cardiovascular fitness may give fresh meaning to the phrase, "Don't get 'bent' out of shape."

DIVING SAFETY

A high degree of muscular strength, cardiovascular endurance, and muscular endurance positively affects your capacity for heavy exertion common to diving. You call on your exercise reserves for extended efforts like long swims and currents, the transient demands of carrying gear around, getting in and out of the boat, particularly in high wind and wave action, and for emergencies.

A diver with high cardiovascular capacity for kicking with fins can easily fin a distance that is hard work to someone with less cardiovascular adaptation. With high muscular power, strength, and endurance you can quickly drag an incapacitated buddy through the water and lift him onto the dive deck or up the shore line, even if the buddy is larger and heavier than you are. Fitter people perceive less exertion at the same exercise intensity so they can dive more before pooping out. For fighting a current, high aerobic capacity may turn a difficult situation into an easy jaunt.

INJURY REDUCTION

Better physical fitness is associated with reduced incidence of joint injury during regular physical activity (Chapter 4 Part III). Pushing beyond capacity and overtraining, both easy to do with low capacity, often result in pain and overuse injury. A good range of joint flexibility also seems to be important to reduce injuries. A tight-jointed diver may have a tendency to muscle pulls and strains, particularly of the back. A diver with a tight shoulder may strain the shoulder capsule with repeated reaching backward to slip through buoyancy compensator straps.

DELAYED AGING

Although not chronologically younger, you can become functionally younger with exercise. It's difficult to separate the toll of aging from just sitting around too much. Still, getting slower and weaker as years pass is not solely an inescapable aging process. To varying degrees, it is a consequence of reduced activity.

Cellular and system functions decline predictably both with aging and without physical activity. Without exercise intervention, muscular strength, speed, and power all drop off sharply as years pass. After about age thirty, the deterioration would run about 0.75 to 1% per year without regular exercise. The maximum amount of oxygen your body can use to make energy, an important indicator of fitness, would drop about 10% each decade from age 20 to 60. Joints tighten with passing years until ordinary reaching and bending can become difficult, and in serious cases, impossible. Regular exercise and stretching considerably slows, even reverses the loss in some cases, making gains equivalent to stopping or reversing years of aging. Effectiveness of exercise shows itself in older people who are physically active. They have many of the functional characteristics of a chronologically younger person.

POSITIVE MOOD

Regular exercise is thought affect your mood positively in several ways. In the short term, a vigorously exercising body is thought to manufacture a class of hormones called endorphins, although specifics are far from established. The word endorphin is a contraction of "endogenous (made from within) morphine-like substance." It's not definitely known, but feasible, that endorphins improve mood after hard workouts by releasing chemicals that stimulate your brain's pleasure center.

In the long term, and more firmly accepted, exercise increases your overall fitness so that you can participate more often and with greater ease in activities you enjoy, such as diving. Regular exercise helps decrease afternoon moodiness and sugar cravings by increasing insulin sensitivity. That means less insulin mobilizes to process a given load of carbohydrate. Your blood sugar remains steadier, reducing the swings that produce food cravings and moodiness.

Greater physical ability, body awareness, and improved body shape and health with exercise might also make you happy. Overall, specifics of improved emotional state with exercise are not clearly mapped. Still there is support for a relation between long-term exercising and increased feeling of well-being and, at least in theory, ability to face emotional stress.

FAT LOSS

Exercise burns calories so you can eat more without getting lumpy. Regular exercise burns fat and shifts your body to a mode where it burns more fat for fuel in general and during exercise. Preferentially burning fat extends the supply of the carbohydrate stored in your muscles and liver, thereby extending exercise capacity.

SUMMARY

Being in good physical condition is beneficial to all divers, even though diving itself is not always physically rigorous. Good fitness reduces risk of several chronic diseases that affect general health and diving health, and increases your tolerance to heat and cold, delays several common effects of aging, and increases muscle while burning fat. Good physical fitness can also improve diving safety and your ability to dive more comfortably and more often. Many benefits of being fit contribute to safe and healthy diving.

- **Increased Heat Tolerance.** Being in shape helps you keep cool in conditions that overheat out-of-shape divers.

- **Increased Cold Tolerance.** Physical fitness improves tolerance to exercise in cold environments.

- **Increased Health**. Regular exercise reduces risk of major diseases, and may decrease risk of decompression sickness

- **Increased Diving Safety**. Fitness improves your capacity for overexertion, common to diving. Fitness can mean the difference between a diving trip and a diving accident.

- **Injury Reduction**. Physical fitness is associated with reduced incidence of joint injury during regular physical activity. Good joint flexibility also seems to be important to reduce injuries.

- **Delayed Aging**. An older people who is physically active can return to many of the functional characteristics of a chronologically younger person.

- **Positive Mood.** Regular exercise is associated with increased feeling of well-being.

- **Fat Loss.** Regular exercise improves body composition.

CHAPTER 6
PART III

ASPECTS OF FITNESS

Swimming, walking, and running increase your cardiovascular (aerobic) endurance, but not strength. One hundred consecutive pushups a day increase muscular endurance but do little for strength or cardiovascular endurance. Sprints don't maximize your ability to do distance work. Weight lifting is usually not aerobic exercise, despite what health clubs tell you. Stretching makes you more flexible, not stronger. Why? Cardiovascular endurance, anaerobic capacity, muscular strength, power, and muscular endurance are different body systems, both structurally and chemically.

- What Is Fitness?
- Why Different Aspects Of Fitness?
- What Are The Different Aspects Of Fitness?

WHAT IS FITNESS?

What is fit? One definition of fitness means being able to do things you need to do. For someone who does no more than a desk job, fitness may be limited to absence of major disease. For participating in sports there's more. Obviously, someone completely out of shape may not fare well during a vigorous scuba dive, yet fitness is also specific to the exercise. Olympian shot putters may be fit to put the shot, but not for gymnastics or scuba diving. The good news is you don't need to do every exercise the gym offers to be fit for diving.

WHY DIFFERENT ASPECTS OF FITNESS?

Different sports need different adaptations. To be a great swimmer, for example, you don't need big biceps. Prime movers for swimming don't include the biceps. For diving, strong biceps, among other things, divide those struggling to lift their scuba tanks from those lifting them easily. Strength, endurance, aerobic ability, anaerobic capacity, and power all contribute to get you out of a current or through surf, and back to the boat or shore. Flexibility reduces injuries and increases comfort when you move through a range of motion required for physical activity.

Recreational scuba diving does not routinely require high capacity in any one aspect of fitness. That's why it can be enjoyed by a wide spectrum of people. You draw on different aspects of fitness for different activities in diving. Since diving is a physically composite activity you'll do better with a little improvement in each area, and possibly, much better with high capacity in each.

WHAT ARE THE DIFFERENT ASPECTS OF FITNESS?

Cardiovascular Endurance. Cardiovascular endurance is also called cardiorespiratory endurance or aerobic capacity. It's the ability of your heart and lungs and their interconnected system of blood vessels to supply oxygen and nutrients to the parts that move you around. Your cardiovascular endurance determines how long you can continue activities like walking, running, swimming, or kicking with fins at your chosen pace. It also affects general health.

Anaerobic Capacity. Not all activities require your body to use oxygen, as with aerobic activities. With rapid-onset, intense activity, your body uses stored fuel, not oxygen, and so, is called *an*aerobic. The stored energy is limited to less than a few minutes worth. If you continue activity at a high intensity, like a surface swim against a current too strong for you, your body can't switch over to its oxygen-using aerobic system to any great extent. Your body continues to try to use the quick and ready stored fuel. But your demand exceeds the supply, forcing you to slow your pace. If you won't slow down, your body will stop you, gasping in your tracks — anaerobic. You need to develop your anaerobic system to breath-hold dive, swim against hard currents, sprint, haul out of the water in full gear, rescue a heavy buddy, or rescue yourself.

Strength. Muscular strength is usually measured by the maximum force your muscles can generate in a single or concentrated effort. You need strength to lift a tank easily rather than struggle, and to easily lift yourself out of the water in full gear. With increasing strength you can move tanks, gear bags, and yourself around more easily, and reduce your chance of musculoskeletal injury from doing it.

Power. Power is how fast you can be strong (velocity times force). You call on power to get through currents and surf, and to rescue a buddy. You increase your muscular power by moving faster against a given load, getting stronger, or both in varying combinations.

Different sports require different ratios of strength to the speed that muscles can contract. To throw the discus and put the shot, you take a moderately heavy weight and hurl it fast and far away. Offensive linemen try to do the same to very heavy defensive backs and tackles. A higher strength component compared to speed of contraction, for example in bench pressing, is called strength-dominated power. Kicking with fins, like swimming, running, jumping, and putting the shot, primarily employs speed-dominated power.

When you learn efficient ways to move your leg segments more rapidly through the water, you'll be able to fin more quickly through the water and increase power without necessarily becoming stronger.

Muscular Endurance. Scuba diving involves many, many leg repetitions against the relatively light resistance of water. High repetitions of low resistance call on muscular endurance. Diving principally needs muscular endurance of the legs for finning. Improved muscular endurance reduces your chance of leg cramps, and eases long swims. For carrying around gear or walking to dive sites in full gear, muscular endurance of the back muscles can make the difference between an uneventful diving day, and a tired, achy back.

Muscular endurance is different from cardiovascular endurance. An untrained muscle may get tired before you are out of breath. Trained muscles have specific enzymatic and cellular adaptations to increase endurance capacity. These adaptations don't change muscle size.

Flexibility. Flexibility is the ability to move easily and safely through a range of motion. There is evidence that with good flexibility, you may suffer fewer injuries to your muscles and the tough fibrous structures called tendons that attach your muscles to your bones. Although not all studies support the conclusion of fewer injuries, the reasoning has good basis. If a muscle is tight, its inflexibility limits the full range it can extend. If you move in a way that surpasses that range, you may strain or tear the muscle and its connecting tendons. With long-term stretching programs, a given muscle can attain a greater length before reaching the tension required to tear it.

Several body areas appear susceptible to injury from poor flexibility. The range of motion required to strain tight low-back muscles is quite small, accounting for many painful backs after a day of diving. Another area is the triple set of muscles behind each thigh called the hamstrings. Tight hamstrings are prone to pulls and are a common contributor to low back pain. Opposite your hamstrings are muscles connecting your hip to your leg in front, called hip flexors. Hip flexors bend your leg forward at the hip. Tight hip flexors, very common in people who sit a lot, add their share of low back pain and limit the range of motion needed for efficient fin swimming. Your Achilles tendon at the back of your lower leg attaches your calf muscle to your heel. Too tight calf muscles and Achilles tendons sometimes leads to tendonitis, knee, and foot pain. Regular stretching reduces these problems.

SUMMARY

- **Cardiovascular Endurance**, also called aerobic fitness - Ability of your heart and lungs, and their interconnected system of vasculature, to supply oxygen and nutrients to the parts that move you around. Enables you to kick with fins farther and longer, with less effort.

- **Anaerobic Capacity** - Your stored fuel system for rapid-onset, intense activity. Enables you to breath-hold dive, exert against hard currents and surf, haul out of the water in full gear, sprint, and make strenuous rescues.

- **Strength** - Ability to move a heavy weight once, or a few times. Increasing your strength makes it easier to lift dive gear and yourself around.

- **Muscular Endurance** - Ability to move a light weight repeatedly. You need muscular endurance of the legs to fin long distances.

- **Power** - Ability to move an object of any weight quickly. You call on power to get through currents and surf, and to rescue a buddy.

- **Flexibility** - Ability to move easily and safely through a range of motion. Flexibility can reduce diving pulls and strains.

CHAPTER 6
PART IV

HOW TO GET FIT

The several different aspects of fitness result from different structural and chemical adaptations in your body. Because each is different, each needs different training to improve. Most exercise can help you get healthier and look better, but not all exercise strengthens. Not all lifting makes you big. Bulking up requires methods that won't help you to fin long distances underwater. Understanding differences among aspects of fitness was covered in Part III of this chapter. This section covers how to train each of them to get in the diving shape you want.

- Cardiovascular Endurance
- Anaerobic Capacity
- Strength
- Muscular Endurance
- Power
- Size
- Firmness
- Flexibility

A little over 2500 years ago, the Greek athlete Milo realized he could increase strength by using workloads above those normally encountered. He began lifting a young calf every day. The calf's maturing weight provided progressive resistance until, it was said, he carried the grown bull around the Olympic arena. He became a military hero, and as an Olympic wrestler was undefeated.

Whether Milo lifted an increasingly heavy calf in legend or in fact, it is well established that fitness improves by progressively increasing the amount done, a process called overload. Routinely carrying increasingly heavy loads, for example, increases strength. Progressively raising the number of times you lift a light weight improves muscular endurance. Progressively swimming farther improves cardiovascular endurance. Increasing your joint range of motion extends flexibility.

CARDIOVASCULAR ENDURANCE

Improve your cardiovascular status through continuous low intensity large muscle activity like walking, running, skating, dancing, cross country skiing, swimming, and kicking with fins.

If your physical work intensity is too high for your fitness level, you will get out of breath and need to stop, cutting aerobic benefits short. If your intensity is too low, as in exercise class floor-work of leg lifts and abdominal crunches, you will also not gain aerobic exercise benefit. Keep an easy moderate pace. Exercise studies find a close match between how hard your body actually works and how hard you consider the activity. That means you can easily monitor your work load. A pace you find to be medium effort, usually is a medium load on your system, and is about right for exercising for general cardiovascular fitness.

Cardiovascular Endurance in a Nutshell: Long-duration, low-intensity, large-muscle activity like walking, running, skating, dancing, cross country skiing, swimming, and kicking with fins.

ANAEROBIC CAPACITY

You need good anaerobic capacity to get you through short hard exertions. In diving you sometimes need to get through currents, climb dive ladders in full gear, quickly catch up to other divers far ahead of you, or rescue a buddy. Improve your anaerobic capacity through high-intensity, short-duration activity like sprint runs, swims, and kicking with fins. Practice dragging a buddy around. Alternate sprints with rests.

As with aerobic activity, you can tell your intensity by how it feels. Unlike aerobic activity, you are anaerobic when you are working hard and fast enough to be out of breath, and the workload feels taxing, even uncomfortable. Train for this, and what was previously uncomfortable becomes possible, and eventually easy. When such a situation occurs while diving, you will be trained to handle it.

Try a 30-second anaerobic bout, followed by active rest, which is easy, mild activity, until your heart rate returns to normal. To maximize training for anaerobic activities, gradually work up to 30 seconds hard anaerobic work, then 1 minute aerobic "rest," then increase, keeping the 1:2 ratio of anaerobic work to active rest.

The fuels you use when you are anaerobic have to be restored after exercising. Replacing these stored fuels, adenosine triphosphate (ATP) and creatine phosphate (CP), takes only a few minutes and requires oxygen. Being in better shape aerobically aids the recovery process. There is nothing you can eat to specifically increase your anaerobic capacity or your ATP-CP stores. Only sprint-specific exercise and plenty of it builds this system.

Anaerobic Capacity in a Nutshell: Short-duration, high-intensity activity like sprints, whether in the water, on a bicycle, or in the water swimming or kicking with fins. Alternate short, hard exertions with easy ones, and practice dragging around buddies and gear.

STRENGTH

Your body makes several adaptations to increase strength when you start a strength training program. First, you usually immediately increase the amount you can lift due to a learning effect, even before any physical changes occur in your muscles. Motor learning increases knowledge of how to do the lifting task, which improves lifting ability. Then, three physical changes begin in your muscles — their size, the rate that nerves serving them can fire, and the number of nerve-muscle units, called motor units, can fire together. All three are trainable to varying degrees.

For the first 3 to 4 weeks of strength training, after becoming accustomed to the task, neural factors predominate to increase strength. After that, strength increases in young males primarily by increasing cross sectional area (size) of the muscle. Older men increase strength less through size than neural mechanisms. Women also increase strength through more neural than size adaptation even with strength changes comparable to those of a young man. Obviously women and older men can increase muscle size through training, but size is not the only predictor of strength. Strong things may come in small packages.

Because maximum strength contributes to winning specific Olympic events, and even more crucial - football games, studies have subjected strength training methods to microscopic scrutiny. It has been found that to get stronger you need to contract muscles at close to the maximum they are able to contract. That takes heavy weight, and is why most exercise class "floor work" does not strengthen. Your leg is not heavy enough. You need a weight that is so heavy that after 8-10 lifts you are just about unable to lift it again. It's almost heretical to say swimming won't make you strong. Like floor work, water is not heavy enough to elicit maximum muscle recruitment. If it were, you would not be able to kick with fins more than 10 times before exhaustion. That doesn't mean swimming, water exercise, and finning during scuba diving are not good for you in other ways. It means they are not major strength builders unless you are debilitated from sickness or injury or do large numbers of laps at high speeds which increase your intensity and total work.

Most studies agree the maximum number of times to consecutively lift a heavy weight to maximize strength gain is between four and eight repetitions or "reps." These same studies find less gain with more or fewer reps. Why? If you can do more reps with the same amount of weight, you are not using a weight heavy enough for maximum strength gain. Fewer reps also don't sufficiently overload a muscle to gain strength. Strength work, relatively heavy weight at 10 or less repetitions, will also "tone" or firm you up more than leg lifts or arm circles, which are light weight with high repetition.

One group of repetitions is called a "set." To maximize strength, do three sets of four to eight reps. Between each of your heavy sets you need rest. Rest allows you to recover enough to maximize muscular tension for the next set of four to eight reps. One to four minutes rest between each set is usually enough. Allow a minimum of a full day between weight training sessions for muscle repair and strength building processes to proceed without interference. When you have progressed to where you can easily lift the weight four to eight reps for three sets, increase the weight. Start easy. Resist going overboard. Try one set to start. After a week or so, if this easy start produces no pain or other problems, increase gradually until you can comfortably do two to three sets of between 8 and 12 reps. Lift the weight through as complete a range of motion as is comfortable. Control your weight to avoid risk of injury. Train all your major muscle groups. Strengthening one group, for example your abdominal muscles, without also strengthening the back muscles opposite them, can result in your "abs" chronically pulling your torso with more tension than the back muscles. Back pain and poor posture can result. Balance is important. Many popular fitness magazines sell protein supplements, stating you need extra protein to build muscle. This is rarely true. The Western diet usually provides much more protein than you need, even with heavy activity. You ordinarily do not need to eat additional protein to increase strength or musculature. Increasing carbohydrate to fuel the exercise you need to increase strength has been found to help.

Some people reject lifting for fear of hurting themselves or becoming bulky. Done properly, you reduce your chances of later injury from other activities, and will look trimmer.

Weight lifting is good for you. Some people reject lifting for fear of hurting themselves or becoming bulky. Done properly, you reduce chance of later injury from other activities, and look trimmer. Weight lifting increases your ability to do the physical work of diving, strengthens, firms, and increases muscle that burns calories and keeps you warm. Weight lifting increases bone density, important for bone health. Lifting is important to every diver's fitness plan. It's a myth that strength, by itself, reduces coordination or flexibility. No diver can be too strong. You can be strong with poor skills, but not too strong.

Weight lifting is good for you. It makes diving tasks easier, burns calories and firms you, and strengthens muscle and bone.

Strength in a Nutshell: Do three sets of six using a heavy weight. Take long rests between sets.

MUSCULAR ENDURANCE

Muscular endurance is the ability of any particular muscle or muscle group to continuously carry on a muscular activity at low intensity. Examples are found any time you exert force against light weights many times, as with leg lifts, peddling a bicycle, or kicking with fins. Training is simple. When you have progressed to where you can easily continue for a set number of kicks, reps, or minutes, increase them. Alternate easy and hard workouts, rest adequately, and don't overdo. The long duration, low intensity, large muscle aspect of kicking with fins also increases cardiovascular endurance to varying degrees.

Muscular Endurance in a Nutshell: Do continuous repetitions using a light weight with no rest between reps.

POWER

Power is the product of strength and speed. Lifting a scuba tank takes strength. Throwing a tank takes power (and no brains either. This is an illustrative example, don't try this yourself or you may get an inkling of why power is also called "explosive strength").

To develop power, lift a weight you customarily need to lift, but lift it more quickly. There are special weight machines specifically made for power training. Be more than a little careful when training for power with weights. Potential for serious injury throwing weights around is high. Never lean over and lift quickly unless you really want to ruin your back. Developing power in the pool for diving is safer and simpler. Increase your fin swimming power by finning hard every few laps. Rest by finning easy laps. Be sure to be well warmed by twenty laps or so before beginning power laps. Practice throwing a rescue line, and dragging willing buddies around. Lift yourself out of the pool without using the ladder. Once done quickly and easily, wear your weight belt, gradually adding more weight while lifting yourself from the pool with and without the ladder.

Power in a Nutshell: Lift a heavy weight quickly. Long rests between sets. Be careful.

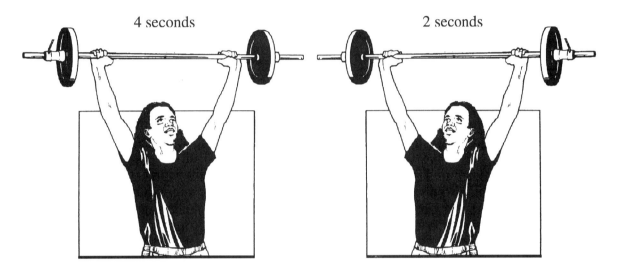

Figure 6.1. The person who can lift a weight in two seconds has twice the power of someone who takes four seconds to lift the same weight.

FLEXIBILITY

Stretching increases range of joint motion required for sports and daily mobility. There is good evidence that stretching prevents muscle injuries and reduces back pain. Although flexibility can reduce injuries, stretching wrong can produce them, both acutely, and in the long term by loosening joints until they don't seat well, thereby increasing wear and tear. Excessive joint laxity also predisposes to sprains and dislocations. Divers need good forward and backward ankle flexibility, but excess looseness on the outsides of your ankle increases your chance of ankle sprains because your ankle can bend at a high angle sideways if you stumble. Lax shoulder capsules may slip out of place from forces that healthier joint capsules tolerate.

Better exercise education and instructor certification programs have reduced several problematic exercises and stretches. Many unhealthy practices are still with us. To keep your stretching healthy, avoid the following still-common stretching practices:

- Don't stretch cold muscles, warm up first. Warming up literally means increasing your body temperature. At cooler muscle temperatures, it takes less force and length to tear muscle fibers. Activities that warm you enough to safely begin exercise are large muscle exercises like pedaling a bicycle or slow jogging. Stretching doesn't raise your body temperature, so it's not a warm up.

- Hold for about 30 seconds without bouncing.

- Several well known stretches hold the joint at an angle that puts too much weight and pressure on ligaments. The hurdler's stretch is a major example. It twists your knee sideways. Instead, keep the non-stretched leg in front of you with your foot on the floor. Clasping hands behind you, then lifting your arms strains the front, and weakest part, of your shoulder capsule. Squatting on your heels is tough on knee ligaments by prying the knee slightly apart, particularly if you have heavy legs. It also is known to damage the small discs of cartilaginous cushion in your knees called meniscus. The bad knees of professional baseball catchers come from chronic squatting. Avoid neck ligament stretchers like the "plow" which involves lying with your legs in the air over your head and much weight on your neck, lengthening it forward. A stretch that puts too much weight on your spine is when you bend over from a stand for toe touching or worse - bouncing while bending over for toe touching. The groin stretch, sitting with knees bent and soles of the feet touching, can overstretch the side of the ankles if the sides of the feet are left on the floor, rather than kept in line with the lower leg.

- Avoid stretching in one direction without countering the stretch in the other. A very common example is stretching forward through toe touching and abdominal crunches, without also stretching the other way by arching backward. Chronic forward bending, particularly with no countering backward stretching is tough on the discs in your spine. A typical result of unbalanced stretching is often seen in dancers who stretch their legs outward without equal stretching inward. The outside of their legs gradually tightens and shortens while the inside loosens until they walk like ducks. Later their hips and knees succumb to early wear. Another example you've probably seen is round shouldered muscle men. They build up the chest without stretching it, and neglect the back except to allow it to stretch through slouching. A problem results called stretch-weakness. Their backs cannot counter the pull of their strong and shortened big chests.

To stretch safely, warm up enough to sweat before you stretch. Then stretch by slowly easing into, then holding the stretch. Don't bounce. Micro-injuries can result. Keep the limb you're stretching in line with the joint to stretch the muscle, not the ligaments. To stretch your hamstrings without hurting your back lie on your back, bend both knees, then leave one foot on the floor and straighten the other leg overhead. To avoid posture problems and back pain from unequal stretching, practice safe backs during stretching. Stretch your upper back, lower back, and hip in each natural direction. Don't overweight your back and neck. Substitute sitting and lying back stretches for standing bent over ones. During the rest of the day avoid sitting with a rounded back. Keep the normal inward curve of your lower back.

Flexibility in a Nutshell: Like most things, moderation works best with flexibility. Stretch enough to move freely through the range of motion you need for activities, but don't force your joints into such looseness that they no longer work properly.

SIZE

An unfortunate number of women and even men shun weight lifting and its associated health benefits on the assumption they will grow huge. The answer to them is simple. Big muscles don't happen by accident. It takes more work than many are willing to do. You can lift weights to get strong, build endurance, gain power, and become healthy. You will get firm and look good but you won't bulk up big without specific and intense work.

One look at power lifters and you know they're strong. Yet they look different than body builders. Power lifters train for strength, body builders maximize size and visual effect. Two things body builders do differently are to increase volume of work and muscle definition.

Volume is the product of how much weight you lift and how many times you lift it. To maximize volume, do more reps and more sets. Lift more slowly than you would for strength or power. You still need heavy weight, but to be able to do more reps, use less weight than for strength training. Use a weight you can lift twelve or so times before muscle failure stops you. Do more sets and take only short rests between those sets. When you can easily lift four sets of twelve, increase the weight and, later on, add another set. Definition comes from losing fat under the skin that covers your nooks and crannies.

Someone with large muscles may not be able to lift as much weight in a single effort as a smaller person who trained specifically for strength. It's difficult to make true assessments about the strength of women or older men, or anyone for that matter, purely on muscle circumference.

Size in a Nutshell: Four slow sets of twelve. Short rests between sets. Exercise and eat low fat so muscles can't hide beneath fat stored under your skin.

FIRM

Firm is easy. Easier than strength and size. Easier than maximizing endurance through marathons. Lifting weights will firm you. You don't have to push it; however, more work makes more firmness.

Firm in a Nutshell: Regularly lift a comfortable weight a comfortable amount of times, for example 10 times, building up to one to three sets.

Scuba diving needs some of each fitness aspect rather than
exceptionally high capacity in any one. Workout in a general
program to optimize all components of fitness rather than maximize
any particular one.

CAN YOU HAVE IT ALL?

Scuba diving needs some of each fitness aspect rather than exceptionally high capacity in any one. You can exercise in a general program to optimize all components of fitness rather than maximize any particular one. Improve scuba fitness with safe and sane weight lifting to develop strength, endurance, and power. Regularly walk, jog, cycle, and especially, swim with fins for cardiovascular endurance. Develop a healthy range of motion and reduce injury potential through regular stretching. Get instruction and start easy, even too easy in the initial weeks of a new program. Get the feel of it first. Then, and this is important, get to like it. Then progressively work up. Exercise does not have to hurt to be effective. You can have gain without pain. If anything hurts, stop, and find out why. Check with your physician before starting any program.

SUMMARY

Hippocrates summed it up over 2400 years ago: "Speaking generally, all parts of the whole body which have a function, if used in moderation and exercised in labours to which each is accustomed, become thereby healthy and well developed, and age slowly." A summary of exercising to develop specific aspects of fitness follows:

- **Cardiovascular Endurance (aerobic capacity).** Long-duration, low-intensity activities like swimming, skating, rowing, cycling, quick walking, cross-country skiing, kicking with fins. Comfortable intensity.

- **Anaerobic Capacity.** Short-duration, high-intensity activity like sprints, whether in the water, on a bicycle, or in the water swimming or kicking with fins. Work hard enough to get out of breath, rest briefly, then sprint again.

- **Strength.** Weight-lifting. Do three sets of six lifts using a heavy weight. Long rests between sets. Train all your major muscle groups to avoid orthopedic problems from unequal strength ratios.

- **Muscular Endurance.** Continuous repetitions of lifts or motions, with light weight and no rest. Vary to avoid overuse.

- **Power.** Weight-lifting, or other activity involving moving a heavy or light object quickly. Fast execution of each lift or motion. Long rests. Great care to avoid injury.

- **Size.** Weight-lifting. Four sets of twelve. Heavy to moderate weight. Lift slowly. Short rests between sets.

- **Firmness.** Regular, comfortable weight lifting. One to three sets of ten reps with a comfortable weight.

- **Flexibility.** Regular comfortable stretching exercises. After each stretch, stretch the opposite way.

CHAPTER 6
PART V

TAILORING FITNESS FOR DIVING

Just about any exercise that improves general health and strength can help diving. There are also exercises that specifically help scuba diving. How can you get in shape for diving? How can you avoid getting out of shape when you're too busy to exercise?

- Results Are Specific To The Exercise
- Don't Worry About Being Exact
- Some Exercises Are Counterproductive
- Getting in Shape For Diving

RESULTS ARE SPECIFIC TO THE EXERCISE

As explained in Part III of this chapter, strength, power, muscular endurance, and cardiovascular endurance are different body systems. Each develops from different kinds of exercise. Stressing one body part, like arms or legs, or one system, such as strength, flexibility, or cardiovascular endurance, does little to influence development of other parts or systems.

Running, for example, makes cardiovascular, metabolic, and structural changes directly related to, or specific to running, not kicking with fins. Trained runners often exhaust themselves during long surface swims, and divers during runs, even though both may have high aerobic capacity. The concept of specificity is important to understanding why going out for a good run every morning can build muscular endurance and cardiovascular endurance that benefits scuba diving fitness, yet doesn't completely transfer to kicking with fins. It's a bit like practicing the tuba. It will not make you a good violin player, even though both are musical skills, with several similarities. Running, peddling a bike, and kicking with fins use lower body muscles differently, which adapt differently. Kicking with fins, therefore, prepares you for diving better than jogging or biking.

DON'T WORRY ABOUT BEING EXACT

Luckily, specificity is not all or nothing. It encompasses a range. For diving fitness you do not need to do the exact motions, ranges, or intensities encountered in diving to gain fitness for diving. There is a certain degree of carryover when you stress a muscles at one joint angle, for example, to the joint angles near it. Weight machine exercise are beneficial to building diving health, and need not be exact duplicates of diving motions.

SOME EXERCISES ARE COUNTERPRODUCTIVE

Some exercises promoted for swimmers and divers are counterproductive. Swimming with hand and/or ankle weights is an example. Like shadow boxing with hand weights, the resistance is in the wrong direction. When boxing, you want the power of your punch to go forward. Hand weights for boxing or swimming weigh your arms downward, preferentially building muscles and neural pathways that resist downward pull by raising your arm upward, which is not what you want. Hand and wrist weights in a pool can contribute to shoulder injury. Ankle weights for kicking have similar problems. They throw off streamline and make poor swimming habits by building the wrong neuromuscular patterns. It doesn't really help you swim without them. Tying weights on is also not the safest thing to do in the water, particularly when not wearing tanks. To improve swimming or finning for scuba you need to increase resistance against your forward progress, not weigh your arms or legs down so that you build patterns that lift upward.

GETTING IN SHAPE FOR DIVING

Some exercises target diving skills more specifically than others. In the water, to maximize the specific skills, muscles, body systems, and nit-picky neurochemical adaptations for diving, swimming with fins is the gold standard. True, you're not lugging tanks under the air-water interface of the pool surface. However, you can make pool practice similar enough to diving for substantial training gains.

In a pool, kick as deeply and slowly as you would in full gear. Wear tanks or simulate tanks by increasing resistance to forward movement. Several devices are available, such as drag suits, webbed gloves, tethers, and other commercial and home-made resistance devices. Tilt a kickboard in front of you to increase the surface area you present to the water. Don't let the increased resistance slow you down enough to change your finning mechanics. Make the effort to fin as much as possible as it is with full gear. Just being in the water helps diving skills by remaining accustomed to the water and to your mask, fins, and snorkel.

On land, carry your own tanks if you're physically able. Carry someone else's tanks, too. Walk around wearing tanks, or even just your weight belt. Avoid bending over wearing tanks, that's tough on your back. Practice climbing ladders in your gear, if you need to do that for boat diving. Invent fun ways to simulate conditions you will find diving. According to respected exercise physiologist Dr. Jack Wilmore, "The more specific you can make your training to the sport, the better off you will be."

Doing non-water, non-scuba-related exercises are also helpful. Cross-training helps liven up old routines and helps prevent burnout. A key to getting fitter is finding activities you love to do, and make your daily routines more active in general.

Is there a magic way to get fit and healthy for diving? Yes. You put the effort in and magic comes out. For now you're off to a good start to diving fitness. Make an appointment with yourself, determine your goals, and stick to your plan.

Kicking with fins in a pool is one of several good preparations
for diving. Doing non-water exercises provide
general fitness, fun, and variety.

SUMMARY

Getting in shape for any activity requires doing that particular activity, and exercising the muscles used in the specific skills. Getting in shape for diving, is best done by going diving, or approximating diving as best you can by swimming with fins, carrying gear around, and practicing climbing up ladders in full gear. Runners who never swim, may be in great shape, but easily poop out in the water. Your muscles make different chemical and neural adaptations depending how you use them. Still, just about any physical activity that benefits your general physical fitness level and health, could be considered to add to your diving fitness, even though it does not translate directly into diving skills. Just don't get too complacent about your bench pressing or other non-diving physical abilities. To be a fitter diver, go diving.

CHAPTER 6
PART VI

GETTING OUT OF SHAPE
AND HOW TO AVOID IT

You may not be an exerciser. Or you may have started a program and got tired of it, or gone on vacation, or got caught up with work. You may have worked hard to get in shape at one time, but gave it up. After a layoff from exercise your problems are more far reaching than just gaining a little weight.

Loss of strength, endurance, and practical skills make tanks heavier, swims longer, safety skills fuzzier. Where did all those improvements you made go? Why should you care? What can you do?

- How To Get Out Of Shape
- What Goes Bad?
- How Long Does It Take?
- Does It Hurt?
- Preventing Getting Out Of Shape

HOW TO GET OUT OF SHAPE

After long periods of not exercising, packages seem heavier than they used to. Following weeks of weightless space flight, astronauts come home with less muscle, blood volume, and bone than they left with. Even after only a day or two in bed with flu, you get up weak and dizzy even though you're not sick anymore. The principle of "Use It or Lose It" is technically known as "reversibility." Physical performance gains made through exercise reverse with inactivity. The deterioration of your physical condition is technically known as "deconditioning."

There are several ways to decondition. Just sitting around for the winter is one. Holiday gatherings and family obligations leave less time for the gym. Winter weather decreases routine outdoor excursions and diving opportunities. These are technically known as "excuses."

Periods of inactivity also follow injury or illness. Deconditioning may be local as in a limb in a cast, or a global problem of whole body inactivity. The common mechanism is disuse. An immobilized limb dramatically decreases in size, strength, and endurance. Bed rest severely reduces the mechanical stresses your entire body needs to stay healthy. Bed rest so effectively deconditions you that aviation scientists use it to study physical decrements following zero gravity in space flight.

WHAT GOES BAD?

Getting fat is only the tip of the pathologic iceberg of getting out of shape. Deconditioning seriously affects the functional state of your entire body. Strength, cardiovascular capacity, blood, mental skills, even your bones and immune system suffer.

Muscle. Without use muscles decrease strength, endurance, and size, and lose blood vessel and nerve associations. They become less able to extract and use oxygen to do work, not only because your entire body's oxygen carrying and delivery system declines, but for chemical reasons of their own.

In-shape muscle is able to burn more fat as fuel than out-of-shape muscle, which uses more carbohydrate. Deconditioned muscles lose intracellular fluid, stored carbohydrate, and contractile protein contributing to loss of muscle tone. Your body gets soft. Eating extra protein will not stop muscle protein loss. Only exercise does that. The bottom line is that when muscles decondition, you may not look as good in a dive suit, can't lift as much gear, swim as far, or rescue yourself or others as easily.

Cardiovascular. A deconditioned cardiovascular system can't process, deliver, or burn enough oxygen to do intense exercise because several of its components go to seed with inactivity. The total amount of blood your heart pumps per minute decreases, probably from overall decrease in blood volume in the initial weeks of detraining. You lose oxygen-carrying molecules called hemoglobin.

The size and contractile force of your heart diminish. The maximum rate your heart can beat doesn't change, yet it has to beat faster and work harder to do the same work you could easily do when you were in better shape. More lactic acid builds up than if you weren't deconditioned. Cardiovascular deconditioning even lowers your ability to regulate body temperature in the heat and cold.

Bone. After your mid-thirties to forties, you usually begin losing bone if you don't exercise, no matter how much calcium you eat. To maintain mineral density, bones need the mechanical stress of muscles pulling on them. Bone loss is a major problem of space flight. As yet no countermeasures completely halt bone loss while weightless. On earth, sedentary lifestyle is a major risk factor for osteoporosis. Once osteoporosis develops, it is not reversible (Bone Health, Chapter 7 Part III).

Body Composition. Although you may or may not avoid overeating during the winter holidays, without exercise you'll lose lean weight and put on some fat. Change in body composition over time includes higher body fat percentage and less lean muscle, even with no change in weight.

Cholesterol. One of several reasons regular exercise decreases risk of coronary artery disease is a favorable change in blood cholesterol. High-density lipoprotein cholesterol (HDL), popularly called good cholesterol, increases. "Bad cholesterol" or low density lipoprotein (LDL) can decrease.

One study of male runners accustomed to 30-40 miles per week found detraining of only two to three weeks resulted in 12% reduction in their aerobic capacity and 7.7% reduction in good cholesterol.

Memory and Coordination. Diving skills not used over a winter dull and fade from active memory. Both memory and specific skills like fine motor coordination appear to involve physical and chemical connections that require practice to stay sharp.

Flexibility. Inactivity, not exercise, reduces flexibility. As joints tighten and your range of motion diminishes for normal, daily activities, you become more likely to pull or strain a muscle, particularly your back and hamstrings. A diver with tight, weak back muscles is a gear-bag accident waiting to happen. Weak, tight back and trunk muscles are the most usual cause of most back pain (Chapter 4 Part III).

How Long Does It Take?

Even brief detraining periods remarkably reduce physical ability. After only days to weeks of stopping exercise, your capacity for exercise decreases. After longer periods of weeks to months, you can become a complete lump. Gains made from a summer in the gym and pool can disappear over a sedentary winter.

The more drastic your inactivity, the greater and more rapid your losses. Complete bed rest for one week can decrease your capacity to use oxygen, your strength, hemoglobin count, and blood volume by up to seven percent. It would take several weeks to deteriorate to the same extent without bed rest even if you didn't exercise.

Does It Hurt?

In one sense you could say getting out of shape doesn't hurt. Deconditioning isn't physically painful. You won't even notice it's happening at first. The harm comes from the fact that getting out of shape is more serious than just gaining a little weight. The global physical decline not only hinders sport activities like diving but activities of daily living.

Capacity for routine walking, lifting, and carrying dwindles. You slowly weaken and as a result do less and push it less. In turn you decondition further. A negative cycle self perpetuates. Risk of cardiovascular disease, falls, back pain, obesity, musculotendinous strains, and certain cancers may increase. For these reasons you could say getting out of shape hurts a great deal.

In older people, deconditioning often continues to the point of severe and even dangerous weakness. Getting out of chairs and activities of self care become too much. A serious handicap results, not from aging, but from preventable and reversible deconditioning.

These people, under physician supervision, benefit by regular weight lifting and conditioning programs. Several studies of exercise for populations debilitated by what we formerly called "aging" found dramatic reversals after simple weight lifting and activity programs. These people no longer needed canes or wheel chairs, decreased medications they took for high blood pressure, arthritis, or diabetes, and went back to unaided daily activities.

Getting out of shape often becomes a downward cycle of weakness, inactivity, and decreased ability to do or enjoy exercise. Serious health problems frequently result.

PREVENTING GETTING OUT OF SHAPE

- **At Least Do A Little.** If you must take time off from exercise, try cutting back, not out. You can hold on to physical fitness even with less frequency of exercise if you maintain the intensity. According to some studies, cutting back from three regular days of exercise to two maintenance days can completely preserve oxygen carrying capacity. Substituting one day for three will not prevent, but can reduce the consequences of detraining.

- **Avoid Bed Rest.** In many instances, the original illness or injury is worsened through the physical degeneration resulting from bed rest. Sometimes irreversible problems develop. Current treatments for most illness and injury involve early ambulation.

- **Get Active, Stay Active.** If you exercise, stay as active as you can all year every year. If you are sedentary, find some kind of regular activity you enjoy and get started. The older you get, the more beneficial exercise, including weight lifting, becomes. Exercise can at least partially counteract the physical deterioration of aging. A few table push-aways won't hurt either.

SUMMARY

Getting out of shape is more serious than just gaining a little weight. It sabotages your cardiovascular condition, strength, endurance, bone health, blood fat status, body composition, and joint range of motion. In a short time, these decrements can become the functional equivalent of aging many years.

Serious problems can result from a vicious cycle of deconditioning, weakness, and poor health. This cycle is easily preventable. Staying in shape once you are active is easier than getting back in shape. You don't have to take care of your entire body, just the parts you want to keep.

CHAPTER 7

NUTRITION FOR DIVERS

Nutrition is increasingly recognized as important to disease prevention. Your food and drink habits influence overall health and diving health. Although bad nutrition may be a strong habit, good, healthy nutrition is not difficult, and can become a regular habit, too.

- Divers and Dieting
- How To Lose Weight Without Dieting
- Bone Health
- Fluid Replacement For Divers

CHAPTER 7
PART I

DIVERS AND DIETING

Dieting is big business. According to Consumer Reports, Americans spend over $33 billion dollars a year on diet services, products, and gizmos. There is no doubt that being too much overweight makes health problems. There are also problems with the safety and long-term effectiveness of fad dieting and calorie restriction as weight-loss methods. Happily, there are effective, simple solutions.

- Poor Food Habits
- Dehydration
- Fatigue
- Reduced Cold Tolerance
- Possible Risk of Heart Disease

Many dieters are familiar with the cycle of repeated losing weight, then regaining, and dieting to lose again. The National Institutes of Health Task Force on the Prevention and Treatment of Obesity looked at 30 years of studies on weight-cycling, or "yo-yo" dieting. They concluded it does not permanently "reset" or hurt your metabolism, as previously thought. The reason fewer calories are needed after dieting, is that the dieter is lighter weight. Smaller people need fewer calories than much larger people. Obesity researcher Susan Yanovsky stated, "For obese people, especially those with a family history (heart disease and diabetes), even a loss of five to ten pounds can bring major benefits. They're better off trying to shed some pounds, even if it means regaining some of that weight later on."

Experimental work, however, shows there is a "set-point" that the body tries to maintain, burning fewer calories when weight is lost, making dieting a dim prospect for weight control. Severe calorie restriction diets without exercise can also undermine general health and diving health to varying extents. Effects may include unhealthy food choices than lead to undernutrition, dehydration, fatigue, reduced tolerance to heat and cold, and possibly, risks to the health of your heart.

POOR FOOD HABITS

To many people, wanting to lose weight means restricting calories, bad tasting food, and fad diets. Restricting calories does not always go along with a life-style switch to healthy food. Diets, particularly fad diets are often nutritionally unsound, leading to fatigue and run-down health from dietary deficiency. Dieting itself is often regarded as a temporary evil, to be discarded when goal weight is met. Dieters then fall back on the only habits they know: Sedentary lifestyle and high-calorie, high-fat meals that predispose to heart and vascular disease, some cancers, and the return of body fat.

DEHYDRATION

Dieters may be familiar with losing "water weight." Water is usually something you are better off keeping. Some of your water stores are in your muscles. When incoming carbohydrate fuel is low, your body does not go first to its stores of fat. It first looks to stored carbohydrate in your muscles and liver, called glycogen, to get the energy you need. Your body can also use muscle protein for fuel when carbohydrate is low. Glycogen molecules hold water. Your muscles lose water as you use stored carbohydrate. You look smaller, but the change is not from losing fat. You have lost water weight.

Too much loss without replacement, and you can run into problems of dehydration, including decreased tolerance to cold and heat, reduced exercise capacity, and possibility of increased risk of decompression sickness (Part IV of this chapter). Water is not fat. Losing water weight has no effect on fat loss. You need water to be healthy. Don't restrict water in hopes of losing water weight.

FATIGUE

Severe calorie restriction diets and fad diets leave you without the calories, carbohydrates, and other nutrients you need for exercise. Loss of muscle with calorie restriction impairs your ability to lift gear, produce body heat, and propel yourself through the water. Loss of water, electrolytes that go with the water, and muscle glycogen combine to further decrease exercise capacity. You become less able to cope with the physical exertion of diving, and less able to drop weight through exercising because you are too pooped.

REDUCED COLD TOLERANCE

Metabolic heat production may decrease when you have too few calories to fuel your needs. Lost muscle from dieting may mean you have less size to store the heat you produce. Reduced capacity for physical activity reduces you ability to produce heat through exercise. Reduced circulating fluid volume from dehydration also contributes to decreased cold tolerance.

POSSIBLE INCREASED HEART DISEASE

Most people who diet usually regain weight, and often return to diet again. Rapid weight gain common after dieting can rapidly raise total blood fat level, increasing fatty deposits in arteries. Dieting alone, without exercise, may also decrease your good cholesterol, called HDL. Low HDL levels add to risk of heart disease.

The repeated cycle of weight gain and loss may be unhealthy for the cardiovascular system, although there is still question regarding extent. Steven N. Blair, epidemiologist at the Cooper Institute for Aerobics Research in Dallas stated, "It's a paradox. Researchers know that gaining weight raises the risks of disease. But it's not clear whether losing weight lowers the risks again."

SUMMARY

Losing extra weight is often important to your joints and cardiovascular system, and general health and well-being. Sometimes it is even crucial. But severe calorie restriction and fad diets rarely work in the long-term for weight reduction, and can be unhealthy.

There is no need to choose between the pros and cons. You can lose weight, and remain hydrated, warm, healthy, and energetic, even more than before the diet. How to do this without calorie restriction follows in the next section.

CHAPTER 7
PART II

HOW TO LOSE WEIGHT
WITHOUT DIETING

You can do many things to lose weight without starvation diets. These alternatives can all become easy, safe, good-tasting, even fun lifetime habits that work.

- Cut Fats
- Increase Complex Carbohydrates
- Don't Go Hungry
- Less Sugar
- Be Prepared
- Take Your Time
- More Physical Activity

John F. Kennedy observed that those who make peaceful revolution impossible will make violent revolution inevitable. Make a few gentle changes now to reduce future problems. Modify your high-fat high-calorie meals to spare you weight gain, diabetes, heart disease, stroke, and joint degeneration from carrying too much weight, and cancer later. Lightening up also lessens orthopedic consequences of overweight: ankle, knee, hip, and back pain. Here's how.

CUT FATS

Studies generally find less relation between total number of calories eaten and body weight, as between calories of fat eaten and weight. Eating less saturated fat also cuts your risk of heart disease and some cancers. Many of your food habits may be high fat without you knowing it, like bacon, which is 80-90% fat.

SUBSTITUTE

When you want to eat foods full of sugar and fat, substitute complex carbohydrates like grains, pastas, potatoes, vegetables, and breads. Meat and eggs have only trace carbohydrates but a high percentage of saturated fat and cholesterol. Complex carbohydrates used to be called starches and were avoided. Studies indicate that eating complex carbohydrates in place of fat and sugar is the key to healthier eating. Try switching from potato chips to pretzels, candy to raisins, banana cake to bananas, cheese burgers to pasta. Find healthy foods you like and stock up. Fry less, and bake, boil, and steam more. Substitute unsaturated oils like olive oil for butter.

DON'T GO HUNGRY

Fasting and semi-starvation make your body hang on to its fat stores. Don't skip meals. Eat low fat snacks in late afternoon. Eat complex carbohydrates often to keep your blood sugar steady. Starving yourself, then snitching candy, can make you moody and want to eat everything you see, usually in the late afternoons, then again at night.

LESS SUGAR

Eat complex carbohydrates like fruit and bagels instead of sugar candy snacks. When you eat less sugar, a magic thing happens—you crave less.

BE PREPARED

You may have made a healthy cupboard and refrigerator for yourself at home, but most offerings away from home at fast food places, restaurants, public events, and snack machines are high fat, high sugar, and low complex carbohydrate. Go prepared. Pack fruit and bagels to munch, so you don't wind up with fries, shakes, and candy. Or go all out and pack a pasta lunch. There are several commercial sport nutrition bars and drinks, some no more than candy with a sporty name, others that are genuine, good, healthy food. Sport bars drinks are not magic energy potions, they are food in a wrapper. Read labels to find those that are low fat. Power Bar® is one example. It comes in several flavors, is easy to pack, and makes a quick, small meal in emergencies, easy snack, or meal adjunct.

TAKE YOUR TIME

Lose weight the way you gained it — slowly. It will pay. Think long term. Food items are not worked off in single death-bouts. Don't get discouraged if your body is not remade by the end of a week, or even a month. Small daily calorie expenditures multiply over time. An easy 150 calorie-a-day walk translates to about 15 pounds a year. Slow weight loss is more likely to stay off, is easier on your heart, and spares bone and muscle. Remember that one extra 150 calorie a day piece of candy can mean you weigh 15 pounds more in one year. If you reduce your activity enough to gain only one pound per year, think how much heavier you will be in 20 years. Small things add up. Make that work for you.

MORE PHYSICAL ACTIVITY

The major factor in overweight is not calories but sedentary lifestyle. Responsible plans for long-term weight loss include exercise. Exercise is, in almost all cases, a healthier, more effective weight loss method than calorie restriction. A University of California study found that most of those able to remain slimmed down were those who started exercising regularly.

The key to fat loss is not calorie restriction but activity.

Exercise doesn't automatically consign you to three weekly punishing sieges, pulse checks, group humiliation, and regimentation. Trade one or two of your daily cookies or sweets for a banana and find an activity you like anyway. If you like to go dancing, find a club and live it up weekly for a fun cardiovascular session. Walk a little extra every day. Grab a friend if that helps you, and do it. Walk to the market and carry home bags for both aerobic and muscular endurance, and depending on weight of the bags, strength. Try bicycling for errands or scenery for aerobic endurance and muscular endurance of the legs. Take nature walks. Help your dive club with chores. Park further away. Forget the golf cart and walk. Use a push mower instead of a power mower. Hide the remote control. Give a friend a piggyback ride. Be a hero and carry things for people. Take house-bound neighbor dogs for walks and romps. Walk-through instead of drive-through. Take reconnaissance walks all over dive sites.

Even your work day can be arranged to transform obligations into opportunities. If you drive to work, park farther away and walk the rest. Why endure an impatient minute for an elevator when you can improve your legs on the stairs? You may get there before the elevator. If you work on a high floor, take the elevator a few flights and walk the rest. Hand deliver interoffice mail any chance you have. Instead of a smoke break, or donut and Danish break, take a walk and stretch break.

Being active in general for fun, and for things you have to do anyway, is the concept of lifetime activity. Your daily activities become more active in a natural way, instead of a sedentary life that has to be made up for by going to a gym. Shake up your concept of exercise from a hated mandatory session with strange rules about heart rates, intensities, and minimum calories to burn, into a daily life exercise playground – yard work, shopping, cleaning, painting. Make opportunities to burn calories as part of your normal daily routine. With a little imagination you could burn an extra 250-300 calories a day depending on your size. You'll lose 2-3 pounds a month. That may not sound like much but it's a clothing size every 3-4 months, and 20-30 pounds by next year. If you're very heavy or haven't had a recent physical, see your physician before starting. Enjoy yourself. Don't overdo.

SUMMARY

Sedentary lifestyle and eating high-fat, low-fiber fast foods are easy to do and often come to seem natural and normal. Likewise, good exercise and nutrition doesn't have to be disagreeable or difficult. They can become easy habits with attention and repetition. Eat healthy and increase your daily activity level by making common lifetime activities part of your exercise. It will pay off in a lifetime of diving enjoyment.

- Cut fats

- Eat more complex carbohydrates

- Don't go hungry

- Eating less sugar-candy makes you crave less

- Be prepared by packing healthy food when you go places you know will have only junk food

- Take your time, small things add up

- More physical activity that you enjoy as part of your regular lifestyle

CHAPTER 7
PART III

BONE HEALTH

"Current recommendations for the prevention of osteoporosis may actually be detrimental to health."

This 1988 warning from University of Ulster researchers referred to dairy products, specifically their use as a calcium source. The Ulster scientists are not alone. There is more to osteoporosis prevention than eating calcium. African Bantu women eat relatively little calcium, yet have low rates of osteoporosis. The very high calcium diet of Eskimos doesn't prevent their suffering the highest rate of osteoporosis in the world. Astronauts lose bone in space no matter what they eat. Osteoporosis is not something that just happens to old people, it begins in youth. Several things can cause you to lose calcium from your bones. Preventing osteoporosis later depends on what you are doing now.

- What Is Osteoporosis?
- Why Young Divers Need To Know
- Factors Affecting Risk
- Where Diving Fits In
- How Much Calcium Do You Need?
- Calcium Sources
- Preventing Osteoporosis

WHAT IS OSTEOPOROSIS?

"Osteo" is a Greek word element meaning bone. "Porosis" means porous. Osteoporosis is a serious degenerative bone disorder that occurs when bones lose mineral density over years, making them porous and fragile. You probably won't know it is happening. Bone loss is completely painless until you break a bone. It is too late at that point to reverse the process.

At-risk sites are the wrist, upper back and upper leg bone where it joins the hip. When upper spine bones crush from osteoporotic fractures, the classic humped-back appears, with height losses up to five inches. Falls may fracture a wrist that would not have otherwise broken. Osteoporosis-induced hip and spine fractures are a major cause of illness and death among older men and women. Complications from broken bones kill a high proportion of older people. Close to fifty percent of those surviving a hip or spine fracture never walk unaided again.

WHY YOUNG DIVERS NEED TO KNOW

Your bone density in later years depends on what you are doing right now. Until your mid-thirties your bones are in an active growth phase that will determine your peak amount. Like stowing more money in the bank now for retirement later, building high peak bone mass in youth allows you to lose bone later in life through normal processes, without falling to dangerously low amounts. After a variable plateau period up to around age 40, bone loss begins silently, varying greatly from your genetically determined potential, depending on food and exercise habits. Risk factors when young can reduce the bone density of a 20 or 30 year old to the equivalent of someone in their 70's.

Like heart disease, bone loss is a gradual process. The time to actively direct its course is now, to prevent it from becoming serious later. Once bone loss becomes serious it is not reversible.

FACTORS AFFECTING RISK

The cause or causes of osteoporosis are not yet completely understood. It is important to know that calcium alone will not protect you against osteoporosis. There are at least four major determinants of how much bone mass you can achieve in your younger years and how much you later lose, and consequently, of fracture risk: genetics, nutrition, hormonal factors, and how much you exercise.

The bones of white people are typically less dense than those of African-Americans at all age groups. Whites have higher rates of osteoporosis. There also may be inherited tendencies to osteoporosis among families. These tendencies can be countered with practices to protect bone density, described later in this section.

Nutritionally, you not only need to get enough calcium, you need to avoid an excess of foods that cause you to lose calcium, such as animal protein. Eskimos have a high calcium diet and are physically active, yet suffer the world's highest rate of osteoporosis, which scientists relate to their high animal protein diet. African Bantu women eat relatively little calcium, yet have low rates of osteoporosis. Their genetic relatives living in the United States eating the Western diet of high animal protein, suffer rates of osteoporosis comparable to the rest of the U.S. population. Caffeine may increase urinary excretion of calcium, but relation to risk is uncertain. Smoking, and drinking alcohol are risk factors, as they are directly toxic to bone cells.

Anorexia nervosa, a condition of abnormal loss of appetite and refusal to eat, results in emaciation and malnutrition. It is a major risk factor for osteoporosis for several reasons. The diet is severely calcium deficient, and the loss of muscle and total body weight decreases resistive forces on bones. Bones need a physical stimulus for maintaining thickness. If menstrual function diminishes from anorexia, the hormone estrogen that is needed to maintain bone density, diminishes along with it. Menopausal women lose high amounts of bone regardless of calcium intake. Estrogen replacement may be the only way to maintain bone mass in the first five years of menopause.

Sedentary lifestyle is a major risk factor. Without exercise, you lose calcium from your bones no matter how much calcium you eat.

WHERE DIVING FITS IN

The job of bones is to support your body against the pull of gravity. Bones develop more when there is more need for them to resist gravity. The physical stress of muscle pulling on bone during activity stimulates bone to thicken and strengthen. By contrast, lack of exercise, prolonged immobility, sedentary lifestyle, and weightlessness during space flight leads to bone loss regardless of how much calcium you eat. Animals that hibernate go without activity for long periods. Their bodies produce chemicals that prevent bone loss. Humans are strongly susceptible to bone loss from inactivity, and require resistive exercise to keep bones dense and strong. Like muscular atrophy from lack of exercise, the bone atrophy of osteoporosis is a "use it or lose it" disease.

The most effective bone-building exercise is lifting weights. Also important is resisting your own body weight during weight-bearing exercise like walking, dancing, running, skating, and skiing. While underwater, scuba diving is not weight bearing. Muscles still pull on bone to move you through the water, but less than during weight bearing.

If you are able, carry your own tanks to get weight lifting exercise. If your back is already osteoporotic, it may not be good to carry or wear your tank before you get into the water. The weight could further compress fragile vertebrae. In this case don your tank in the water. Buoyancy underwater is an advantage to offset the weight of a tank. Check with your physician about diving safely if you have osteoporosis.

HOW MUCH CALCIUM DO YOU NEED?

With so many interacting variables, calcium need varies. You need more calcium if you lose calcium from smoking, drinking alcohol, and eating high amounts of animal protein. You may do well with less calcium if you exercise and reduce factors involved in calcium loss. Although much is unknown, it is established that calcium intake influences bone mass until adulthood. In this way calcium reduces subsequent osteoporosis risk, since someone with high bone mass at age 30 may lose bone through normal aging yet have sufficient bone remaining at 75. It is not known if calcium intake over a certain minimum during adulthood influences bone density. Neal Barnard, M.D., President of the Physician's Committee for Responsible Medicine (PCRM) reminds us that, "Excessive calcium intake does not fool hormones into building much more bone, any more than delivering an extra load of bricks will make a construction crew build a larger building." PCRM filed a complaint with the Federal Trade Commission against certain ads showing celebrity milk moustaches, stating a few deceptively imply that milk will prevent bone loss.

In 1994, the NIH recommended 1000 milligrams (mg) of calcium daily for men and non-pregnant women up to age 65, 1,200-1,500 mg for pregnant and nursing women, and 1,500 mg daily for men and women over 65 and menopausal women over 50 not on estrogen replacement. Table 7.1 gives a few examples of common high calcium foods.

CALCIUM SOURCES

Although dairy products are the prevailing calcium source in many Western countries, they are not the only source, or even in many cases, the best source.

Dairy is one of the most potent causes of allergy, and is a major source of fat and cholesterol. Many people lose ability to digest dairy after childhood. It is not difficult to get adequate calcium without dairy products. Many non-Western people get more calcium than the average American, from non-dairy sources.

Table 7.1. High calcium foods.

Source	Milligrams of Calcium (mg)
1 cup tofu processed with calcium sulfate	868
1 cup dulse seaweed	600
1 cup navy beans & 2 corn tortillas	370
1 cup milk	291
1 cup amaranth	280
1 cup kale	200
1 cup broccoli	180
1 cup soybeans	175
1 tablespoon blackstrap molasses	140
1 cup fortified orange juice	120

PREVENTING OSTEOPOROSIS

- Get regular exercise. An effective bone-building exercise is lifting weights. Also important is resisting your own body weight during weight bearing exercise like walking, dancing, running, skating, and skiing.

- Get adequate calcium from a variety of sources, and spread intake throughout the day

- Quit smoking

- Drink less alcohol

- Avoid high-meat diets

- Estrogen replacement after menopause may be the only way to maintain bone mass in the first five years

SUMMARY

Calcium is not the whole story in bone health. Adequate calcium intake remains a sound strategy, but without other critical factors, it is not a cure-all. Osteoporosis affects both men and women. Factors in risk are how much exercise you get, nutrition, heredity, and hormone status. Attaining high peak bone density when younger reduces the chance of lowering bone mass to unhealthy levels in later life. Lack of exercise, smoking, high alcohol intake, and high protein diet increases calcium loss. Reducing calcium loss may be as important as getting enough. To reduce bone loss, limit calcium-robbing foods and increase physical activity.

Factors in Bone Density

Consider Estrogen Replacement. Estrogen replacement, under physician supervision, may be the only way to maintain bone mass in the first five years after menopause.

Exercise. The most effective exercise for building bones is regular weight lifting. Weight bearing exercise such as walking, dancing, running, skating, skiing also loads bone by using your body weight.

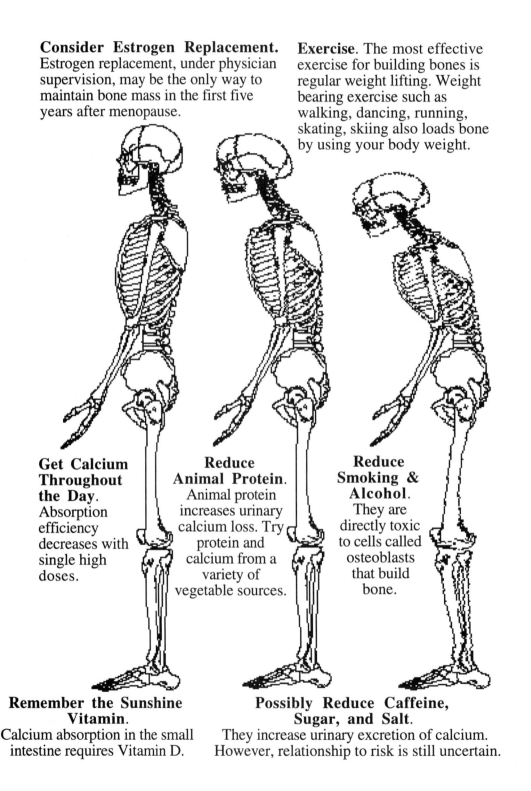

Get Calcium Throughout the Day. Absorption efficiency decreases with single high doses.

Reduce Animal Protein. Animal protein increases urinary calcium loss. Try protein and calcium from a variety of vegetable sources.

Reduce Smoking & Alcohol. They are directly toxic to cells called osteoblasts that build bone.

Remember the Sunshine Vitamin. Calcium absorption in the small intestine requires Vitamin D.

Possibly Reduce Caffeine, Sugar, and Salt. They increase urinary excretion of calcium. However, relationship to risk is still uncertain.

Figure 7.1. Several factors influence risk of bone loss, and subsequently, osteoporosis.

CHAPTER 7
PART IV

FLUID REPLACEMENT FOR DIVERS

Divers need good hydration for diving health. Contrary to popular diving belief, sport drinks do not dehydrate you, and do not need to be diluted. Are they helpful? Which fluids are best? Is beer a good carbohydrate or fluid replacer? What's the difference between an electrolyte drink and a carbohydrate replacer? What is an electrolyte? What should divers do for healthy hydration?

- Why Not Dehydrate?
- How You Lose Body Water
- How You Conserve Body Water
- Why Replacement?
- Water
- Electrolyte Replacers
- Carbohydrate Loaders
- Carbohydrate Replacers
- Not Harmful To Divers
- Alcohol
- Caffeine
- Preventing Dehydration

WHY NOT DEHYDRATE?

Dehydration greatly reduces exercise capacity, tolerance to heat, and may increase risk of decompression sickness.

Skin blood vessels dilate in the heat to cool you. They need more blood supply to do that. If you are active in the heat, your working muscles need blood too. With dehydration, competition between heat-induced vasodilation and muscular activity like carrying dive gear, leaves you without enough circulating blood volume to go around. Your blood pressure falls, and your heart pumps less blood with each heart beat, which increases your heart rate. You may overheat, feel faint, be unable to carry all your gear or yourself around, or safely finish your dive. Your body would rather cut your exercise ability than let you continue to generate heat through exercise.

With dehydration, your body temperature rises higher at the same exercise workload. But you are less able to cool yourself through sweating and vasodilation. There just isn't enough water to go around. Dehydration is also a small factor in reduced tolerance to cold (Chapter 3).

With less water in your circulating blood volume, blood fluids called plasma volume decrease, but cell content stays the same. Blood viscosity increases, blood vessels constrict, and blood flow decreases in previously supplied areas. These conditions put a strain on the circulatory system and are thought to relate in some, as yet unidentified, way to getting rid of inert gas absorbed under pressure, and so, to decompression sickness.

Dehydration is usually unnoticeable at first, one reason it can be so common. With progressing dehydration you feel unwell, but don't generally know why. Severe dehydration in the heat puts a person, particularly an older or obese person, at risk of collapse. Another reason to avoid dehydration on dive trips is that after a dive it may be difficult to distinguish the general malaise of dehydration from decompression sickness.

Dehydration increases your chances of overheating, fatigue, feeling generally unwell in the heat, and possibly, risk of decompression sickness.

HOW YOU LOSE BODY WATER

Everyone loses body water several ways all day and all night as part of the normal metabolic processes of living. You lose body water through sweat, in liquid and solid waste, and through your skin and respiratory tract in a process called insensible perspiration. Insensible does not mean it is not a sensible way to sweat, but fluid loss that you are not aware of. Divers lose body water during diving activities:

- High sweating in wet or dry suits before dives increases normal fluid loss.

- Divers often deliberately don't drink fluids to reduce their need to "go" on dive boats without facilities, or when dry-suit diving. Healthy alternatives are in Chapter 2.

- Immersion, particularly in cold water, increases the need to "go" (Chapter 2).

- Alcohol and caffeine can increase your output to the point that you lose more fluid than you drank.

- Water, juice, or other fluid replacers may not be available at dive sites.

- Divers may become queasy on dive boats, giving up large fluid offerings to the downwind altar of Earl the SeaSick God, or travel to countries with customs and bacteria foreign to their gastrointestinal tract.

One factor in how much moisture you lose through breathing is how much water content, called water vapor, there is in the air around you, compared to the content of your lungs. Water vapor, like heat and nitrogen, travels from greater quantity to lesser. There is normally more water vapor pressure in the air in your lungs than the atmosphere, so you lose moisture from your lungs to the environment. As the vapor pressure of air in hot conditions increases, the gradient for water loss through breathing decreases, so you lose less. With cold it increases, and you lose more. That is why your throat may feel dry in very cold weather.

Your skin is not very permeable to water passing in or out through it, which is a good thing. If it were, you would gain and lose much water when surrounded by environments of different concentrations than your insides – water would flow in or out, trying to make you and the environment the same concentration. You would swell up with water every time you immersed in fresh water, which is more dilute than your body, lose body water while in salt water, and dehydrate entirely while standing in air. Normally, only about 300-400 ml of water diffuses out through your skin each day, a little over a cup. If your outer, non-permeable layer of skin were removed, as after extensive burns, evaporative loss could increase to 3-5 quarts (liters) per day. Fluid balance is a major problem in treating burn patients.

HOW YOU CONSERVE BODY WATER

As with heat loss pathways (Chapter 3), water loss pathways interact with each other. If some increase output and lose more, others decrease output to conserve. In normal temperatures without exercise, you lose a little under half a cup of sweat in a day (about 100 ml). In hot weather, sweating generally increases about 14 times (to about a quart and a half or 1400 ml), and with heavy exercise up to 50 times or so (around 5 quarts or 5000 ml) and more. Insensible water loss of about 350 ml per day does not change, nor does the 100 ml or so you lose daily with solid output. To compensate for extra fluid loss through sweating, urine volume decreases, sometimes considerably, from an average of 1400 ml at rest in normal temperature to 1200 ml in the heat, to 500 ml (about a pint) with heavy exercise. Decreased urine output is your body's way of reducing dehydration by conserving more. Loss from your respiratory tract drops by about a third in hot conditions, further conserving body water.

WHY REPLACEMENT?

Your body manufactures a small amount of water during normal metabolism, and you get a bit of water from your food, but you gain body water principally through drinking. If you don't drink as much as you lose, you dehydrate.

You need to add to your body water stores before and after activity, and sometimes during activity depending on length of the activity. Fluid replacement is particularly important in the heat. Depending how long and how intensely you exercise, you may benefit by adding electrolytes and carbohydrates during exercise. After exercise you need to restock carbohydrates you used for fuel, and replace lost electrolytes. Different drinks benefit different durations of exercise and at various times before, during, and after exercise. Options follow.

WATER

You normally lose a bit over 2 quarts (2300 ml) of water each day, over 3 quarts (3300 ml) in hot weather and 6 or more quarts (6000 ml) with heavy exercise. You need to replace equivalent amounts. Drink 8 glasses of water a day, and up to another pint (half liter) every 15-20 minutes during exercise in the heat.

Water replacement during activity reduces fatigue and feeling poorly in the heat. Replacing lost body water is a major factor in preventing overheating. Water is a good, inexpensive, and easy fluid replacer for diving. For ordinary short duration activity, your regular meals replace other things you need, such as certain minerals and salts called electrolytes.

The most overlooked athletic ability aid is water. You need to replace body water before and after activity, and sometimes during activity, depending on duration, particularly in the heat.

ELECTROLYTE REPLACERS

A persistent rumor among divers is that sport electrolyte drinks will dehydrate you and must be diluted. There is no basis for these stories, explained later in this section.

Electrolyte drinks replace water and amounts of each electrolyte you need. They eliminate the need to stop to eat, and are convenient to keep in your dive bag. Unlike plain water, electrolyte drinks stimulate thirst, which encourages more drinking. The electrolytes help you absorb more water and more carbohydrate for energy. Once in your bloodstream these drinks help you retain water. When you drink plain water, your body pees much of it back out, due to lack of electrolyte content to retain it.

What Is An Electrolyte? An electrolyte is a substance that, when you dissolve it in liquid, becomes electrically conductive, because it breaks up into ions. Ions are atoms or small molecules with at least one electron more or less than normal, giving them a positive or negative electric charge. Table salt, for example, becomes the positively charged sodium ion, and the negatively charged chloride ion. Both are principle ions in your body. In physiology, the ions themselves are called electrolytes.

No current flows through pure water. Dissolving even a trace of electrolytes in water makes water conductive. Why does your body need an electric current? Your cells use ions to regulate processes such as flow of water across the cell membrane. Ions propagate signals along nerves for all the thousands of functions that nerves control to keep you alive, moving, and thinking. The difference between electric current in, say, a flashlight, and in your body is that electronic signals race through wire at up to half the speed of light, passing the charge by electrons. The electrons themselves don't move far, but pass the charge like toppling dominos. In your body, nerve signals propagate thousands of times more slowly, along dissolved ions.

Why Replace Electrolytes? Losing electrolytes with sweat is a good thing, to an extent. If you lost only water, your blood would get very concentrated with electrolytes. Dogs are more susceptible than humans to that. Dogs pant, not sweat, to cool themselves, and panting removes only water and no electrolytes. Burros can sweat, but burro sweat contains little salt. In both dogs and burros, blood concentrations can rise too high in the heat if they don't have water to drink.

Your sweat contains water and electrolytes. When you sweat, you lose proportionately more water than minerals, leaving your blood slightly more concentrated than normal, or hypertonic. That does not mean you should avoid drinks containing electrolytes. Substantial electrolyte loss with prolonged sweating creates a real need for electrolyte replacement. Without replacement, your levels fall too low and your ability to exercise decreases. With extreme electrolyte loss during long exercise, with only water to drink, you may abnormally dilute your body fluids and cells, a condition called water intoxication. Effects range from weakness to convulsion and occasionally death. Water intoxication is also called hyponatremia (high-poe-nay-TREE'-me-uh) meaning low sodium. Cases are usually reported in hikers and distance runners who drink only water. Occasionally, serious cases of hyponatremia occur in infants swallowing pool water during parent-infant swimming lessons.

When to Replace Electrolytes. Except for extreme endurance activities, you usually eat and drink enough or more electrolytes with your regular meals to keep you going for short duration activity. Diving does not deplete electrolytes enough to affect athletic ability or health. For that reason, after a one hour dive, you don't ordinarily need to replace electrolytes immediately. It is also unnecessary to take extra electrolytes ahead of time to offset any loss predicted during the dive. You don't lose enough to affect performance or fatigue level. Unless you work slinging tanks in the tropics with limited chance to eat and drink fluids other than water, health problems from electrolyte loss is low for divers.

Two Stimuli For Thirst. You have two different stimuli for thirst. One is hypovolemic, the other is osmotic.

Your "low on water" or hypovolemic thirst signal comes when you lose fluids. If you replace only water, your body sees that you have more fluid relative to electrolytes, because you have also lost electrolytes. Your body helpfully responds by "peeing" out some water. Electrolyte drinks avoid this problem.

Regardless of your body's total water volume, high electrolyte content stimulates osmotic thirst, or "high on electrolyte particles" thirst. That is why salty things make you thirsty, even when you are drinking (and why bars serve you salty finger food). Small amounts of sodium in electrolyte drinks stimulate your osmotic thirst, then help you retain what you drink. That is why people consume more of these beverages than plain water. The first commercial drink to solve the electrolyte replacement need along with fluids during long exercise bouts was developed at the University of Florida, and named Gatorade® for their Gators mascot.

CARBOHYDRATE LOADERS

Carbohydrate is an important fuel for activity. Because athletes exercising at high intensities for long periods can delay fatigue with carbohydrate drinks, thereby working longer and harder, misunderstandings result. Drinking carbohydrate preparations will not transform you into a better athlete or diver. Submaximal exercise like scuba diving does not improve from any particular food or drink.

Carbohydrate loaders have three main applications. During intense, long-duration exercise they provide fuel to delay fatigue. For athletes who can't eat enough calories through regular meals and snacks to maintain their weight with all their strenuous workouts, the drinks add calories. For people unable to eat a regular meal before physical activity because of time restraints or jittery stomach, the drinks become a temporary meal substitute or adjunct.

Carbohydrate drinks are not magic energy elixirs or stimulants. They won't give you a performance edge if taken before or during exercise much shorter than an hour or so, like a recreational dive, aerobics class, a half hour to hour of cycling, skiing, or basketball, or even a six to ten kilometer jog. Carbohydrate drinks are most effective to delay fatigue when carbohydrate concentration is between 6 and 8% and when exercise is tough stuff lasting over an hour. Athletes generally have enough of their own stored carbohydrate, called glycogen, to last about an hour to 90 minutes. The commercial drink Bodyfuel 450®, for example, is 4.5% carbohydrate, Gatorade® is 6.0%, and Exceed® is 7.0%.

CARBOHYDRATE REPLACERS

Carbohydrate replacement drinks have a higher carbohydrate content than carbohydrate loader drinks. Replacement drinks are for after hard activity to restock your muscle and liver glycogen. Glycogen is an important fuel. Long, intense exercise depletes glycogen. You need to replace glycogen as soon as possible after exercise. If you don't eat enough carbohydrate, your body won't make enough glycogen to replace the loss. Your muscle and liver reserves remain low even days later, limiting further exercise potential.

The first 30 minutes after hard exercise are crucial to the major restocking. The next two hours are the second important stage. You benefit by eating high carbohydrate food as soon after exercise as you can. Unfortunately, people usually get changed, pack away their gear, and return home before eating anything. By then a critical maximum restock window has passed. For this reason, high carbohydrate replacement drinks were developed for right after exercise. Regular food eaten with water would do just as well. Replacement drinks serve the market of people who prefer to drink rather than eat and drink right after exercise, or who just want something pre-packaged and ready to swallow. For divers they make a handy after-dive snack. High carbohydrate content means the drinks are high calorie. Go overboard with these and the extra calories will store not as glycogen, but fat.

What Sport Drinks Do

- Increase palatability, compared to plain water, so you drink more

- Replace needed water, then help absorb and retain water

- Stimulate your osmotic thirst mechanism to keep you drinking

- Provide carbohydrate during long exercise bouts to delay fatigue

- Replace carbohydrate after exercise

NOT HARMFUL TO DIVERS

Commercial electrolyte and carbohydrate sport drinks are not harmful to divers. They will not overload you with electrolytes, dehydrate you, or sit in your stomach as sometimes thought. It is also not the case that they must be diluted or taken in small quantities.

Commercial sport drinks do not dehydrate you.
There is no physiologic need to dilute them.

Won't Harm Blood Electrolytes. There's little risk of injurious electrolyte concentrations to an otherwise healthy diver from even high concentration drinks. As a point of reference, your body has about 97,000 milligrams (mg) of sodium and about 170,000 mg of potassium. In one hour of light exercise, you might sweat 400-700 mg sodium and 80-200 mg potassium. Contrast that with one cup of cream of mushroom soup with 1000 mg of sodium. Sport drinks have far less sodium. Gatorade®, for example, with 110 mg of sodium has less sodium than a slice of whole wheat bread or a glass of milk.

Your body continually makes adjustments to keep all its workings in a narrow range of sameness. It restricts electrolyte loss when supply is low, and gets rid of excess when you eat or drink too much. When you are inactive, the major exit avenue for surplus electrolytes is urine and feces. With high loss through sweating, your body restricts this loss. When you sweat and your supply of sodium falls below normal, your body secretes a hormone called aldosterone (al-DOHS'-tur-own) into your bloodstream to help you retain sodium. Most people in Western society eat many times more salt than their bodies require, sometimes in astounding quantities in fast foods, and that's before they even pick up their salt shaker. When you eat more salt than you require, your body retains water to dilute the salt, and aldosterone drops to encourage your kidneys to excrete the excess. Ordinarily the body handles large ranges of excess, with exceptions in salt-sensitive people. Much research in blood pressure regulation continues in this area.

Limits exist, of course. Drinking sea water is an example. Sea-going birds such as penguins, sea gulls, and albatross can drink sea water. Special glands in their heads excrete excess salt. Humans have no salt glands. You have to get rid of the extra salt because it is just too much for your system. Contrary to popular belief, your blood is not similar in composition to sea water; blood is several times more dilute. If it were like sea water, you could safely drink it, which is not the case. The human kidney draws water from the body's supply to dilute the salt and get rid of it, a process so dehydrating that if sea water were the only fluid replacement available, you could die of thirst faster by drinking sea water than if you didn't. Human inability to drink sea water for fluid replacement is reflected in Samuel Taylor Coleridge's ballad *Rime of the Ancient Mariner* — "Water, water everywhere, nor any drop to drink."

Your blood is not similar in composition to sea water.
Sea water is about three times more concentrated.

Human blood is also not similar to
what we believe was the concentration of the
primordial ocean.

Won't Dehydrate You. A popular diving myth is the scientific sounding, but false statement, that sport drinks and sugary or salty juices and food pull water from your body into your intestine to balance their high electrolyte or sugar content, temporarily dehydrating you.

Sport drinks are not hypertonic, or more concentrated with electrolytes than your blood. They are similar concentration, or isotonic, to your body fluids. Your body also maintains a 1.3 to 2.6 gallon (5-10 liter) circulating reserve of water, salivary, gastric, biliary, pancreatic, and intestinal fluids that mix, change the chemical attributes, and dilute your food and drink. Repeated studies of exercise in the heat show that people prefer the taste of a salty drink, so drink more. The small amount of salt in these drinks helps retain water, and further stimulates your thirst mechanism to keep you drinking. The net effect of all of this is to gain, not lose fluid.

Not Sweet Drinks. Statements that high sugar content pulls water out of your body to the intestine can also be put to rest. On one hand, it is a physiologic principle that fluids are drawn across certain body membranes into other fluid compartments with higher particle amounts. That's called osmosis. It does not apply to sweet things in your stomach and intestine. Sugar is not osmotically active in the intestine. In other words it is unable to draw water out of your body into the gut.

In hospital settings, a patient may need to reduce unhealthy body fluid levels. Solutions of 50% sugar like sorbital or mannitol are injected directly into a vein bypassing the intestine. The sugars are not absorbed by body cells. The extreme and sudden blood concentration, as with sea water, makes you "pee" out body water. This is not the case with sugary beverages. Sport drinks usually range only 6-10% sugar, and are not injected directly into circulation – you drink them. The sugar content in sports drinks allows more water absorption through the intestine than from a solution just of salts, equal in concentration to your body. In other words, the sugar aids water absorption, helping replace needed water. The sugar in sports drinks is also absorbed by your cells, allowing cells to draw water osmotically along with it. The net effect is more, not less fluid everywhere.

Not Salty Food or Juices. Eating salty food will not dehydrate you. Just the opposite occurs. Salt is well known to help you retain water. Extra salt stimulates thirst, then makes you retain the water you drink with meals. Some "salt-sensitive" people with high blood pressure need to restrict salt, to allow them to lose the extra water that salt retains.

According to Dr. Scott Montain of the US Army Research Institute of Environmental Medicine in Natick, Massachusetts, even fruit juices and non-caffeine sodas with relatively high sugar and salt content (hypertonic) will not dehydrate you. He stated that a very small bit of water may temporarily cross into the intestine to balance an unusually hypertonic mixture, however the amount is inconsequential compared to total body water, and that juices give more fluid than they withdraw from circulation. He added that the small amount of sodium in sport drinks is needed to help carrier molecules transport the carbohydrate out of the intestine, making the drinks more effective.

Dr. Carl Gisolfi, one of the best known researchers in fluid regulation in the heat, also confirmed that there is no dehydrating effect of juices. He stated that drinking large quantities of some juices just before exercise may delay stomach emptying due to the high carbohydrate content, or cause upset stomach, making them unsuitable as sports drinks, but they have no dehydrating effect unless they give you diarrhea.

The American Red Cross points out that they serve pretzels, donuts, and juices in bloodmobiles after blood donations. The combination of fluids, sugar, and salt begins restoring lost blood fluid volume.

Finally, don't forget that you have a kidney, usually two. Many physiologic processes determine fluid balance, not just passive fluid movement across membranes according to their gradients.

Won't Upset Stomach. Although hard to tell in every case, studies of marathon runners reveal the usual reasons for gastrointestinal upset are high core temperature, dehydration, and decreased sweating at high levels of dehydration, not sport drinks.

Some sports drinks may leave the stomach slightly slower than water because of the calorie content. However, once in the small intestine, glucose and sodium speed up absorption. The slight difference in stomach emptying should not cause major stomach upset in most people. Drinks of 6% sugar like Gatorade® enter the blood as fast as plain water. Recent studies on drinks that use small chains of sugar called glucose polymers, show they are no more or less rapidly absorbed, and no more or less effective than other drinks.

No Need To Dilute. A popular misconception among divers is that sport drinks must be diluted or taken in small quantities. Dr. Robert Murray, Director of the Gatorade Exercise Physiology Laboratory, points out that diluting the drinks lessens their effectiveness. The drinks are designed to be taken in large volumes for rehydration. Since diving is rarely a maximal athletic endurance event, if you don't like the taste full strength, it makes little difference to dilute. The importance is to replace fluids and electrolytes during long exercise.

ALCOHOL

Alcohol has several characteristics making it unsuitable as fluid replacement for physical activities. Taken before an activity, it reduces output of glucose by your liver, producing early fatigue. It is unsuccessful as a loader or replacer drink because, although alcohol is a concentrated source of carbohydrate calories, the calories are not metabolized like carbohydrate, making it ineffective as an endurance energy source. As a central nervous system depressant, alcohol interferes with mental and motor control. The electrolyte content in beer is insufficient to use it as a replacement drink. Hard alcohol suppresses antidiuretic hormone (ADH). ADH, as explained in Chapter 2, inhibits fluid loss. When this inhibiting influence is removed, you put out more fluids. Less concentrated alcohols like beer have limited effect on ADH. It takes large volumes of beer before ADH suppression becomes involved in diuresis. The typically high output from beer is due to sheer volume overload, rather than suppression of ADH. Beer can contribute to dehydration. Alcohol's place is not with diving or exercise.

CAFFEINE

Caffeine may help athletic endurance. Caffeine also increases irregular heart beats, nervousness, and diuresis. Don't drink coffee, tea, or soda, or take caffeine tablets just to get a boost for diving. If you drink lots of caffeine drinks, cut down if you comfortably can. If you are so accustomed to your coffee and sodas that missing your dose would hinder your diving, drink extra water to help offset diuresis.

PREVENTING DEHYDRATION

Your diving health benefits by good hydration. Bring plenty to drink to dive sites and boats, and drink throughout your dive trips. Which drink you choose is a matter of personal taste.

If you prefer sport drinks then enjoy yourself. Sport drinks won't transform you into super diver. They are quick and simple fluid, electrolyte, and carbohydrate replacement, and live up to claims for endurance events where you can't stop to eat or drink.

Try different drinks to determine which works out best for you. Everyone's system differs in what it tolerates. Drink before you're thirsty. Drink more than you think you need in the heat. Just as emergency oxygen is becoming regular safety equipment, make large drink coolers standard equipment aboard dive boats and at all your dive sites.

SUMMARY OF FLUID REPLACEMENT CHOICES

- **Water.** The most overlooked athletic ability aid. Replacing lost body water prevents dehydration. Dehydration increases your chance of overheating, fatigue, and not feeling well in the heat. It also seems to be involved (somehow) in decompression sickness.

- **Electrolyte Replacers**. These drinks replace and retain needed electrolytes and water after long duration exercise in the heat. They stimulate thirst, resulting in greater fluid replacement.

- **Carbohydrate Drinks**. These drinks provide fuel and fluids to delay fatigue in long events, supplement calories, and can be a temporary meal substitute or adjunct. They are not magic energy elixirs or stimulants. They often are combined with electrolytes.

- **Carbohydrate Replacers**. With a higher carbohydrate content than regular carbohydrate drinks, replacement drinks restock muscle and liver glycogen along with fluids after hard activity.

- **Alcohol**. Alcohol has several characteristics making it unsuitable as fluid replacement.

- **Caffeine**. Cut down if you comfortably can. If you are so accustomed to your coffee and sodas that missing your dose would hinder your diving, drink extra water to help offset diuresis.

ANNOTATED GLOSSARY

A

ADH See Antidiuretic Hormone.

Aerobic Capacity   See Endurance, Cardiovascular.

Adrenal Glands [From Latin *ad*, near +*renes*, kidney. Also called suprarenal gland.] Small glands sitting like hats, one on each kidney. The outer covering, called the cortex, secretes more than 30 different steroid hormones including hydrocortisone and aldosterone. The cortex is about one centimeter (0.4") thick. The inside, called the medulla, which comes from a word meaning middle, secretes adrenaline and noradrenaline, also called epinephrine and norepinephrine. See Aldosterone, Epinephrine, Kidney, and Norepinephrine.

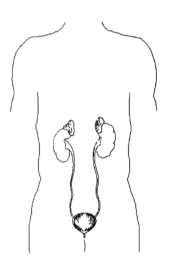

Adrenaline   Another name for epinephrine. See Epinephrine.

Advection [From Latin *ad*, to, toward, or near + *vehere*, to carry.] Meteorologic term for heat transfer from movement of an air mass. Its effect to rapidly remove body heat by convection and evaporation from the skin is responsible for the wind-chill factor. See Wind Chill.

Air Embolism [From Greek *emballein*, to insert.] Any bubbles of air that obstruct blood flow. Compare to Embolism.

Aldosterone   (al-DOHS'-tur-own) [Named for its chemical structure containing an aldehyde and a sterol.] Steroid hormone secreted by the adrenal gland and regulated by the kidney. Helps you retain salt and water, and excrete potassium, to maintain their healthy balance in your body. See Kidney, Renin, and Renin-Angiotensin-Aldosterone Cascade.

Algorithm   [From Latin *algorismus*, doing calculations with Arabic numbers, from Arabic *al Khuwa-rizmi*, 9th c. Arab mathematician.] A step-by-step rule or procedure for doing a procedure or calculation. Has a finite number of steps and a known result. In diving computers, refers to internally programmed computational procedures for estimating compartment nitrogen tensions, and so, depth and time limits for a dive. Sometimes applies to the formulas or equations themselves.

Allergy   [From Greek *allos*, other + *ergon*, action.] Heightened response to specific substances, such as pollen, foods, microorganisms, which cause no reaction in other people. Term coined by Austrian physician Pirquet, around the early 1900's.

Ambient Pressure   [From Latin *ambi-*, around; + *ire*, to go.] Surrounding pressure. On land, exerted by the weight of air above you. Under water, by the combination of air plus water pressure. As distance down increases, pressure increases. When considering sea level as a zero starting point, pressure measured under water is called gauge pressure and does not include atmospheric pressure (14.7 psi, 760 mmHg, or 101.3 kPa). All air and water pressure together is called absolute pressure, starting with one ATA at sea level (units are atmospheres absolute, abbreviated ATA, or more preferred, atm abs). See Atmosphere, and compare to Hydrostatic Pressure.

Anaerobic Capacity.   Ability of your body to use special stored fuel, not oxygen, for rapid-onset, short duration, and intense activity. Because it is not an oxygen-using (aerobic) system, it is called **an**aerobic. You use your anaerobic system for breath-hold diving, swimming against hard currents, sprints, to haul out of the water in full gear, or rescue a heavy buddy. Compare to Endurance, Cardiovascular.

ANF   See Atrial Natriuretic Factor.

Angiotensin   [From Greek *angeion*, little vessel or blood vessel + tension.] Three hormones, Angiotensin I, II, and III. The angiotensins counterbalance low blood fluid and salt volumes and help regulate arterial blood pressure. Angiotensin I has no great biologic activity and rapidly converts to angiotensin II (chiefly in the lungs) and angiotensin III (various sites). Both constrict blood vessels. Angiotensin II acts on the kidneys to retain salt and water two ways. A powerful vasoconstrictor, it reduces fluid and salt loss by restricting kidney blood flow. It also stimulates the outer covering of the adrenal gland called the cortex, to produce the hormone aldosterone. Aldosterone acts on the kidney to excrete more potassium instead of sodium. Increased body sodium helps retain body water. Angiotensin III is less of a vasoconstrictor, but more active on the adrenal cortex. When angiotensin production is inhibited by atrial natriuretic factor, you excrete more salt and fluid. See Adrenal Gland, Aldosterone, Atrial Natriuretic Factor, Kidney, Renin, and Renin-Angiotensin-Aldosterone Cascade.

Antibody   A protein produced by, or introduced into the body, that destroys or weakens a specific bacterium, toxin, or foreign cell invader called an antigen.

Antidiuretic Hormone (ADH)   Another name for the hormone vasopressin. ADH works normally to limit fluid output from the kidney, constrict blood vessels, and raise blood pressure. When ADH is suppressed through immersion, high alcohol intake, or other stimuli, fluid output increases, blood vessels relax, and blood pressure lowers. See Aldosterone, Angiotensin, Atrial Natriuretic Factor, P Phenomenon, Renin.

Antigen   [From antibody + Greek *gennan* to produce; from the Greek root *gen* we get words like gene, gender, genesis, and generate.] A substance the body thinks is an invader. Examples are toxins, bacteria, foreign blood cells, and cells of transplanted organs. Antigens stimulate production of antibodies as part of the immune response.

Antihistamine   An agent, either produced in the body or taken, that reduces effects of an inflammatory chemical produced in the body called histamine. Antihistamines work by blocking or displacing histamine at its sites of action. See Histamine.

Apnea   (AP'-nee-uh) [From Greek *a*-, without + *pnoia*, breathing.] Temporary halt to breathing. Examples are voluntary breath holding during snorkeling and breath-hold diving, and involuntary lapses from sleep disorders involving snoring.

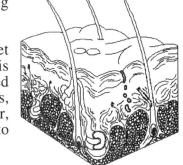

Apocrine Sweat Glands   [From Greek *apokrinein*, to set apart, named because part of the secreting cell is released along with sweat]. Type of sweat gland related to emotional, not thermal sweating. Found in palms, soles, arm pits, groin, and upper lip. Contains water, lipids, a bit of color, and musky odor. Compare to Eccrine Sweat Glands.

Arrhythmia   [From Greek *a*, without + *ruthmia*, rhythm.] Irregular heartbeat. Arrhythmias occur normally now and then in the middle of normal heart beats, without ill effect or you being aware of them. Too many arrhythmias occurring too often can be harmful.

Arterial Gas Embolism (AGE)   Small bubbles of air that obstruct blood flow in arteries. Also called air embolism.

Arteries   Muscular, elastic, branching system of thick-walled tubes carrying blood away from the heart to all the body. Compare to veins.

Atmosphere   [From Greek *atmos*, vapor + Latin *sphaera*, sphere] Abbreviated atm. In decompression, one of several units of pressure of the air or water around you. At sea level, pressure is approximately 14.7 pounds per square inch (psi), 33 feet of sea water (fsw), 10 meters of sea water (msw), 760 mmHg, or 101.3 kPa. At 18,000 feet of altitude (almost 5.5 km), air pressure drops to half that at sea level. At 10 miles up (16 km) pressure falls to 0.1 atm, and by 20 miles up (32 km) pressure is only 0.01 atm. Atmospheric pressure varies with weather conditions. Underwater, pressure increases by one atmosphere for every 33 feet (10 meters) descent, reaching two atmospheres absolute at 33 feet (10m), three at 66 feet (20m), four at 99 feet (30m) and so on. Because 33 feet of depth is two atmospheres absolute but one atmosphere by gauge pressure, it can be inconsistant to call the surface one atmosphere, and confusing calculational problems occur when people use atm and ATA interchangeably underwater. If sea level were defined as 0 atm, it becomes interesting to express sub-atmospheric pressures. This is sometimes handled with negative numbers (0.5 ATA would be -380 mmHg, or -16.5 fsw), other times by defining sea level as one atmosphere. See Atmosphere Absolute.

Atmosphere Absolute   Abbreviated atm abs or ATA. Atmospheric pressure plus water pressure. For scientific use, the SI units pascals (Pa) and kilopascals (kPa) are preferred, or the term atm abs. See Atmosphere, SI System, and Technical Atmosphere.

Atrial Natriuretic Factor (ANF)   A substance (or factor) secreted in the upper chambers of the heart, called atria. ANF inhibits renin, a kidney enzyme. With renin inhibited, your body produces less angiotensin. Angiotensin conserves body fluid and salt. ANF blocks that, making you "have to go." ANF also decreases circulating levels of aldosterone, ADH, and catecholamines, which furthers the effect. ANF is the most powerful vasodilator known, and also tells the kidneys to excrete sodium, a process called natriuresis (nay-tree-you-REE'-sis). See ADH, Aldosterone, Angiotensin, P Phenomenon, Renin.

B

Baroreceptors   [From Greek *baros*, weight or pressure (from which we get words like barometer, hyperbaric, and bariatrition - a physician who cares for the obese) + receptor.] Sensory nerve endings in blood vessel walls, particularly of the heart and neck, that respond to change in blood pressure.

Bert, Paul   French physiologist who determined the connection between nitrogen bubbles and decompression sickness, published in 1878. He made several important gas discoveries, such as describing central nervous system oxygen toxicity from exposure to high oxygen pressure, which is called the Bert Effect, in his honor. See Central Nervous System Oxygen Toxicity.

Boyle's Law   Physical principle that, at a constant temperature, the volume of a confined ideal gas is inversely proportional to pressure, or in other words, as pressure increases, volume decreases, all other things kept the same. Named for Robert Boyle (1627-1691) Irish-born British physicist and chemist. Boyle invented the vacuum pump, which he used in experiments of pressure reduction, and filled J-tubes with mercury and measured the compressed trapped air volume in relation to pressure applied. These experiments added to understanding of decompression sickness. Although much of the work was done by his assistant Robert Hooke, the pressure-volume relationship is named for Boyle, originator of the concept. In 1662, Boyle stated this pressure-volume relationship was evidence that the atmosphere must become less dense with altitude above earth, based on decreased pressure readings at altitude in 1648 by French mathematician Blaise Pascal, or more accurately, by Pascal's brother-in-law, who Pascal sent up a mountainside with a mercury barometer. This was evidence that the atmosphere was far higher than the 5 miles predicted if it were uniformly 14.7 psi, as at the surface. Boyle did much important work, including experiments upholding Galileo's theories (against Aristotle) that heavy and light objects fall at the same rate in a vacuum, experiments with blood transfusion, and was the first to publish that the human body had a fixed temperature, higher than room temperature. Boyle's meticulous work in chemistry began its modern separation from alchemy. See Ideal Gas.

Bradycardia   [From Greek *brady*, slow + *kardia*, heart.] Slow heart rate in an adult human, usually fewer than 60 beats per minute.

Bronchi   (BRON'-kai) [From Greek *bronkhos*, windpipe.] Plural of bronchus. The two branches of your windpipe leading to your lungs.

C

Cabin Pressure   Air pressure in an aircraft cabin. In unpressurized aircraft, cabin pressure is close to the air pressure outside the aircraft, at whatever altitude. In pressurized aircraft, cabin pressure is usually maintained at a higher pressure (lower altitude) than flight altitude. Cabin pressure of commercial air flights is not always equivalent to 8,000' as often thought, but usually equivalent to lower altitude (higher pressure), varying  with cruising altitude and type of aircraft. Cabin pressure is usually gradually brought to the pressure of the destination airport so that the rapid change in pressure on landing is minimized.

Caisson Disease [From Italian *cassone*, augmentative of *cassa*, box, meaning big box. From Latin *capsa*.] Caissons are watertight boxes allowing bridge and tunnel construction laborers to carry out work under water. Pressurized air keeps water out. In the late 1800's, laborers began returning to the surface after work suffering joint pain and paralysis. The bent over posture to ease pain from this "caisson disease" popularized the name "the bends" which became understood as decompression sickness. See Decompression Sickness.

Carbohydrate [From Latin *carbon* + Greek *hudro*, water, because they are made of carbon, hydrogen, and oxygen.] Organic compounds including sugar, starch, and cellulose. Found only in plants, they are a major energy source for many animals, including humans.

Carbohydrate Loader Drink   Beverage containing carbohydrate to replace fluids and delay fatigue in long endurance events.

Carbohydrate Replacer Drink   High carbohydrate beverage to replace fluids and restock your body's carbohydrate supply after long endurance events.

Catecholamine   (cat-eh-COAL'-uh-meen) [Named for its chemical structure derived from a catechol and an amine, and so, catechol-amine.] Important family of nervous system chemicals that work as both neurotransmitters and hormones to transmit signals in your body. Your body makes catecholamines (dopamine, norepinephrine, and epinephrine) in several steps, all starting with the amino acid tyrosine. Each step requires a specific enzyme that turns each resulting catecholamine into the next, first making DOPA, then from DOPA, dopamine, then norepinephrine, then epinephrine (same as adrenaline). See Adrenal Glands, Epinephrine, and Norepinephrine.

Central Nervous System (CNS) Oxygen Toxicity Acute reaction to breathing high partial pressure of oxygen (PO_2), above a range of about 1.4 to 2.0, or seven to ten times normal. May include sudden convulsion, which is potentially dangerous underwater. Also called the Paul Bert effect, to honor the discoverer. See Paul Bert, Free Radical, Oxygen Toxicity, and contrast to Pulmonary Oxygen Toxicity.

Cerebral Arterial Gas Embolism (CAGE) Bubbles of air that obstruct blood flow in the arteries of the brain. See also Air Embolism.

cgs System. Measurement system using metric units. Based on the centimeter (c), gram (g), and second (s). Differs by powers of ten from MKS units (meter, kilogram, and second). MKS units became the foundation for the International System (SI). SI units are preferred over English units for scientific use. Note that cgs is small case letters, and MKS is upper case. See English System, Metric System, and SI, and compare to MKS System.

Charles' Law Physical principle that, at a constant pressure, the volume of a fixed quantity of ideal gas varies directly with temperature. In other words, as temperature increases, volume increases, all other things kept the same, which means that heating a scuba cylinder with resultant pressure rise is not an example of Charles' law as sometimes stated in scuba books, but another law more completely described by Joseph Louis Gay-Lussac. Charles' Law is also called the volume-temperature law.

Charles' Law is named for Jacques Alexandre César Charles (1746-1823) French physicist whose observations led to the concept of the Kelvin temperature system. His volume-temperature experiments were said to be spurred by the excitement of that time over hot-air balloons. He constructed the first hydrogen balloon, and made several flights. Compare to Gay-Lussac's Law, and see Ideal Gas.

Circadian Variation [From Latin *circa*, around + *dies*, day.] Body changes with a cycle of increasing and decreasing of approximately 24 hours. Circadian cycles include heart rate, blood pressure, hormone release, sleep-wake cycles, and core temperature. Synchronized by the light-dark cycle of the 24 hour day, and regulated by a brain structure in the hypothalamus called the suprachiasmatic nucleus (SCN), which is about the size of the head of a pin. Jet travel across several times zones can confuse your circadian rhythms, causing jet lag. Contrasts with ultradian cycles (ultra + circadian), those physiologic activities ebbing and flowing more than once every 24 hours, and infradian, those less than 24 hours.

Clo [From clothing.] Universal standard insulating unit of clothing, introduced in 1941 by Gagge, Burton, and Bazett. One clo is the amount of insulation needed to keep a person comfortable at rest in a room at 70°F (15°C), with relative humidity less than 50%, and air movement less than 20 feet per minute. A man's suit is about one clo. As temperature falls, you need garments of higher clo. In warmer temperatures and/or with increased heat generation through exercise, a protective suit of less clo value will do. To sleep comfortably in freezing temperature (32°F, 0°C) your needed clo value is about seven. For moderate work, three, and heavy work, only about one. There are other units of clothing insulation; for example the "tog" unit, introduced around 1946, roughly equal to 0.645 clo.

Coelenterates (cell-EN'-ter-ates) [From New Latin *coel*-, hollow; + Greek *enteron*, alimentary canal.] Invertebrates with a sac-like, or hollow body. Includes jellyfishes, hydras, sea anemones, and corals.

Cold Absence or loss of heat, involving slowing of motion of molecules. Cooler objects have less molecular motion than warmer objects. The coldest temperature where all molecular motion stops, meaning it has no thermal energy, is absolute zero, -459.67°F (-273.15°C). See Heat.

Compartment For decompression computations, your body is divided (theoretically) into a number of compartments, which are body areas similar in rate of inert gas uptake. These may be different areas scattered all over your body. For example, a 5 minute half-time compartment encompasses all body areas that take up inert gas at the same 5 minute half-time rate. Often called tissues, but compartment is preferred. See Half-time and Tissues.

Complement Cascade of immune reactions in the body to disable foreign things like bacteria, viruses, and decompression bubbles. Involves at least 20 different blood serum proteins and two different pathways. One action of activated complement is to release a chemical that attracts special engulfing cells called phagocytes. Then, both pathways, the classical pathway and the alternate pathway, lead to two possible effects, opsonization (a process like poking forks in the foreigner, to make it more easily grasped by phagocytes) or assembling a battering ram-like process called the membrane attack complex, or MAC attack. The MAC attack rams holes in the invader's membrane. In the classical pathway, the body picks out the target by sticking antibodies on it. The body has to recognize the invader as foreign from previous experience with it. Then complement component C1 sticks to the antibody and starts the cascade. The sequence of activation is C1 -> C4 -> C2 -> C3 and then either opsonization (C3b) or the MAC attack (C5 through C9). The alternative pathway constantly dusts particles on everything the blood contacts. Cells that belong in the body quickly inactivate the cascade with special factors on their skin. Foreign particles can activate the complement cascade. The complement is also called alexin, from the Greek meaning "to ward off." Consequence of the complement cascade to diving and microbubbles remains unknown.

Conduction [From Latin *conducere*, to lead.] Heat transfer through a medium without movement of the medium itself.

Controlling Compartment. The half-time compartment that reaches its maximum tolerated nitrogen tension (M-value) before the others. Decompression tables and computers base dive time/depth limits for the entire body on the controlling compartment. See M-value.

Convection   [From Latin *convectio*, to carry together.] Heat transfer through a medium involving absorption of heat at one point, movement of the medium, and then release of heat at another point.

Core   In thermoregulation, the interior of the body.

Counter-Current Heat Exchange   Anatomic system of exchanging heat between arteries and veins in the extremities, reducing convective heat loss in the blood. Heat from warm arterial blood transfers to venous blood returning to the body, thereby keeping heat in the body's core. Cold venous blood returning from the extremities cools outgoing arterial blood. Heat is not lost to the extremities, and cold blood from the extremities does not cool the core.

Cryptorchidism   (cript-OR'-kid-izm). [From Latin *crypt*, hidden + *orchis*, testicle, and from which we get the word orchid, for the shape of the bulbs.] Undescended testicle(s). Also called cryptorchism.

Critical Supersaturation   Point in compartment supersaturation where bubbles form, or a compartment pressure above ambient beyond which bubble formation is likely. There are researchers who believe bubbles are probable after any degree of supersaturation. See Saturation.

D

Dalton's Law   Description of partial gas pressure relationship to total gas pressure: the part of total pressure exerted by only one gas in a mixture is the partial pressure, and the sum of all partial pressures equals total pressure. Expressed in numbers as $P_1 + P_2 + P_3... = P_{total}$. Or P(nitrogen) + P(oxygen) + P(argon)... = P(air). Dalton's law only holds exactly for ideal gases, but in practice applies closely to real gases. Named for British chemist John Dalton (1766-1844). His pioneer work in gas properties led to his formulation of the atomic theory, now commemorated by naming the atomic mass unit the Dalton. He also contributed to knowledge of color-blindness by studying his own lack of red-green color vision, now named Daltonism.

Decompression Sickness (DCS)   Diving injury of pain, numbness, and/or paralysis. Results from too rapid ascent, which allows inert gas that was absorbed at depth from the breathing mix to come out of solution and form small bubbles in the body. Bubbles mechanically and chemically damage the body. Called bends, and formerly, caisson disease. May be grouped with arterial gas embolism as decompression illness. See caisson disease.

Decompression Illness (DCI)   Single category grouping bubble problems of air embolism and decompression sickness.

Decompression Mixes. High oxygen breathing mixes of varying percents, or fractions (FO_2), up to 100%. Used during the decompression stops of deep and technical dives. High oxygen mixes increase the nitrogen offgassing gradient with the aim of reducing decompression hang times and risk of decompression sickness. Because of oxygen toxicity, they are not for use at depth. Also called intermediate mixes and hang mixes.

Defensive Stinging   A guard against perceived attack by predators. Venom sites of defensive stingers are usually located around the tail, as in the stingray. Compare to Offensive Stinging.

Denature   To thermally or chemically change a protein's structure, eliminating some or all of its biological activity.

Diffusion   [From Latin *fundere*, to melt.] Random motion of the particles of two or more substances that results in their intermingling.

Disc   [From Greek diskos, to throw.] Round, flat, fibrocartilage cushion between bones. Vertebral discs lie between the bones of your spine. Commonly injured over time by bad sitting, standing, and lifting postures.

Dissolve   [From Latin *dissolvere*, to release.] To pass into solution.

Diuresis   (die-uh-REE'sis) [From Greek *dia,* completely + *ourein,* to urinate.] Increased urine output from any cause. Compare to P Phenomenon. See Kaliuresis and Natriuresis.

Divers Alert Network (DAN)   Non-profit membership organization offering diving safety information, accident insurance, and oxygen administration training. PO Box 3823 Duke University Medical Center. Durham, NC 27710, USA. (919) 684-2948 for non emergency questions, 9 a.m. - 5 p.m. ET; 24 hour emergency number (919) 684-8111.

Dive Reflex   Decreased heart rate and limb blood flow from the various effects of immersion. Does not reduce oxygen need in humans as it does in marine mammals.

Doppler Ultrasound   Device used to hear inert gas bubbles zipping by in the blood. It is ultrasonography using the Doppler effect to shift the frequency of returning sound, although not all events heard with this ultrasound are heard because of the Doppler shift. Named for Austrian physicist and mathematician Christian Johann Doppler (1803-1853), who in 1842 first described the principle known as the Doppler effect. Doppler studied the apparent shift in frequency of light waves occurring when source and observer move relative to each other. Frequency increases when they approach, and decrease when they move apart (each shifts the color). Today the term is also applied to the same phenomenon with sound waves (shifts the pitch). In medical uses, the Doppler device gives information about direction and velocity of blood flow. The moving targets are blood cells. In decompression research, Doppler is used to listen for bubbles to help understand decompression dynamics, and to test decompression tables and profiles before release. Dopplering is done on divers after they come up from the dive. It does not hurt. An ultrasound probe is placed, like a stethoscope, on the body at various sites that overlie veins. The chest site is called the precordial site, because it is over the precordium, the area over the heart. Subclavian sites listen under (sub) collarbones (clavicles) for bubbles from each arm, on their way in the blood back to the heart. Occasionally, other sites like the femoral (inguinal) veins, or behind knees are used to hear bubbles in blood returning from each leg. Bubbles often sound like names of Ikea furniture: Blik! Kaweee! Kerplick! The clicks, pops, and bliks of bubble signals must be differentiated from similar-sounding heart valves, and are often hard to hear above the smoosh-wump (not lub-dub) of heart sounds, blood turbulence, and other messy, noisy, normal internal body events.

E

EAN   See Enriched Air Nitrox.

Eccrine Sweat Glands   [From Greek *ekkrinein*, to secrete.] Heat-activated sweat glands. Compare to Apocrine Sweat Glands.

EL Model   (or L-E Model). Decompression model where inert gas uptake is exponential (E), as in Haldane models, but as soon as supersaturation occurs, a slower linear (L) offgassing is used to limit bubble formation. Developed by Capt. Ed Thalmann and his group at the Naval Experimental Diving Unit (NEDU) for combat swimmer profiles.

Electrolyte   [From Greek *electro* + *lytos and lysis*, soluble or loosening, from which we get such words as dialysis, electrolysis, and analysis.]   Any substance which, when dissolved in a liquid, becomes electrically conductive, because it breaks up into ions. Ions are atoms or small molecules with at least one electron more or less than normal for it, giving it a positive or negative electric charge. For example, table salt (sodium chloride) becomes the positive sodium ion and the negative chloride ion. Pure water does not conduct electricity. Why not? Water molecules rarely spontaneously dissociate into ions. Water molecules tightly bond all the electrons of its two hydrogen and one oxygen atoms, and there are no free places on the water molecule where electrons can be added or taken away. Acids, bases, and salts are electrolytes, and dissolving just a trace of them in water makes water conductive to varying degrees. Your cells use ions to regulate processes such as flow of water across the cell membrane. Ions propagate signals along nerves for all the thousands of functions that nerves control to keep you alive, moving, and thinking. The difference between current in electronic equipment and in your body is that electronic signals race through wire at up to half the speed of light, passing the charge by electrons. The electrons themselves don't move far, but pass the charge along like toppling dominos. In your body, nerve signals move along dissolved ions, thousands of times more slowly than electric current in wires. Like electrons, the ions themselves don't move far in the nerve, but propagate the signal by positive and negative ions switching places on either side of the nerve membrane. That makes neighboring positive and negative ions want to switch places too, in a continuing action called the action potential. In physiology, the term electrolyte usually refers to the ions, rather than the original substance. Two of the principal positively charged ions (electrolytes) in your body are sodium and potassium. Magnesium and calcium are two more positive ions. Two important negatively charged ions are chloride and bicarbonate.

Electrolyte Drink   Beverage containing electrolytes, and usually, carbohydrates to supply fluid, electrolytes, and carbohydrate before, during, or after exercise. Commercial electrolyte preparations do not contribute to dehydration, as popularly thought by divers.

Embolism   [From Greek *emballein*, to insert.] Obstructing foreign thing, or embolus, traveling around in a blood vessel. In medicine, often a blood clot, sometimes a clump of bacteria, piece of tissue, or globule of fat. In diving accidents, most often small bubbles of air. See Air Embolism and Fat Embolism.

English System   Units of measurement, historically based on royal anatomy and pottery; the foot, gallon, pound, etc. Still used in some former colonies, such as the United States. Almost all the rest of the world has adopted the metric system, where comparable units are the meter, liter, and kilogram. Therefore, the interesting result is that English units, used in the United States, are not the metric units used in England. The English system uses a hodge-podge of varied units assimilated over centuries from different cultures. The metric system, by contrast, was deliberately designed to make interconversions easy. The International System of Units (SI), which uses metric units, is preferred over the English System for scientific use, although English units of pressure such as feet of sea water (fsw) are still often seen in diving applications. SI pressure units are pascals (Pa) and kilopascals (kPa). See cgs System and MKS System, and compare to Metric System and SI.

Endorphin   [Composite word from endogenous (made from within) morphine-like substance.] A class of hormones produced after extended hard exercise. Not confirmed, but along with other opiate chemicals produced in the body, possibly associated with positive mood after good workouts.

Endurance, Cardiovascular   [From Latin *indurare*, to harden.] Ability of the heart and lungs to get oxygen and nutrients to the body for fuel during exercise. Determines duration you can continue at a given pace. Needed for continuous, mid- and low-intensity walking, running, skiing, swimming, cycling, etc. Also called cardio-respiratory endurance, aerobic capacity, or functional capacity. Compare to Anaerobic Capacity.

Endurance, Muscular   [From Latin *indurare*, to harden.] Ability of muscles to move a relatively light weight repeatedly. Walking, swimming, finning, cycling, running, even sitting and standing up straight all day require muscular endurance.

Enriched Air Nitrox (EAN)   Breathing mixtures with higher oxygen percentage or fraction (FO_2), and lower nitrogen fraction than regular air. Used to reduce decompression sickness risk on the same profile as an air dive, or to extend bottom time with similar risk. Because increased oxygen increases risk of oxygen toxicity at depth, EAN mixes are not used to extend depth range. Also abbreviated EANx. Also called Oxygen Enriched Air (OEA). See Nitrox, NOAA Nitrox I, and NOAA Nitrox II.

Enzyme   [From Greek *en-*, in + *zume*, yeast, from which we get the word *zymurgy*, the branch of chemistry dealing fermenting and brewing alcohol. From the Greek word *zein*, to boil.] A protein which speeds up chemical reactions. In other words, an organic catalyst. Enzymes function by holding one or more other molecules in just the right way so that they can react, either making a new bigger molecule or splitting a big molecule into smaller pieces. Enzymes make reactions go faster, but are not themselves burned up in the reaction. Examples are lactase, which breaks down lactose in milk; amylase in your saliva, which starts breaking down carbohydrates; papain, a plant enzyme used in meat tenderizer that breaks down protein; and zymase, the enzyme in yeast that breaks down sugar into alcohol and carbon dioxide. With notable exceptions, names of most enzymes end in the suffix -ase. All enzymes are proteins. Enzymes that you eat are digested before they can pass into your blood stream and reach your body tissues. Digesting means breaking down to components until it is small enough to pass through the intestinal wall. It will not automatically reassemble into the original enzyme on the other side of the intestinal wall. Eating ordinary enzymes, even those promoted as health foods (except digestive aids), will not raise body enzyme levels.

Epinephrine [Kidneys are called *nephros* in Greek and *renalis* in Latin, so the chemical produced in the gland atop the kidneys is called epinephrine (on the kidney, or adrenaline (near the kidney). The gland itself is the adrenal.] Major nervous system chemical, released during conditions of physical and mental stress such as fear, injury or pain, including pain response to severe cold. Increases heart rate, blood pressure, metabolic rate, blood glucose and vasoconstriction. See Adrenal Glands and Catecholamine, and contrast to Norepinephrine.

Equivalent Air Depth (EAD) Depth defined by your partial pressure of nitrogen. EAD using a breathing mix with less nitrogen than air, is shallower than actual depth. The equation to find EAD is: $EAD (fsw) = [(1-FO_2) (D+33) / 0.79] - 33$.

Evaporation [From Latin *e*, out + *vapor*, steam.] Process of passing from liquid form into vapor form. The substance that evaporates absorbs heat from its surroundings, and cools the surroundings. For example, sweat absorbs heat from your body when it evaporates, cooling your body.

Exponential [From Latin *exponere*, to expound (to place or give details).] Various mathematical expressions describing a quantity that gains or loses a fixed percentage of its resulting value with every passing fixed interval. Increments may be of time, distance, or some other value. The percentage change is constant, the amount gained or lost changes each time. Many events occur in exponential fashion. World population grows at a certain percentage of its new size each year (although food supply does not). Radioactive plutonium-239 loses one half its remaining value every 24,360 years. During a dive, compartment nitrogen tension increases by half every fixed interval of time, from minutes to hours for different compartments. Heat transfer in your body and in machines is exponential; for every unit of time, half the remaining heat in the hotter of two regions transfers across the boundary between them. Light diminishes exponentially as the distance from the source increases; for each doubling of distance, the light is 1/4 as strong. Compound interest follows exponential increase; for example a dollar invested at 10% interest compounded daily would double just about every seven years. The f-stops on cameras are an exponential series of diameters that admit light. Cell division increases exponentially during growth phase. A single cell divides into two. Each later divides, resulting in four. Those four divide, yielding eight, then 16, then 32. Cancerous cells don't stop. Exponential change differs from arithmetic change, which is a constant absolute increase or decrease per interval, like birthdays every year, or a pile of magazines growing by the same number each month.

Exponential equations may represent regular changes of any percentage. In the half-time exponential, it is 50%. See Half-time.

F

Fast Compartments Body areas that absorb and release inert gas rapidly. In anatomic tissues, uptake and release rate depend on blood flow and solubility of gas in that area. In most decompression models, blood flow establishes half-time speed.

Fat Embolism [From Greek *emballein*, to insert.] Small globules of fat that obstruct blood flow. Compare to Air Embolism.

Fat Face-Chicken Legs Effect Term coined to describe a phenomenon occurring during space flights where, due to zero gravity, body fluids float out of the legs adding visible volume to the upper body, and reducing girth of the lower limbs.

Flexibility [From Latin *flexibilis*, to bend.] Ability to move safely and comfortably through a range of motion required for various activities.

FN$_2$ Fraction, or percentage, of nitrogen in a gas mixture. For calculating decompression schedules, FN$_2$ of regular breathing air is considered to be 0.79 or 79%. The fraction does not change with depth because the composition of the breathing gas is not changed, only the pressure on it. Compare to PN$_2$ and PO$_2$.

FO$_2$ Fraction, or percentage, of oxygen in a gas mixture. In regular breathing air FO$_2$ is 0.21 or 21%. The fraction does not change with depth because the composition of the breathing gas is not changed, only the pressure on it. Compare to PN$_2$ and PO$_2$.

Foramen Ovale (for-RAY'-men oh-VAHL'-ay) [From Latin *foramen*, opening, + *ovalis*, oval.] Small opening in the partition between the right and left upper chambers of the heart, present before birth in the fetus but usually closed soon after. A patent (pronounced pay'-tent) foramen ovale remains open after childhood, resulting in an amount of blood sometimes passing from the right side of the heart directly to the left, bypassing the lungs.

Free Radical An atom, molecule, or macromolecule existing temporarily with at least one unpaired electron in the outer orbit. Electrons usually prefer to be paired. Being unpaired makes them reactive and eager either to acquire another electron or to lose the unpaired one. Some free radicals are beneficial, such as those involved in muscle contraction and in the immune response, while others are detrimental, such as those involved in certain disease processes and oxygen toxicity. Free

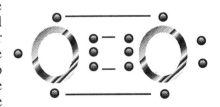

Oxygen free radical with extra electron

radicals occur normally as a byproduct of breathing, and in increased numbers during exercise, in smog, from cigarette smoke, and in high pressure oxygen environments. In 1954, Rebecca Gershman and her colleagues, in a theory now widely accepted, proposed that the damaging effects of oxygen toxicity are caused by oxygen free radicals. An oxygen free radical has one unpaired electron. It strongly wants to take an electron from other molecules, particularly fatty acids and proteins. When oxygen free radicals grab electrons from hemoglobin, cell membranes, or protein enzymes, those substances are rendered ineffective at their former jobs. In addition, they become free radicals themselves, with a strong propensity to grab electrons from others, starting a chain of destructive events (like a game of tag). The body produces various antioxidant substances to neutralize many free radicals.

fsw   Feet of sea water. Unit of pressure, not depth. Other examples of units of pressure are meters of sea water (msw), pounds per square inch (psi), and atmospheres absolute (ATA). In scientific writing, International System units are preferred: pascals (Pa) and kilopascals (kPa). See English System, Metric System, and SI.

G

Gay-Lussac's Law   Physical principle that, at a constant volume, the pressure of a confined ideal gas is proportional to temperature, or in other words, as temperature increases, pressure increases, all other things kept the same. An example is leaving a scuba tank out in the sun, with resultant pressure rise. Also called the pressure-temperature law. Named for Joseph Louis Gay-Lussac (1778-1850) French chemist and physicist, who worked on understanding gas behavior with Jacques Alexandre César Charles. He is also known for his work with Louis-Jacques Thenard in isolating the elements potassium and boron. Sometimes spelled Guy-Lussac. Contrast Gay-Lussac's Law to Charles' Law, and see Ideal Gas.

Glycogen   [From Greek, *glukos*, sweet + *gen*, making or producing.] Chief form of carbohydrate storage in animals, stored primarily in liver and muscle. It converts to glucose as needed to meet the body's energy needs.

Goose Bumps   Temporary fluffed hair follicles in humans in response to cold exposure and sometimes fear, looking like the rough skin of a plucked bird. Also called goose flesh and goose pimples. It is ineffective for cold protection in humans. See Piloerection.

Gradient   [From Latin *gradi,* to walk or go.] Difference in some quantity between two points in space or time. A hill is a height gradient. Acceleration is a speed gradient. Gradients drive things, such as gas molecules or heat energy, from an area of higher to an area of lower quantity or density. Going underwater, higher nitrogen tension in surrounding water pressure than within the body promotes nitrogen ongassing. On ascent, higher nitrogen tension within compartments than in the surrounding water drives nitrogen offgassing. Heat is another example. Heat flows from warmer to cooler areas. Cool skin is a good adaptation to lessen heat loss in cold environments. This is called a low skin-to-environment gradient.

H

Haldane, John Scott. Scottish born British physiologist (1860-1936). Together with Arthur E. Boycott and British naval officer Guybon C. Damant, he co-developed the first scientific attempt to estimate amounts of inert gas absorbed and released by the body. The work was published in 1908. J.S. Haldane sometimes used his young son, John Burdon Sanderson Haldane (1892-1964), as an experimental subject. J.B.S. Haldane grew up to be a geneticist, Marxist, and devotee of Hindu culture.

Haldane Decompression Model   One of several methods, and the first scientific attempt, to estimate amounts of inert gas absorbed and released by various body areas, computationally handled as compartments. Named for co-developer John Scott Haldane. The majority of current decompression tables and computers are based on versions of the Haldane model. See Haldane.

Half-time   Time required for half the maximum amount that the body can hold of a drug or other substance to be taken up or eliminated by normal biological processes. Written $T^{1/2}$. Also called biological half-life. In anatomic tissues, the half-time of any substance is determined both by blood flow to the tissue and by solubility of the substance. In decompression equations, half-times describe speed of nitrogen or other inert gas transit into and out of the body. The equation describing half-times is exponential. It models only blood flow to each compartment, not solubility of the gas in that compartment. Use of half-times allows calculation of estimated nitrogen tension in several different body compartments, given varying length and depth dives. See Exponential.

Hang Mixes   See Decompression Mixes.

Heat   Energy associated with motion of atoms and molecules. Conducted through solids, liquids, and gases, convected through liquids and gases, and radiated through empty space. Units of measure are usually the calorie or British Thermal Unit (BTU). Until the 1800's, heat was mistakenly thought to be a substance called caloric, along with another substance carrying cold called frigoric. American-born Benjamin Thompson, who later became British physicist Count Rumford of Bavaria (1753-1814) found that heat is not a substance, but related to motion. British physicist James Joule (1818-1889) established the modern kinetic theory of heat and codified the first law of thermodynamics. Contrast to Cold.

Heat Rash   Heat-related inflammation of sweat gland ducts characterized by small red bumps. Also called prickly heat.

Heat Cramps   Heat-related spasm of muscle. Although much attention seems to surround electrolyte theories and suggestions to eat bananas, better evidence points to inadequate blood flow as the main factor in heat cramps.

Heliox   Breathing mixture of helium and oxygen. Helium replaces some or all nitrogen, and a portion of the oxygen in a breathing mix. Used to reduce or eliminate nitrogen narcosis on deep dives, and by reducing oxygen partial pressure exposure, reduces risk of oxygen toxicity.

Hemoglobin [Shortened form of hematinoglobulin. Contains an iron group called heme, and globulin, a protein. Symbol Hb or Hbg.] Molecule in red blood cells of vertebrates that transports oxygen. Has four iron atoms that each loosely bind one oxygen molecule, so each hemoglobin molecule has room for four atoms of oxygen. At one atmosphere, about 97% of oxygen is carried in combined form with hemoglobin called oxyhemoglobin ($Hb-O_2$), the rest dissolved in blood. Hemoglobin removes carbon dioxide (CO_2) to a small extent (15 to 25% of total CO_2) in the form carbaminohemoglobin (CO_2HHb). Unlike oxygen, CO_2 bonds with the protein subunit so they do not ordinarily compete for sites and can be carried simultaneously. Most CO_2 dissolves in blood, reacting with water to form first carbonic acid, then rapidly dissociating into a hydrogen ion (H^+) and a bicarbonate ion (HCO_3^-).

Hemoglobin-Oxygen Buffer System Body regulatory system controlling pressure of oxygen delivered to body tissues from blood hemoglobin. Ensures that within limits, oxygen is delivered to tissues at nearly normal pressure, even though pressure of inspired oxygen may be higher or lower than normal pressure, as at depth or at altitude. Past extreme limits, however, such as at high altitude, there is not enough oxygen for your body to extract. Conversely, with too much oxygen, depending on depth and partial pressure of oxygen in the breathing mixture, the buffer is overwhelmed, leading to high oxygen pressure, overproduction of free radicals, and CNS oxygen toxicity. See Henry's Law, Free Radical, and Oxygen Toxicity.

Henry's Law Physical principle that, at a constant temperature, the solubility of a gas in a liquid varies directly with partial pressure of the gas on the liquid. In other words, as pressure increases, solubility increases, all other things kept the same. Named for English chemist William Henry (1775-1836) who studied gases and is best known for this law of solubility. A major exception to this law is when chemical reactions occur between the gas and the dissolving medium, as with oxygen. During diving, nitrogen tensions increase in the body according to Henry's Law. Oxygen tensions do not. Although increased pressure with depth can dissolve more oxygen in your blood, blood vessel constriction caused by oxygen, and the hemoglobin-oxygen system prevent it all from being delivered to your cells. The body's hemoglobin-oxygen buffer system regulates release of oxygen to cells, delivering oxygen to your body tissues at almost normal pressure even when you breathe higher or lower than normal pressure oxygen, as at depth or altitude, but only within limits. See Free Radical, Hemoglobin-Oxygen Buffer System, and Oxygen Toxicity.

Histamine [An amine created from the amino acid histidine, and so, hist-amine.] Chemical substance released by the body in several situations including skin injury and allergic reaction. Large amounts produce swelling and inflammation. An agent that blunts the effects of histamine is an antihistamine. See Antihistamine.

Homeostasis [From Greek *homos,* same + *stasis*, standstill.] Continuous regulation of all the body's goings-on, using physiologic checks and balances to return the system to its set equilibrium. Body temperature, oxygen levels, pH, water balance, plasma ion regulation, calorie utilization, and many other processes are all tightly regulated. Walter Cannon, Harvard physiologist, coined this term for the principle first described by French Physiologist Claude Bernard.

Homeotherms [From Greek *homos,* same + *therme,* heat.] Animals who generate and regulate heat internally to maintain a largely constant body temperature that is independent of and typically above surrounding temperature. Birds and mammals are homeotherms. Sometimes called endotherms. Contrast to Poikilotherms.

Hormone [From Greek *horman,* to urge on.] Chemical messengers, usually peptides or steroids, produced in one body tissue and traveling through the blood to stimulate or suppress activity in another tissue. Examples, among many, are insulin, adrenaline (epinephrine), and antidiuretic hormone (ADH). Hormones regulate body processes as diverse as growth, metabolism, and reproduction, and modify behavior.

Hunting Reflex, or Hunting Reflex of Lewis Cold induced, alternating skin vasodilation and vasoconstriction, perhaps to reduce cold injury to extremities from prolonged vasoconstriction. Named for its characteristic of "hunting" for a skin-temperature equilibrium point.

Hydrostatic Pressure [From Greek *hudro,* water or liquid + *statos,* weight, or standing]. Pressure exerted by the weight of fluids. Examples are sea and fresh water pressure, and pressure in your blood vessels due to weight of your blood in the vessels. Pressure at the surface of a body of water is at atmospheric pressure. As depth increases, pressure rises. When you are standing up on land, pressure in the veins of your feet is higher than at your heart. With leg movement, contracting muscles squeeze blood upward. This venous muscle pump ordinarily keeps pressure in the legs from rising as high as when standing still. Soldiers at attention may lose up to 20% of blood volume from the general circulation to the legs, swelling the legs, occasionally causing fainting. The weightlessness of space flight removes the effect of gravity to pool fluids in the lower limbs. Pressure underwater more or less balances, and so counteracts your internal hydrostatic pressure. Both cause more blood to remain in the upper body rather than pool in your legs, regardless of whether you are head up or head down. This is one of the triggers for the dive reflex, and also for having to "go." Hydrostatic pressure operates all the time in your body, from normal processes, to swelling with injury, to swollen bellies in starvation. Hydrostatic pressure inside capillaries pushes fluids out of the capillaries, because hydrostatic pressure inside is higher than interstitial pressure outside. Because blood proteins cannot also move out, osmotic pressure from plasma proteins, called colloid osmotic pressure or oncotic pressure, rises inside capillaries. Farther along the capillary at the venous side where there is less hydrostatic pressure, the relatively higher oncotic pressure inside draws fluids back in by osmosis. The oncotic draw prevents high fluid loss into interstitial spaces. In other words, the arterial side pushes out more fluid than the venous side pulls back. The extra fluid is drained by the lymph system. With tissue damage from injury, proteins leak from broken capillaries, dropping vessel oncotic pressure, leaving the vessel no way to draw fluids back in. Swelling results. During starvation, there is not enough plasma protein from the diet to maintain plasma oncotic pressure. The vessels can't draw fluids back in resulting in the characteristic swollen bellies of the starving. See Venous Pooling.

Hyper- Prefix meaning more or above.

Hyperbaric [hyper + Greek *baro,* weight or pressure]. Pressure higher than normal atmospheric pressure, as occurring underwater or in a hyperbaric chamber. Contrast to Hypobaric.

Hyperbaric Bradycardia Decreased heart rate at depth when breathing compressed air, due to increased gas partial pressure and density of the breathing gas with depth. This heart rate decrease occurs through mechanisms different from the dive reflex.

Hyperbaric Chamber Room or enclosure capable of sustaining air pressure greater than one atmosphere, which simulates depth. Used for scientific study of effects of pressure, and in conjunction with oxygen delivery, to treat decompression illness and other injuries.

Hypercapnia [hyper + Greek *kapnos*, smoke.] Excess carbon dioxide in the blood. Also called hypercarbia.

Hypertonic [hyper + Greek *tonos*, tension.] In chemistry, a solution containing a higher concentration of dissolved particles compared to a reference solution, usually blood or body tissues. For example, sea water is hypertonic to your blood (about three times more concentrated). Compare to Hypotonic and Isotonic.

Hypo- Prefix meaning less, or under.

Hypobaric [hypo + Greek *baro*, pressure.] Pressure lower than normal atmospheric pressure, as occurring at altitude. Compare to Hyperbaric.

Hypothalamus [hypo + thalamos, named for its location in the brain below a major brain relay station called the thalamus.] Part of the brain that regulates many metabolic and autonomic activities, including hunger, thirst, sleep, secondary sex characteristics, and body temperature.

Hypothermia [hypo- + Greek *therme*, heat.] Condition of core temperature below 95°F (35°C) in humans. Does not refer to skin temperature. Hypothermia is one of several cold injuries.

Hypotonic [hypo + Greek *tonos*, tension.] In chemistry, a solution containing a smaller concentration of dissolved particles compared to a reference solution, usually blood or body tissues. For example, fresh water is hypotonic to your blood.

Hypoxia [hypo + oxia, oxygen.] Condition in which insufficient oxygen reaches body tissues. Distinct from hypoxemia, which is insufficient oxygenation of blood

Hypoxic Mix Breathing mixture with oxygen concentration too low to sustain consciousness at the surface. Becomes able to support life (normoxic) with higher PO_2 at depth. Used at depth to keep PO_2 below that risking oxygen toxicity. Compare to Normoxic Mix.

I

Ideal Gas An imaginary gas that exactly obeys all the gas laws of Boyle, Charles, Gay-Lussac, and Avogadro. Most gases behave near-ideally around the standard temperature of 0°C and standard pressure of one ATA. With large deviations, such as in a scuba tank, gas behavior is not ideal, but follows a behavior called "real."

For this reason, mixtures of gas vary from expected concentrations when mixed according to partial pressure calculations. Gas analysis to determine actual concentrations in your tanks is important when using any calculated gas mixes for diving. The laws of Boyle, Charles, and Gay-Lussac can be combined into the Ideal Gas Law, also called the Generalized Gas Law. See Boyle's Law, Charles' Law, and Gay-Lussac's Law.

Inflammation   [From Latin, *in* + *flammare*, to set on fire.] Response of body tissues to an injury, bite, sting, or infection. Characterized by warmth (calor), redness (rubor), swelling (tumor), and pain (dolor). Inflammation attracts immune cells, which secrete free radicals to kill bacteria and other invaders. See Free Radical.

Ingassing   Transfer of dissolved gas into the body. Also called uptake or ongassing.

Insensible Perspiration   Moisture loss through skin that you are not aware of.

International System of Units   See SI.

Ischemia   (is-KEE'-me-uh) [From Greek *iskhein*, to hold back +*haima*, blood. From *haima* we get words like hemoglobin, hemorrhage, and hemorrhoid.] Decrease in blood supply to cells. Pain and loss of function follows ischemia.

Isotonic   [From Greek *isos*, equal + *tonos*, tension.] In chemistry, a solution containing the same concentration of dissolved particles as a reference solution, usually your blood or body tissues. For example, many commercial sport electrolyte drinks are isotonic to your blood. Your blood is not isotonic to sea water, it is much less concentrated, or hypotonic. Even many sea creatures have different tonicities than the sea. Some are higher, some lower. They have to constantly pump stuff in or out to keep their bodies within normal levels.

K

Kaliuresis   (ka-lee-you-REE'-sis) [Latin *kalium*, potassium, which is from Arabic *qily*, alkali + Greek *ourein*, to urinate.] Excretion of potassium (periodic table symbol K) in the urine. See Diuresis and Natriuresis.

Kidney   Bean-shaped, paired organ, about 4" (10 cm) long, in back of the abdominal cavity, incompletely covered by the lower ribs. Often, the right kidney hangs a bit lower than the left. Kidneys have several important functions. They regulate sodium-water balance, acid-base balance, convert Vitamin D from inactive to active form, and when kidney blood and oxygen levels drop during exercise, kidneys release the enzyme erythropoietin (eh-rith-throw-poe-ee'-tin) that stimulates red blood cell production. In that way, exercise beneficially increases red cell count. Human kidneys have tremendous range, from very concentrated fluid output to conserve water, to very dilute. Of about 180 quarts of fluid daily that they filter, kidneys efficiently return 98 to 99% of the water and dissolved salts to the body according to needs. About 20% of your blood shunts to the kidney on each circulatory pass. There blood travels through tiny juicers called glomeruli (about a million per kidney) which squeeze out another 20% of the liquid part of blood into long, twisty tubules. Red cells, white cells, and protein particles do not pass into the tubules. They stay in the blood, unless your kidneys are sick. Through most of the tubule, valuable particles reabsorb into the body: glucose, sodium, potassium, bicarbonate, etc. The juice becomes very dilute, and the surrounding kidney very concentrated. Depending on body needs, more or less water and salts reabsorb and return to your blood. Antidiuretic hormone tells your kidneys to keep more water. Aldosterone tells the kidney to save sodium, which helps keep more water, too. Angiotensin II tells the kidneys to retain salt and water. Atrial natriuretic factor tells the kidneys to excrete more water and sodium. All water, particles, and wastes not reabsorbed go to your bladder to be excreted into your diving suit. See Adrenal Glands, Aldosterone, Angiotensin, Antidiuretic Hormone, Atrial Natriuretic Factor, and Renin.

L

Latent Heat Amount of heat a body can absorb without changing temperature. See Heat.

Latent Heat of Evaporation Amount of heat absorbed or released by a substance changing its state, such as sweat evaporating into vapor. Also called heat of transformation. Changes in sweat as electrolyte content varies.

Ligament [From Latin *ligare*, to bind.] Tough, fibrous bands connecting bones to each other, cartilage at a joint, or supporting an organ.

Look-Up or Table-Based Computers Decompression computers that give their final answer by looking up the dive profile against the already worked out values of a decompression table. Very few decompression computers work this way. Compare to Model-Based Computers.

Lorrain Smith Effect Pulmonary oxygen toxicity. Named for Lorrain J. Smith, 19th Century scientist who first demonstrated and described it. See Oxygen Toxicity, Pulmonary Oxygen Toxicity, and contrast to Central Nervous System (CNS) Oxygen Toxicity.

Lung Overexpansion Injury Injury from expanding air in the lung, usually from breath-holding ascent or other obstruction to air trying to leave the lung on ascent. Can result in embolism and/or pneumothorax. Also called pulmonary barotrauma, or pulmonary overpressure syndrome (POPS).

M

M-Values Maximum nitrogen (or other inert gas) tensions that compartments are thought to tolerate before supersaturation produces a harmful amount of bubbles. Each compartment has its own M-value. Surface M-values are written M_0, pronounced M sub zero. M_0 is the maximum tension you can build up and still return to the surface with acceptable risk. If any compartment would exceed its surfacing M-value (M_0), you make a decompression stop to allow compartments drain down until they are below M_0. M_{10} is the maximum tension you can build up and get to within 10 feet of the surface, with acceptable risk. If tensions would exceed M_{10}, a still deeper stop is made for offgassing, and so on.

Metabolism   [From Greek *metaballein*, to change.] Physical and chemical processes in cells and living systems as a whole, necessary for energy synthesis to maintain life.

Metric System   [From Greek *metron*, measure]. Originally, a system of units based on the centimeter, gram, and second (cgs system). Now more broadly, any system of units based on powers of ten. The symbols for metric multipliers 1,000 and smaller are written in lower case: k for kilo (x 1,000), h for hecto (x 100), da for deka (x 10), d for deci (x 0.1), c for centi (x 0.01), etc. For multipliers greater than 1,000, the symbols are upper case: M for mega (x 1,000,000), G for giga (x 1,000,000,000). Metric multipliers are used with International System (SI) units of measure. English units of measure have their own unique multipliers, with a few exceptions (e.g., kilotons, megatons, etc.) To be a bit confusing, metric multipliers that are within the set 10 raised to the power n, where n is a multiple of 3, are sometimes called engineering units, whereas any power of 10 is called a scientific unit. See cgs System, and compare to English System and SI.

MKS System   Measurement system using metric units: meter (m), kilogram (k), and second (s). Predecessor (and subset) of the present International System (SI), preferred for scientific use over the English System. Note that MKS uses upper-case letters, compared to cgs, in small case. See cgs System, Metric System, and compare to English System and SI.

Model-Based Computers   Decompression computers programmed with a decompression calculation algorithm. They calculate decompression for the actual depth time profile in real time. Compare to Look-Up or Table-Based Computers. Most decompression computers are model based.

msw   Meters of sea water. Unit of pressure, not depth. Other examples of units of pressure are feet of sea water (fsw), pounds per square inch (psi), and atmospheres absolute (ATA). In scientific writing, International System units are preferred to describe pressure: pascals (Pa) and kilopascals (kPa). See English System, Metric System, and SI.

Multi-Compartment Model   Use of several grouped body areas that absorb and release gas at different rates to construct a working example of decompression in your body. Almost all decompression tables and computers are multi-compartment models. See Tissue.

N

Narcosis   [From Greek *narkosis*, numbing.] Stuporous, usually reversible, condition produced by any drug or chemical that depresses nerve excitability. In diving, due to the effect of breathing various, usually inert, gases under pressure. When due to nitrogen under pressure it is called nitrogen narcosis. Helium is less narcotic than nitrogen, and according to some, non-narcotic. Argon and neon are more so, with argon being about twice as narcotic as nitrogen. Other gases like oxygen may also be involved. Gas narcosis is poorly understood. Reduced mental and motor ability reduce diving safety. Although also called "rapture of the deep," effects are not always rapturous. In conditions of cold and limited visibility, narcosis is often associated with fearful, unpleasant mental states.

Natriuresis   (nay-tree-you-REE'-sis) [From Latin *natrium*, sodium + Greek *ourein*, to urinate.] Extra excretion of sodium in the urine. See Diuresis and Kaliuresis.

Negative Pressure Breathing   Breathing where the pressure at your mouth, and so the pressure inside your lungs, is lower than the ambient pressure on the outside of your chest. Occurs in head-out immersion, with breathing from a hard-to-breathe regulator, and during snorkel breathing.

Nematocyst   [From Greek *nemat*, thread + *kustis*, small sac or bladder.] A barbed, threadlike tube that propels a paralyzing sting. Found in certain coelenterates like jellyfish. Also called stinging cell.

Neurotransmitter   [Neuro from Greek *sinew or s(neu)*, meaning string or nerve + transmitter.] Chemical your body produces to send nerve impulses from one nerve ending to the next, across a space called a synapse. Examples of neurotransmitters, among many, are acetylcholine, serotonin, and catecholamines such as dopamine, norepinephrine, and epinephrine.

Nitrogen Tension   Partial pressure of nitrogen in body compartments. In the English System of measurement, units are commonly feet of sea water (fsw) and meters of sea water (msw). The International System of Units (SI), preferred for scientific work, uses pascals (Pa) and kilopascals (kPa). Also called gas loading.

Nitrox   Various breathing mixtures of nitrogen and oxygen. The term nitrox historically referred to mixtures with less than 21% oxygen, commonly used in habitats and saturation situations. When oxygen percentage is above the normal 21% of regular air, it is called enriched air nitrox (EAN) and/or oxygen enriched air (OEA), although the terms are often confused and interchanged. There are several different nitrox mixes, the most common are NOAA Nitrox (EAN32) and NOAA Nitrox II (EAN36). See Enriched Air Nitrox.

NOAA Nitrox I   Enriched Air Nitrox of 32% oxygen and 68% nitrogen. Also called EAN32. See Enriched Air Nitrox, Nitrox, and NOAA Nitrox II.

NOAA Nitrox II   Enriched Air Nitrox of 36% oxygen and 64% nitrogen. Also called EAN36. See Enriched Air Nitrox, Nitrox, and NOAA Nitrox I.

Non-Shivering Thermogenesis   [From Greek *therme*, heat + *gen*, making or producing.] Internal heat generation through chemical, not shivering processes. Also called chemical thermogenesis.

Norepinephrine   (nor-eh-pin-NEF'-rin) Important nervous system catecholamine neurotransmitter made in the adrenal gland and nerve endings. Works normally to produce vasoconstriction and increased heart rate, blood pressure, and blood sugar. Also called noradrenaline. See Adrenal Glands, and contrast to Epinephrine and Catecholamine.

Normoxic Mix   Breathing mixture with oxygen level equivalent to the 21% of air at the surface. The PO$_2$ of normoxic mixes is around 0.21 ATA regardless of depth. Mixes of oxygen fractions less than the normal 21% become normoxic at depths where their PO$_2$ rises to 0.21. Compare to Hypoxic Mix.

O

Oculocardiac Reflex   Reduction in heart rate upon pressing the eyeballs.

Offensive Stinging   Action to kill prey. The venom delivery system is usually near the mouth, as in the anemone and sea snake. Contrast to Defensive Stinging.

Offgassing Transfer of dissolved gas out of the body. Synonymous with outgassing and elimination.

Ongassing Transfer of dissolved gas into the body. Interchangeable term with ingassing.

Osteoporosis   [From Latin *osteo*, bone + Greek *poros*, passage, pore.] A progressive disease where bone, particularly of the upper back, hip, and wrist, becomes porous and easily fractured. Healing is difficult and slow. Occurs mainly in post-menopausal women, and elderly men. Resistive exercise, like weight lifting, is an important part of prevention. Also important is resisting your own body weight during weight bearing exercise like walking, dancing, running, skating, and skiing.

Outer Ear   Part of the ear you can see (auricle or pinna) and the canal that you can stick your finger into (external auditory canal). It is the part of the ear involved in swimmer's ear. It is a blind alley and does not, except in ruptured eardrum, communicate with the middle or inner ear. It is not associated with pressure injuries to the middle and inner ear. See Swimmer's Ear.

Outgassing   Transfer of dissolved gas out of the body. Also called offgassing and elimination.

Oxygen Enriched Air (OEA)   See Enriched Air Nitrox.

Oxygen Toxicity   Damage from higher than tolerated amounts (partial pressures) of oxygen. Mammals, fish, birds, insects, bacteria, and plants have varying susceptibility. Certain bacteria like gangrene cannot live with oxygen (called anaerobes), and can be killed by oxygen treatments. Hyperbaric oxygen is an effective therapy for gas gangrene, which is caused by anaerobic bacteria. Even aerobic bacteria, like some strains of *E. coli* which live in your gut, (*Escherichia coli*, named for German physician Theodor Escherich), will swim away from regions of high O$_2$. In humans, long, low exposure may damage the lungs. High, short exposures affect the central nervous system. See Central Nervous System (CNS) and Pulmonary Oxygen Toxicity.

P

P Phenomenon   Affectionate expression for increased fluid output called diuresis, in rapid response to immersion. Abbreviated PP. See Aldosterone, Atrial Natriuretic Factor, Diuresis, Renin, and Renin-Angiotensin-Aldosterone Cascade.

Paradoxical Undressing   Phenomenon where people freezing to death have sometimes felt so warm, reputedly from skin vasodilation, that they remove their clothing and are found dead and naked.

Parallel Model   Decompression model where all compartments are considered to ongas and offgas separately to blood. Using this theory, all compartments are assumed fed by arterial blood supply, so all receive the same inert gas pressures. No gas transfer is (usually) assumed between compartments. Decompression tables and computers based on the Haldane model assume parallel gas transit in each half-time compartment. Compare to Series Model.

Partial Pressure   The part of total pressure exerted by one gas in a mixture. The sum of all partial pressures is total pressure, described by Dalton's Law. Pressure of a gas is caused by molecular collisions – the more gas in a space, the more collisions, and the more pressure. The partial pressure of inert gas you breathe relative to the partial pressure of that gas accumulated in your compartments, determines uptake and elimination. To calcualte partial pressure: Partial pressure equals total pressure times the fraction (%) of gas. See Dalton's Law, PN_2, and PO_2.

Perfusion   [From Latin *perfundere*, to pour.] Blood flow.

Physiology   [From Greek *phusio*, nature + *ology*, study.] Study of functions of living beings and their parts.

Piloerection   [From Latin *pilo*, hair + *erectus*, to set up.] Fluffed up fur, feather, or hair follicles by erector pili muscles associated with the follicles. In nonhumans, traps an insulative layer of air next to the skin as part of an animal's cold protection system. In humans, it remains as a small response called goose bumps, which are ineffective for cold protection. See Goose Bumps.

Plasma   [From Greek *plassein*, to mold.] Clear, yellowish, noncellular fluid portion of blood. Makes up about 55% of blood volume. Plasma without the clotting protein fibrinogen is called serum.

Pleura   [From Greek *pleura*, side or rib.] Thin, double membrane, one around the lungs, the second lining the rib cage. The extremely small, air tight space between them is called the pleural space.

PN₂   Abbreviation for partial pressure of nitrogen. For calculating decompression, PN_2 in regular air is usually considered to be 79% of the total air pressure, because the 1% of other inert gases like argon, helium, krypton, and xenon are all lumped together with the 78% of nitrogen in air. See Partial Pressure.

Pneumothorax   [From Greek *pneuma*, wind or breath + *thorax*, chest.] Injury in which air or other gas enters the normally airtight pleural cavity. Air occupies lung space, preventing expansion. Lung collapse may follow. May occur from breath-holding ascent or diving with certain lung injuries.

PO₂   Abbreviation for partial pressure of oxygen. At the surface breathing regular air, where oxygen is 21% of the total air pressure, PO_2 is 0.21 ATA. At 33 feet/ 10 m of depth (two atmospheres) PO_2 doubles to 0.42 ATA. At 66 feet/ 10 m (three atmospheres) PO_2 triples to 0.63 ATA. See Partial Pressure.

Poikilotherms   [From Greek *poikilos*, various + *therme*, heat.] Animals, such as fish and reptiles, whose body temperature varies depending on surrounding temperature. Sometimes called ectotherms. Contrast to Homeotherms.

Poison   [From Latin *potio*, meaning the act of drinking a dose of medicine or poison.] A chemical causing serious or fatal illness. May be distinguished from venom, where poison is eaten, venom injected. See Venom.

Power   [From Latin *potere*, to be able.] Ability to move an object of any weight quickly.

Pressor Effect. From Latin, *press-*, to press.] Increase in blood pressure by vasoconstriction, in response to various stimuli.

Prime Mover   Muscle or muscles mainly responsible for a particular movement.

Prosthesis   [From Greek *prostithenai*, to add.] Artificial device replacing a missing body part.

Pulmonary Oxygen Toxicity   Lung and air-passage damage from long exposure to partial pressure of oxygen (PO_2) elevated above about 0.5 to 0.6 (equivalent of 50 to 60% O_2 at the surface), as in hospital oxygen treatments, and occasionally, in extra long hyperbaric chamber treatments. Up to a large point, it is reversible with return to normal oxygen pressure. Also called oxygen poisoning or the Lorrain Smith effect, after Lorrain J. Smith, who first studied and described it in the late 1800's. See Oxygen Toxicity, and contrast to Central Nervous System (CNS) Oxygen Toxicity.

R

Radiation [From Latin *radius*, ray.] In thermoregulation, heat emitted in rays or waves. Because it does not require a medium to travel through, as do conduction and convection, heat can travel (radiate) through the vacuum of space to reach us from the sun.

Recreational Diving Conventionally referred to as diving on air, with no decompression stops, with a maximum depth of 130 feet (approx. 43 meters). There is much discussion regarding these parameters and the definition of a recreational diver.

Reduced Gradient Bubble Model (RGBM) One of several non-Haldane decompression models. Uses reduced surface gradient on repetitive dives. Surface gradients are much like M-values, where shorter half-times have larger values than longer half-times. Developed by theoretical physicist Dr. Bruce Wienke and partly based on the work of Yount and Hoffman.

Renin [From Latin *renes*, kidney.] In 1898, researchers Tiegerstedt and Bergmann found that injecting ground up kidney extract would raise blood pressure. Although the kidney itself does not contain a blood pressure raising agent, it makes a substance called renin that makes another substance called angiotensin I, that turns into angiotensin II, which increases blood pressure. Renin is a kidney enzyme. It breaks off part of a 14 amino acid molecule (a tetradecapeptide) called angiotensinogen, made in the liver, to make the hormone angiotensin I (a decapeptide). Angiotensin converting enzyme (ACE) breaks two more amino acids off angiotensin I to make the octapeptide angiotensin II (A-II). A-II acts strongly to raise blood pressure and reduce fluid and salt loss. A-II also goes to your adrenal glands to cause them to synthesize and release aldosterone which increases sodium and so, water retention. These combined effects counterbalance low blood volume. Medications called angiotensin converting enzyme (ACE) inhibitors block this blood pressure-raising effect, and so are useful to control hypertension. By relaxing vasoconstriction, ACE inhibitors also ease resistance to heart function, so are used in some treatments of heart failure. Because ACE inhibitors also inhibit bradykinin, a mediator of inflammatory response, users of ACE inhibitors sometimes experience skin rash and nagging cough as side effects. See Adrenal Gland, Aldosterone, Angiotensin, Enzyme, and Renin-Angiotensin-Aldosterone Cascade.

Renin-Angiotensin-Aldosterone Cascade The main system in conserving healthy body fluid, blood pressure, and salt levels. The kidney enzyme renin acts to make angiotensin I, which quickly converts to angiotensin II. Angiotensin II increases blood pressure and retains salt and water, and also stimulates the cortex of the adrenal gland to produce aldosterone. Aldosterone acts on the kidney to excrete more potassium instead of sodium. Increased body sodium helps retain body water. Renin production is stimulated by low blood salt content, low water content, and low blood pressure. Restored body levels then shut off stimulation of renin release. The renin-angiotensin-aldosterone system keeps body fluid and salt levels fairly constant, even when a person eats very large or very small amounts of salt. Counterbalances the ANF-ADH system. Immersion suppresses the system, resulting in increased diuresis. See Adrenal Gland, Aldosterone, Angiotensin, and

Renin. Compare to Antidiuretic Hormone (ADH) and Atrial Natriuretic Factor (ANF).

S

Saturation   [From Latin *saturare*, to fill, to be sated.] In chemistry, when a substance is present in the highest possible concentration under a given set of conditions. For example, water vapor forms dense clouds when the air is saturated; adding any more water causes the vapor to condense into rain. In diving, a compartment is considered saturated when it contains all the nitrogen or other inert gas it can hold at a given pressure, and therefore depth. Occurs when compartments have enough time to become equal with inspired inert gas partial pressure (more or less, and subtracting out water vapor pressure and carbon dioxide). Compare to Critical Supersaturation.

Saturation Diving   Alternative method to repeated decompression after repeated underwater work bouts. Divers remain under pressure for days, weeks, or longer, working, living, and sleeping in habitats, or 'communting' to work at depth in dry bells, becoming saturated with nitrogen or chosen inert gas in the breathing mixture. Incurs only a single decompression obligation, and, once equilibrated with external pressure, or saturated, time to decompress remains constant regardless of length of stay.

Sensitized Response   Increased response to a substance, such as a bee sting, after one exposure, where the first exposure caused little or no ill effect.

Series (or Serial) Model   Decompression model where inert gas is assumed to pass from compartment to compartment. Only one compartment is considered exposed to the ambient pressure reached in the blood stream. The Canadian DCIEM (Defence and Civil Institute for Environmental Medicine) tables are a series model. Also called serial model. Compare to Parallel Model.

Shallow Water Blackout   Term originally used in 1944 by Barlow and MacIntosh for blackout from too high CO_2 levels (hypercapnia) using closed circuit scuba. During World War II, British divers using oxygen rebreathers were passing out without warning. The problem subsided after improving the carbon dioxide absorption canisters. Later the term was applied to unconsciousness from too low oxygen (hypoxia) on ascent from breath holding. The mixup has continued into common use.

Shell   [From Germanic for husk, shell, or shield, related to Old Norse skalli, for a bald head.] Adjustable temperature area surrounding your body core, including skin and subskin tissue. Shell thickness changes with the amount of blood flowing through it, varying the degree of insulation.

SI   [From French, *Système International (d'Unités)*, International System (of Units)]. The Standard International System of Units, agreed on in 1960, uses metric units to standardize one named unit for any given measurement. SI base units are the meter (m) for length, kilogram (kg) for mass, and the second (s) for time. The SI system also measures temperature in kelvin (K), electric current in amperes (A), luminous intensity in candelas or candles (cd), and moles for the amount of a substance. Every other quantity can be described as a ratio of SI base units, for example, one atmosphere is 10,332.27 kilograms per square meter. SI units for pressure are the pascal (Pa) kilopascal (kPa), and megapascal (MPa), etc. See cgs System, MKS System, and Metric System, and compare to English System.

Slab Model A non-Haldane decompression model that uses one compartment, called a slab, rather than several separate compartments. Gas diffuses through one area of the slab to get to another. The British Sub-Aqua Club (BSAC) tables are a slab model.

Slow Compartments Body areas that absorb and release inert gas slowly. In anatomic tissues uptake and release rate depend on blood flow and solubility of gas in that area. In most decompression models, blood flow alone establishes the half-time speed.

Solubility. [From Latin *solvere*, to loosen or release.] The ability of a substance to dissolve, or pass into solution.

Spicules [From Latin *spiculum*, little point.] Small needlelike frameworks supporting sponges. Spicules can puncture the skin making entry portals for venom and germs.

Spontaneous Pneumothorax Pneumothorax occurring seemingly by itself without an obvious injury. Openings on the lung surface may come from a weakened area that ruptures. Occurs more often in young males who smoke. See Pneumothorax, and compare to traumatic pneumothorax. History of spontaneous pneumothorax is a contraindication to diving.

Statistical Model Decompression tables approaching decompression statistically – out of so many dives of a specific type, so many DCS incidents are expected. The NMRI (US Naval Medical Research Institute) tables are are statistical tables. They use maximum likelihood calculations developed by Dr. Paul Weathersby.

Strength [From Old English *strang*, strong.] Ability to move a heavy weight one or few times.

Stroke Volume (Abbreviated SV). Amount of blood ejected from the heart with each beat. Stroke volume times heart rate is cardiac output, or SV x HR = Q. If stroke volume increases with increased venous return, as with immersion or lying down, heart rate decreases to keep cardiac output constant.

Supersaturation Situation when compartment inert gas partial pressure (tension) exceeds ambient pressure, meaning the compartment has more nitrogen than it can contain in equilibrium. Occurs when ambient pressure drops on ascent. See Critical Supersaturation.

Supersaturation Ratio Compartment nitrogen tension at depth divided by total pressure at the surface or at the required decompression stop. Exceeding the supersaturation ratio produces bubbles or likelihood of bubbles. Each half-time compartment has its own supersaturation ratio.

Surface Area-To-Mass Ratio   Proportion of exposed surface area relative to internal mass. Fingers and ears have a high surface area-to-mass ratio. Your torso has a low ratio.

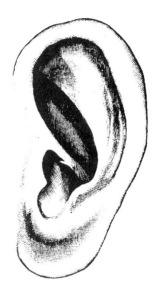

Swimmer's Ear   Painful infection or inflammation of the outer ear, which is the part you can see (the auricle) and stick your finger into (the canal). Cotton swabs and scratching the canal contribute to swimmer's ear by removing protective cerumen (ear wax). Ear plugs rarely keep water out, and often create conditions good for swimmer's ear, by rubbing away wax, and holding water in the canal. Swimmer's ear usually is easily prevented and treated with white vinegar or Otic Domeboro drops. Swimmer's ear is not related to middle ear or inner ear injuries caused by pressure, or to congestion of the middle ear, so decongestants do not help. Swimmer's ear does not automatically require stopping swimming or diving, in many cases, just drying the ears afterward. For serious and recurring cases, see your physician.

T

Table-Based Computer   Synonymous with Look-Up Computer. Decompression computers that give their final answer by looking up the dive profile against values that have already been determined by a decompression table. Very few decompression computers work this way. Compare to Model-Based Computers.

Technical Atmosphere   Pressure unit occasionally used in Europe. The technical atmosphere is 735 mmHg or 98.06 kPa. Usually abbreviated "AT" or "ATA" if absolute. This is in contrast to the atmosphere absolute (ATA or atm abs) of 760 mmHg or 101.325 kPa. Confusion and misinformation is possible where these units are used interchangeably. See atmosphere, atmosphere absolute, and SI System.

Temperature   [From Latin *temperare*, to mix, and from which we get words like temperate and temper.] Measure of intensity of heat energy. Different from heat in that a substance at high temperature may not necessarily have more heat energy than one at a lower temperature. Your body, like other heat sinks, can lose or gain great amounts of heat energy with little change in temperature. Size, density, type of material, and temperature determines amount of heat energy contained. The heat a body can absorb without changing temperature is called latent heat. See Heat.

Tendon   [From Latin *tendere*, to stretch. This definition is interesting, as tendons don't stretch greatly except with injury.] Tough, fibrous, inelastic modification of the ends of muscle, that connect muscle to bone.

Tension [From Latin *tendere*, to stretch or extend.] Inert gas partial pressure in body compartments. See Nitrogen Tension.

Tension Pneumothorax Potentially lethal complication of pneumothorax, where air forced into the pleural space progressively compresses the heart, decreasing its ability to function, and may collapse one or both lungs.

Thorax [From Greek *thorax* meaning breastplate or chest.] Area of your body between neck and diaphragm, partially enclosed by your ribs.

Tissue [From Latin *tela*, meaning web or net, and from which we get words like architect, technology, and technical.] In anatomy refers to body areas with structurally similar properties, such as muscle tissue. In decompression, refers to body areas, wherever they may be, that are similar in rate of uptake of inert gas, for example, a 5 minute or 10 minute tissue. They are now more often called compartments. Compare to Compartment, and see Half-time.

Traumatic Pneumothorax Injury from an accident where air enters the chest area outside the lung. Diving lung overexpansion injury may lead to traumatic pneumothorax. See Pneumothorax and Lung Overexpansion Injury.

Trimix Mixture of three gases for diving beyond the air range, usually helium, oxygen, and nitrogen.

Toxic [From the Greek *toxikon*, a poison for arrows.] Able to cause injury or death, especially by chemical means.

U

Undersea and Hyperbaric Medical Society (UHMS) International professional society devoted to clinical and research information in diving physiology and hyperbaric medicine. Open to professionals in the field, and others interested. Annual and branch meetings of recent advances. Publishes *Undersea & Hyperbaric Medicine* quarterly, technical works, and workshops. 10531 Metropolitan Avenue Kensington, MD 20895-2627 USA. Phone (301) 942-2980. Fax (301) 942-7804.

Uptake Transfer of dissolved gas into the body. Also called ongassing or ingassing.

V

Valsalva (or Valsalva's) Maneuver [Named for Antonio Maria Valsalva (1666-1723), Italian anatomist. His treatise on ear anatomy, published in late 1600's, is considered a classic work.] Technique to equalize, or "pop" the ears by forcing air from the mouth up through the Eustachian tubes to the middle ear, increasing air pressure on the inside of the eardrum to match increasing water pressure on the outside. Accomplished by breathing out against a closed mouth with nostrils pinched shut. It may be technically incorrect to call this a Valsalva maneuver. The technique originally described by Valsalva was to forcibly exhale against a closed glottis, by closing the vocal cords together, as in a cough. This technique would not equalize the ears. Now, both techniques are commonly called a Valsalva maneuver. Either technique may increase pressure in the chest cavity, impeding venous return of blood to the heart, and because of that, is often used to study cardiovascular effects of decreased cardiac filling and output. It is possible that English physician Joseph Toynbee (1815-1866) may have developed the maneuver for exhaling against a closed nose and mouth. To make things confusing, Toynbee also developed a different, gentler equalization method that we call the Toynbee, consisting of swallowing with the nose and mouth shut.

Varying Permeability Model Non-Haldane decompression model limiting bubble size on ascent to a critical volume, and quantity to below a critical number. Developed by a group of University of Hawaii researchers led by Drs. Yount and Hoffman, called the Tiny Bubble Group.

Vasoconstriction [From Latin *vas*, vessel + Latin *constrict*, to compress.] Decrease in diameter of blood vessels, usually arterioles.

Vasodilation [From Latin *vas*, vessel + Latin *dilatare*, to enlarge.] Increase in diameter of blood vessels, usually arterioles.

Vasopressin [From Latin *vas*, vessel + Latin *press*, to press.] Synonymous with antidiuretic hormone, which limits fluid output from the kidneys. Originally named for its effect to raise blood pressure, because it constricts blood vessels. See Antidiuretic Hormone.

Veins Membranous, branching system of thin-walled tubes that carry blood from all areas of the body back to the heart for transport to the lungs. Compare to Arteries.

Venom [From Latin *venenum*, meaning poison.] A chemically harmful secretion transmitted by a bite or sting. May be distinguished from poison where poison is eaten, venom injected.

Venous Gas Emboli (VGE) In diving, small inert gas bubbles in the veins. See Embolism, and compare to Arterial Gas Embolism (AGE).

Venous Pooling Blood collecting in the veins of your legs when at rest on land, and to a smaller extent, your arms at your sides. Immersion removes venous pooling in the following way: Your blood flows in blood vessels that are stretchable, like rubber tubes. When you stand upright on land, blood pools in your legs because gravity pulls down the entire column of blood. Blood pressure rises in your legs, which pushes out on your tubes. Your vein tubes stretch more than your artery tubes, so blood accumulates there – venous pooling. If you had veins of iron there would be no distention, and no pooling, no matter how great the gravity. Forces opposing stretching are the elastic-restoring force of the tube (how strong and stiff your blood vessels are), and ambient pressure. In air, ambient pressure is small, so you get pooling. Water pressure is higher – enough to counter pooling. Water pressure increases with depth for the same reason that venous blood pressure, on land, increases toward your feet (or your head if you stand on it); gravity pulls down on both, so the water at one level feels the weight of all the water above it. The increase in water pressure with depth is almost identical to the increase in blood pressure towards the part of your body that is lower (head or feet), regardless of your postural orientation and, up to an extreme point, how deep you are, so it "cancels" venous pooling. Without extra accumulation of blood in the legs, more blood returns to the thorax. Increased blood volume returning to the chest is one trigger for both the dive reflex and the urge to "go." Removal of venous pooling is sometimes mistakenly attributed to the hydrostatic gradient – greater pressure with deeper depths squeezing your blood from foot to head. However, the countering water pressure does not progressively squeeze blood upward, it matches the increasing venous pressure with distance down your vessels, and operates equally on you in any posture. You may notice venous pooling on land in several situations: With sudden standing, the rush of venous pooling briefly lowers available supply and pressure to your head, and you may feel light headed. Bending over allows gravity to restore blood, relieving dizziness. After sitting still long periods, such as on a plane, your feet swell with pooling fluids. Contracting your leg muscles while sitting or moving around, pumps blood upward, helping to relieve pooling. Extreme venous pooling has caused occasional cases of fainting when climbing out of water. It has also been fatal to beached whales. See Hydrostatic Pressure.

Venous Return   Blood flowing back to the heart from the body. The amount of blood flowing back to the heart determines how much the heart pumps back out, called stroke volume.

VO_{2max}   (pronounced vee-oh-tu-max) VO_2 is how much oxygen you consume. Max VO_2 is the maximum amount of oxygen your system can extract and use to do exercise.

W

Water Intoxication   Abnormally dilute body fluids and cellular fluids due to drinking too much water and too little electrolytes. May occur in long endurance events like ultra-marathons and long hikes, with only water and no electrolyte replacement. Occasionally occurs in infants swallowing pool water during swimming lessons, with serious health consequences. Also called hyponatremia (high-poe-nay-tree'-me-uh) meaning low sodium.

Water Vapor Pressure   Pressure exerted by evaporated water on its surroundings. Just like any other gas, water vapor follows Dalton's Law of partial pressures. There is normally more water vapor pressure in the air in your lungs than the atmosphere. This slightly reduces the inspired nitrogen (or other inert gas) pressure that your body will ingas. It also affects how much water you lose through your respiratory tract. Just as heat and nitrogen travel from greater quantity to lesser, you lose moisture from your lungs to the environment. As the vapor pressure of air in hot conditions increases, the gradient for water loss through breathing decreases, so you lose less. With cold it increases, and you lose more. That is why your throat may feel dry in very cold weather, although water vapor pressure is only one factor determining total respiratory water loss. Saturation water vapor pressure falls exponentially with decreasing temperature, or in other words, cold air holds far less water vapor than warm air. That's why moist air masses can't hold as much water vapor when they cool. Water vapor then condenses, coalesces into drops, and falls as precipitation. See Saturation.

Weight-Bearing Activity Exercise where body weight provides the resistance, as in walking, running, dancing, skiing, skating, hiking. Regular weight bearing exercise is known to increase bone density and reduce risk of osteoporosis.

Weight-Loading Activity Exercise where external weight provides the resistance, as in weight lifting and carrying packages. Regular weight loading is known to increase bone density and reduce risk of osteoporosis.

Wind Chill Cooling effect of wind. More calories of heat are lost per unit area of the body as wind speed increases, even though air temperature remains the same, because advection, convection and evaporative cooling are enhanced by the air motion. Wind chill temperature is the temperature that calm air would need to be to cause the same cooling effect. See Advection, Convection, and Evaporation.

APPENDIX

PRESSURE CONVERSIONS

A few units of pressure used in this text, such as fsw, msw, ATA, psi, and mmHg, are commonly seen in several kinds of diving applications, although the International System of Units (SI) is preferred for scientific use. SI units of pressure are the pascal (Pa = Newton x m^{-2}), the kilopascal (kPa), and the megapascal (MPa). The SI and English systems are explained in the glossary, along with the metric system and metric units used in SI.

This table gives conversions and notes from the Standard Practice for Use of the International System of Units (SI). Document E380-89a, American Society for Testing and Materials, Philadelphia, PA, 1989.

1 atm	=	1.013247 bar	1 torr	=	133.322 Pa [a]
1 atm	=	1.013247 bar	1 atm	=	33.08 fsw
1 atm	=	101.3247 kPa	1 bar	=	32.646 fsw [b,d]
1 atm	=	14.6959 psi	1 fsw	=	3.063 kPa
1 atm	=	760.00 torr [a]	1 fsw	=	22.98 torr
1 bar	=	100.000 kPa	1 psi	=	2.251 fsw
1 bar	=	100,000 kPa	1 atm	=	10.13 msw
1 bar	=	14.50377 psi	1 bar	=	10.00 msw
1 bar	=	750.064 torr	1 msw	=	10.000 kPa [c,d]
1 MPa	=	10.000 bar	1 msw	=	1.450 psi
1 psi	=	6,894.76 Pa [a]	1 msw	=	75.01 torr
1 psi	=	51.7151 torr			

[a] Signifies a primary definition, from which other equalities were derived

[b] Primary definition for fsw; assumes a density for seawater of 1.021480 at 4°C (the value often used for depth gauge calibration.

[c] Primary definition for msw; assumes a density for seawater of 1.01972 at 4°C.

[d] These primary definitions for fsw and msw are arbitrary since the pressure below a column for seawater depends on the density of the water, which varies from point to point in the ocean. These two definitions are consistent with each other if a density correction is applied. Units of fsw and msw should not be used to express partial pressures and should not be used when the nature of the subject matter requires precise evaluation of pressure; in these cases, investigators should carefully ascertain how their pressure-measuring devices are calibrated in terms of a reliable standard, and pressures should be reported in pascals, kilopascals, or megapascals.

FIGURES

Figures 2.1, 2.2, 2.3, 3.1, 3.3, 5.2, and 5.3: Adapted or reprinted from images in NAUI Textbook I, with permission; Figure 5.1: Adapted from Instructor's Visual Aid Master P22 with permission of the National Association of Underwater Instructors Michael J. Williams, Director, Member Communications, NAUI.

Figures 3.2 and 5.5: Reprinted from Sea Life images by AAH Computer Graphics.

Lateral skeleton in Figure 7.1, and six blood cells in Figure 1.2: Adapted with permission and licensed; Adrenal and skin segment illustrations in the glossary, reprinted with permission and licenced from LifeART Super Anatomy Collection 1, Copyright © 1991 by TechPool Studios, Cleveland, OH.

Images making up Figure 3.4 of surface area to mass ratio, Figure 6.1, and glossary images except adrenal, skin segment, balloon, and hard hat diver: Adapted or reprinted from Zedcorps Desk Gallery CD-ROM collection.

Chapter opening art woodcuts, hot air balloon and decompression diver in the glossary: Pictorial Archive Trades and Occupations, selected by Carol Belanger Grafton, Pictorial Archive Men, selected by Jim Harter, and Pictorial Archive for Collage Harter Woodcuts, all copyright free from Dover Publications.

*I*NDEX

A

Acclimatization
  cold 70
  heat 81
Achilles tendon 156
Acne 95
ADH (Antidiuretic hormone) 45, 50, 195
Advection 55
Aerobic capacity 92, 151, 155
AGE (Arterial gas embolism) 108
Aging 120, 153, 171
  reduce effects with weight lifting 170
  reduce effects with exercise 152
Air consumption 98
  work load 98
Alcohol 194
  causing cluster headaches 134
  congeners 136
  effect on antidiuretic hormone 195
  fluid replacement 194
  treatment for swimmer's ear, 140
Aldosterone 46
Algorithm 7
Allen's rule 65
Allergic response 143
Altitude 22, 32, 86, 120, 123, 124, 131
  testicular implant testing 86
American Red Cross 146, 194
Anabolic steroids 98
Anaerobic 92
Anaerobic capacity 155
Anatomic tissues 8 *see Compartments*
Anemones 144
ANF (Atrial natriuretic factor) 46
Anorexia nervosa 181
Antibodies 143
Antidiuretic hormone (ADH) 45, 50, 195
Antigens 143
Antihistamine 144, 146
Antioxidants 130, 131, 132
  Vitamin C 130, 131, 132
  Vitamin E 130, 131, 132

Aristotle 79
Arterial gas emboli 118
Arterial gas embolism (AGE) 108
  AGE and ascent rate 120
  cerebral (CAGE) 108
Ascent rate 21, 120
Asthma 111
ATA 11, 13, 128-129
  technical ATA 13
Atrial natriuretic factor (ANF) 46
Auditory canal 139
Auerbach, Paul M.D. 145

B

Back pain 95, 156, 159
  abdominal muscles 96
  exercises 96
  major contributors 95
Bacon, Francis 69
Balding 87
Bangasser, Susan Ed.D. 100
Barnard, Neal M.D. 182
Bell, diving 21
Bends 5 *see Decompression sickness*
Bennett, Peter Ph.D., D.Sc. 120
Bergman's rule 65
Bert, Paul 5
  Bert effect 127
Beta blockers 67
  non-shivering thermogenesis 67
Blood
  centralization 38-39
  compared to sea water 192
Blood-brain barrier 118
Body fat *see Fat, body*
Body position underwater
  diuresis 44
  dive reflex 40
  venous pooling 40
Bone health 180-184 *see Osteoporosis*

Bottom mix 33
Botulism 123
Bove, Alfred M.D., Ph.D. 110
Box jellyfish, 144
Boycott, Arthur E 5
Boyle, Robert 5
Boyle's law 5
Bradycardia *see Heart rate*
Breath-hold injury 108
Breath-holding 39
Breath-holding time 37
Breathing rate
    carbon dioxide 134-135
    narcosis 36
    partial pressure of oxygen 36
    work of breathing 36
British Sub-Aqua Club (BSAC) 28, 90
Bronchitis 110
Brooklyn bridge 5
Brown fat see *Fat, brown*
Bubbles 4
    arterial 114
    bone marrow 118
    brain 118
    joint space 116
    neurons 117
    not all bad? 121
    patent foramen ovale 115
    silent 114
    skin 118
    tendons and ligaments 117
    venous 114
Buoyancy
    air consumption 99
    horizontal trim 93, 106
    negate blood pooling 40, 42, 44, 45,
    52
    oxygen cost 93, 99
    power output 99

C

Cabin depressurization 22
CAGE (Cerebral arterial gas embolism)
    108 *see Air embolism*
Caffeine 49, 195
Caisson disease 5 *see Decompression
    sickness*
Caissons 5, 120
Calcium
    how much do you need? 182

Carbohydrate
    loaders 190
    replacers 191
Carbon dioxide 39, 134, 135
    dilate brain blood vessels 134
    retention 134
Catalase 126, 132
Catecholamines 47, 73
    epinephrine 47, 73
    norepinephrine 47, 73
Catfish 145
Central nervous system (CNS) oxygen
    toxicity 127 *see Oxygen toxicity*
Cerebral arterial gas embolism (CAGE)
    108 *see Air embolism*
Cerumen 138, 139
Cholesterol
    bad 98
    good 174
Clark, James M.D. 110
Clo 69
    three dog night 69
Coelenterates 144-145
Cold 119
    Allen's rule 65
    bald men 102
    Bergman's rule 65
    clo 69
    effects of 72-78
        arrhythmias 74
        decompression 75
        dive reflex 38
        diuresis 46-47
        endurance, cardiovascular 74
        fatigue 75
        frostbite shorts 103
        gasp response 72
        hunting reflex of Lewis 73
        manual impairment 73
        mental function 74
        metabolism 74
        narcosis 75
        renal 74
        respiratory effects 72
        thermostat 75
        vascular effects 72
    hypothermia 64, 101
    infertility 87
    male genital injury 103
    paradoxical undressing 73
    preventing cold injury 76
    rewarming 76
    shivering 59, 61, 62, 64, 68, 70, 75,
        76

surface area-to-mass ratio 65, 101, 102
susceptibility 64-71
why do you get cold? 54-63
Cold and heat 53-84
Cold tolerance 174, 150, 186
   acclimatization 69
   age 67
   behavior 67
   dehydration 70
   gender 69
   medication 67
   physical fitness 68
   protective clothing 68
     three dog night 69
   rest and exercise 67
   skinfold thickness 102
Cold water
   overheating in 68
Compartments 6, 8
   blood flow 9
   identifying experiments 9
   fast and slow 17
   which is which? 17
Complement 116, 117
Conduction 55
Congeners 136
Convection 55, 80
Coral 144
Cortisone 98
Cortisporin 141
Counter-current heat exchange 59
Cross, Maurice M.D. 85, 111
Crush injury 131
Cryptorchidism 86

D

Damant, Guybon C. 5
Decompression mix 33
Decompression sickness (DCS) 113-132
   arterialized bubbles 114, 118-119
   biochemical effects 116
   bone marrow 118
   brain 118
   bubbles not all bad? 121
   complement activation 116
   extravehicular travel 22
   is it DCS or AGE? 118-119
   joint space 116
   marine mammals 37

   mechanical effects 115
   nervous system 117
   patent foramen ovale 115
   prevention 121
   previous 120
   skin bends 118
   tendons and ligaments 117
   venous bubbles 114
   risk 75, 119
     aging 120
     ascent rate 120
     cold and heat 119
     dehydration 119
     exercise 121
     fat 100-101, 120, 122
     fatigue 121
     gender 120
     repeated exposure 120
Decompression stops 20, 134
   exercise during 121
   oxygen use 130, 134
Decompression tables and computers 1-34
   DCIEM tables 25-26
   EL model 27
   Haldane model 6, 14, 17, 20, 23, 27, 30
   history 5
   Kidd-Stubbs model 25
   pneumatic analog computer 25
   model-based computer 23
   multi-compartment models 9
   reduced gradient bubble model 28
   series (serial) model 25-26
   slab model 27
   table-based computer 23
   tiny bubble model 28
   U.S. Navy (USN) standard air decompression tables 20
   varying permeability model 28
   what tables and computers calculate 6
Deep and technical diving *see Technical diving*
Defence and Civil Institute of Environmental Medicine (DCIEM) 25
Dehydration 47, 97, 104, 119, 174
   cold tolerance 77
   drinking sea water 192
   how you conserve body water, 188
   how you lose body water, 187
   obesity 187
   prevention 195
   problems with 186
   rehydrating underwater 50

why replacement? 188
Desaturation 20
    when are you desaturated? 20
Diaper rash 49
Dieting 97, 173-175
    "yo-yo" 173
    problems with 173
Diuresis 43-52, 74
    age 47
    aldosterone 46
    antidiuretic hormone (ADH) 45, 50, 195
    atrial natriuretic factor (ANF) 46
    cold 46-47
    buoyancy 44
    dive boat options 49
    dry hyperbaric chambers 47
    drysuit options 49
    emotion 47
    exercise 47
    fluid density 46
    hydration 47
    kaliuresis 45
    microgravity 44
    natriuresis 45
    temperature 46
    time of day 46
    rehydrating underwater 50
    renin 46
    renin-angiotensin-aldosterone system 46
Dive reflex 36, 74
    arrhythmias 37
    cold 38
    heart rate 37
    individual variation 38
    limb blood flow 37
    marine mammals 37
    mechanisms 38
    metabolism 37
    role in humans 37
Divers Alert Network (DAN) 93, 121
Diving Diseases Research Center (DDRC) 87, 100
Donald Duck voice 31, 32
Doolette, David M.D. 32
Doppler 100
Doyle, Arthur Conan Sir 144
Drag 105
DSAT recreational dive planner 20, 100

E

E. coli (*Escherichia coli*) 131
Ear plugs 138, 139, 140, 141
Eating disorders 97, 148
    cold and heat tolerance 97
    dehydration and other problems 97
Edmonds, Carl M.B. 105
EL Model 27
Electrolytes 81, 189
    conservation 81
    what is an electrolyte? 189
Electrolyte drinks 189
    not harmful 192
    no need to dilute 194
    why replace electrolytes? 189
Emphysema 111
Embolism
    arterial (AGE) 108
    ascent rate 120
    cerebral (CAGE) 108
Endorphins 152
Endurance
    cardiovascular 151, 155
    muscular 151, 155
Enriched air nitrox (EAN) 29, 129
    decompression sickness 31
    hyperbaric chamber treatment 31
Envenomations 142-146 *see Marine stings*
Enzymes 125, 143
    catalase 126, 132
    peroxidase 126
    superoxide dismutase (SOD) 130
Epinephrine 47, 73
Equivalent air depth (EAD) 30
Erectile function 93
Eustachian tubes 139
Evans, Janet 91
Evaporation 55-56, 80
    sweat 56
Exercise 121, 147-171
    aging 152
    body fat loss 152
    cancer risk 151
    carbon dioxide retention 134
    cold water 68
    counterproductive exercises 166
    decompression sickness 151
    endorphins 152
    free radicals 126
    insulin sensitivity 152
    mood 152
    specificity 165

Exercises for divers 157-164
Exponentials 9, 16
External otitis 138-141 *see Swimmer's
    ear*
Extravasation 144

F

Fat, blood 174 *see Cholesterol*
Fat, body 120, 173, 174, 177, 178, 191
    decompression risk 100-101, 120,
        122
    diving 148
    insulation 59
    loss with exercise 152
    helps sports 148
    hinders sports 148
    shivering 59
Fat, brown 67
Fat, food 173, 176, 177, 178, 183
Fat-face-chicken-legs-effect 45
Fat emboli 116
Fatigue 75, 121, 174
Fife, Caroline M.D. 141
Fire coral 145
Fitness
    air consumption 98
    cold 68
    different aspects 154
    heat 80
    what is fitness? 154
Flexibility 94, 156, 161-162
    ankle 161
    reducing back pain 156
    reducing joint injury 151
    stretcher's scrotum 96
Fluid replacement 186-196
FN_2 11 *see Nitrogen*
FO_2 10, 11, 12, 128 *see Oxygen*
    FeO_2 (fraction expired) 10
    FiO_2 (fraction inspired) 10
Foramen ovale 115
Free radicals 116, 125
    antioxidants 130, 131, 132
        Vitamin C 130, 131, 132
        Vitamin E 130, 131, 132
    autoimmune disease 125
    cigarette smoke 126
    exercise 126
    formation 126
    function of 125

heart attack, cancer, stroke, and
    emphysema 125
hydrogen peroxide 125, 126
immune system 125
inflammation 144
lipid membranes 127
muscle contraction 126
reperfusion injury 127
scavenging enzymes
    catalase 126, 132
    peroxidase 126
    superoxide dismutase (SOD) 130
superoxide (O_2^-) 125
Frostbite shorts 103
fsw 13
Full face masks 135

G

Gangrene 123
Gas switching 33-34
Gasp response 72
Gatorade® 191, 194
Gender 85-106, 120
    aerobic capacity 92
    air consumption 98
    anabolic steroids 98
    back pain 95
    cardiovascular health 93
    decompression sickness 100
    dehydration 104
    diving accidents 93
    eating disorders 97
    electrolyte loss 104
    fat 100-101
    flexibility and joint injury 94
    growth hormone 98
    heat injury 103
    hernia 99
    horizontal "trim" 105
    hypothermia 101
    joint structure and injury 94
    overweight 96
    shell 101
    slipping weight belt 99
    spontaneous pneumothorax 94
    stretcher's scrotum 96
    sudden death 93
    sweating 104
    work load 91-92
Gisolfi, Carl Ph.D. 194

Growth hormone 98

H

Habitats 21, 29, 139
Hair restoration 87
Haldane, John Scott 5, 21, 120
Haldane model 6, 14, 17, 20, 23, 27, 30
Half-Times 14
    elimination 14
    equation 16
    exponentials 9, 16
    not just theoretical 16
    Novocain 17
    penicillin 17
    radiation 16
    uptake 14
    Valium 16
    which half-times are used? 16
Hamilton, Bill Ph.D. 24, 32
Hang mix 33
Hangover
    diving as cure? 133
    migraine and cluster headaches 133
    oxygen's lack of effectiveness 134
Headache 133-137
    breathing 100% oxygen 133
    caffeine 136
    carbon monoxide poisoning 136
    cigarette smoke 136
    diving as cause? 134
    diving as cure? 133
    National Headache Foundation 137
    prevention 136
    temporomandibular joint 136
    tyramines 136
Heart disease 174
Heart rate
    cold water 38
    immersion effects 38-39
    warm and hot water 38
Heat, diving in 79-84
    shirts vs. skins 82
Heat injury 83
    prevention 83
Heat conservation 58
    counter-current heat exchange 59
    insulation 58, 59, 60, 63, 65, 67, 68
        clo 69
        clothing 68-69, 70, 73
        fat 54, 59, 65, 68, 76

        muscle 59, 60, 62, 68
        shell 58, 59, 60, 73
    vasoconstriction 58
Heat gain 60
    brown fat 67
    exercise 56, 57, 59
    shivering 59, 61, 62, 64, 68, 70, 75, 76
    non-shivering thermogenesis 61, 67
Heat loss
    breathing helium 32
    conduction 55
    convection 55
    evaporation 55
    gradient 57
    head 56
    polar bears 57
    radiation 55
    respiration 32, 56
    shell-to-environment gradient 102, 103
    sweating 80
Heat shock proteins 81
Heat tolerance 150
    acclimatization 81
        electrolyte conservation 81
        heat shock proteins 81
        plasma volume increase 81
        sweating increase 81
    age 81
    body size 82
    dehydration 81
    gender 82
    physical fitness 80
Heliox 31-32
    decompression time 31-32
    Donald Duck voice 31, 32
    speech unscramblers 31
Helium
    colder breathing helium? 32
    speed of sound 31
    thermal capacity 32
    thermal conductivity 32
Hemoglobin 124
    free radicals 125
Hemoglobin-oxygen buffer 124
Hennessy, Tom Ph.D. 28
Henry's law 4, 19, 124
Hernia 99
High pressure nervous syndrome (HPNS) 33
Hill, Kelly M.D. 85, 90
Hills, Brian Ph.D. 118
Hip flexors 156

Hippocrates 164
Histamine 143
Histidine 144
Homeotherms 54
Hot or warm water
    diuresis 46
    heart rate 38
    male fertility 87
    vasodilation 46
HPNS (High pressure nervous
   syndrome) 33
Hsu, David Ph.D. 116, 124
Hunting reflex of Lewis 73
Hydrogen peroxide 125, 126, 140
Hydroids 144, 145
Hydrostatic gradient 39, 45
Hyperbaric bradycardia 40
Hyperbaric chamber treatment 31, 126,
   128, 130, 133
Hypercapnia 135 *see Carbon dioxide*
Hyperostoses 140
Hyperthermia 80, 103-104
    surface area-to-mass ratio 65, 103
Hyperventilation 135
Hypothalamus 75
Hypothermia 64, 101
    bald men 102
    risk 58, 101
    surface area-to-mass ratio 65, 101,
    102
Hypoxia 135
Hypoxic mix 33

I

Immersion
    face 39
    full body 39
    head-out 39
Immersion effects 35-52
Implants
    hair 87
    chest in males 89
    mammary 86, 89
    penile 86
    testicular 86
Inappropriate fatigue 116
Inert gas narcosis *see Narcosis*
Infertility, male 87
Inflammation 144
    free radicals 144

Inguinal hernia 99
Injuries, diving 107-146
Institute for Naval Medicine (INM) 67
Insulation 58, 59, 60, 63, 65, 67, 68
    clo 69
    clothing 68-69, 70, 73
    fat 54, 59, 65, 68, 76
    muscle 59, 60, 62, 68
    shell 58, 59, 60, 73
Integumentary sheathe 145

J

James, Philip M.D. 112, 118
Jellyfish 143, 144
Jet fighter pilots 87
Jones, Bruce Lt. Col. M.D. 94

K

Kaliuresis 45
Kidd-Stubbs decompression model 25
Kilopascals (kPa) 11, 13
Kindwall, Eric M.D. 121
Korean diving women 69

L

Lanphier, Edward Rev. M.D. 121, 134
Leukocytes 116, 118
Lion's mane 144
Lionfish 145
Lipid peroxidation 127
Look-up or table-based computers 23
Lorrain Smith effect 126
Lung
    as bubble filters 115
    capacity 98
Lung injury
    asthma 111
    bronchitis 110
    emphysema 111
    pneumonia 111
    prevention 112
    overexpansion 108, 118
    pneumothorax 109, 110 *see*
    Pneumothorax

M

M-values 6, 7, 20, 22
    different depths 23
    units 22
Man-of-war 144, 146
Marine stings 142-146
    coelenterates 144-145
    coral 144
    defensive stings 142
    general wound care 146
    jellyfish 143, 144
    offensive stings 142
    panty hose 146
    prevention 146
    stingrays 145, 146
    stonefish 142, 145, 146
    treatment 144
    urinating on the wound 145
Martin, Lawrence, M.D. 111
Maskus-too-tightis 136
Meat tenderizer 145
Men divers *see Gender*
    anabolic steroids 98
    chest muscle enhancement implants
    89
    cryptorchidism 86
    genital injury from cold 103
    hair implants 87
    hernia 99
    infertility 87
    minoxidil 87
    offspring gender 87
    overweight 96
    penile implants 86
    "roid" rages 98
    sleep apnea 96-97
    snoring 96
    stretcher's scrotum 96
    testicular implants 86
Menopause 181
Middle ear 139
Migraine and cluster headaches 133, 136
    see Headaches
Minoxidil 87
Model-based computers 23
Montain, Scott Ph.D. 193
Multi-compartment models 9
Murray, Robert Ph.D. 194

N

Nappy rash 49
Narcosis 31, 32, 36, 37, 75, 128, 135
Natriuresis 45
Naval Experimental Diving Unit (NEDU)
    27
Negative pressure breathing 44
    diuresis 44
Nematocyst 144
Neuman, Tom M.D. 121
Nishi, Ron 25
Nitrite compounds 136
Nitrogen
    elimination 3
    uptake 3
    narcosis *see Narcosis*
    neural depressant 33
Nitrogen tension 12
    compartments 14
    on land 13
    underwater 13
    units 13
NOAA Nitrox I 29, 129
NOAA Nitrox II 29, 129
Non-Haldane models 20, 24-28
Non-shivering thermogenesis 61, 67
    beta blockers 67
    brown fat 67
Norepinephrine 47, 73
Normoxic 33
Novocain 17
Nunneley, Sarah M.D. 56
Nutrition for divers 172-196

O

Obesity *see Overweight*
Ocean sunfish 142
Oculocardiac reflex 40
Offgassing
    exponential 27
    linear 27
    only on ascent? 18
    slow compartments 18
Offspring gender 87
Oral contraceptives 89
Osmosis 193
Osteoporosis 97, 180-184

calcium need 182
calcium sources 182
factors affecting risk 181
hibernation 182
lifting weights 182
prevention 183
Overheating 103 *see Hyperthermia*
Overweight 96, 173, 176, 187
dehydration 187
hernia 99
major factor 177
orthopedic problems 176
osteoporosis 149
sleep apnea 96-97
snoring 96
Oxygen
constricts brain blood vessels 124, 133
football players 31
mood effect 31
Oxygen enriched air (OEA) or enriched air nitrox (EAN) 29, 129
decompression sickness 31
hyperbaric chamber treatment 31
Oxygen toxicity 30, 33, 123-132
antioxidants 130, 131, 132
Vitamin C 130, 131, 132
Vitamin E 130, 131, 132
E. coli (*Escherichia coli*) 131
enzymes, scavenging
catalase 126, 132
peroxidase 126
superoxide dismutase (SOD) 130
deep and technical diving 128
depth ranges 127
hyperbaric chamber 128
hyperbaric oxygen treatment 130
iron 117
prevention 130
recreational air diving 127
reperfusion injury 127
susceptibility 129
treatment 130

P

P phenomenon 43-52 *see Diuresis*
P-valves 49
Paradoxical undressing 73
Parallel model 25, 26

Partial pressure 10
calculating 12
units 11
why you use 12
Pascals (Pa) 11, 13
Patent foramen ovale 115
Paul Bert effect 127
Paulev, Poul-Erik M.D. 37
PCO_2 134 *see Carbon dioxide*
Pendergast, David Ph.D. 92, 98, 105
Penguins 59, 76
Penile implants 86
Peptides 143
Peroxidase 126
Physicians committee for responsible medicine (PCRM) 182
Platelets 116, 118
PMS 105
PN_2 10, 11 *see Nitrogen*
Pneumonia 111
Pneumothorax 109
diving injury after 110
spontaneous 109
tension 109
traumatic 109
PO_2 11, 12, 33, 126, 129, 129, 130, 131, 132 *see Oxygen*
Poikilotherms 54
Poison 142
Polar bears 57, 76
Porcupine fish 142
Power 155
speed-dominated 155
strength-dominated 155
Prednisone 98
Pregnancy 89
death from 89
Pressure
absolute 2
ambient 2, 4, 21
gauge 2
Protein
heat shock 81
supplementation 159
Proteus 139
Pseudomonas aeruginosa, 139
Puffer fish 142
Pullen, Fred M.D. 140
Pulmonary barotrauma 108 *see Lung injury*
Pulmonary oxygen toxicity 126 *see Oxygen toxicity*

R

Radiation, atomic 16
Radiation, heat 55, 80
Rebreathers 135
Reduced gradient bubble model 28
Rehydration 186-196
Rehydrating underwater 50
Renin 46
Renin-angiotensin-aldosterone system 46
Reperfusion injury 127
Repetitive dives 120
Rice, Stephen M.D. 94
"Roid" rages 98

S

Safety stops 18, 28, 120, 122
Saturation 19, 29
    when are you saturated? 19
Saturation diving 20
Scalp reduction surgery 87
Schwarzenegger, Arnold 91
SCUDA 50
Sea urchins 146
Sea wasp 144
Sea water
    drinking 192
    compared to blood 192
Seals 37, 76
Sensitization 143
Series (serial) model 25
Shallow water blackout 135
Sharks 105
Shell, body surface 58, 67, 101
Shell-to-environment gradient 102, 103
Shivering 59, 61, 62, 64, 68, 70, 75, 76
    critical shivering temperature 61
    thin people 59
Sinus 136, 139
Skin bends 118
Skinfold thickness 102
Slab model 27
Sleep apnea 96-97
Snoring 96
Space shuttle 22
Sponges 144, 145
Spontaneous pneumothorax 94
Squeezes

ear 136
mask 136
sinus 136
tooth 136
St. Leger Dowse, Marguerite 87, 100
Staphylococcus aureus 139
Starfish 146
Statistical model 24
Stingrays 145, 146
Stonefish 142, 145, 146
Strength 151, 155
    and back pain 159
    protein supplementation 159
Stretcher's scrotum 96
Superoxide (O_2^-) 125
Superoxide dismutase (SOD) 126, 130
Supersaturation 21
    critical 21
Supersaturation ratio 21
Surface area-to-mass ratio 102
    curves 103
    heat 67
    hypothermia 102
    individual body parts 66
Sweat 187
    insensible 187
Sweat glands
    apocrine 82
    eccrine 82
    number 82, 104
Sweating 56, 80, 81, 82, 150, 188
    electrolyte 81
    heat loss 82
    insensible 82
Swimmer's ear 95, 138-141
    causes 139
    ear plugs 138, 139, 140, 141
    prevention 141
    symptoms 139
    treatment 140

T

Table-based computer 23
Technical diving 29-34
    antidiuretic hormone 50
    bottom mix 33
    breathing rate 36, 134, 135
        elevated carbon dioxide 134-135
        high partial pressure of oxygen 36
        narcosis 36

work of breathing 36
carbon dioxide retention 134
colder breathing helium? 32
decompression mix 33
diuresis 43-52
    diapers 49
    diaper rash 49
    dive boat options 49
    drysuit options 49
    external catheters 49
    p-valves 49
Donald Duck voice 31, 32
enriched air nitrox (EAN) or oxygen
  enriched air (OEA) 29, 129
    chamber treatment after 31, 130
    mood effect from EAN? 31
gas switching 33-34
heliox 31-32
high pressure nervous syndrome
    (HPNS) 33
hypoxic mix 33
narcosis 31, 32, 36, 75, 128, 135
NOAA Nitrox I 29, 129
NOAA Nitrox II 29, 129
normoxic mix 33
oxygen toxicity 128-129
    susceptibility 129-130
    treatment 130-131
tank oxygen analysis 34
travel mix 33
trimix 32-33
Tell-tale 146
Temperature, body
    core 57, 101, 150
    deep skin 58, 102
    men's skin 102, 103
    skin 57, 102
    sweating 104
    woman's skin 102, 104
Testicular implants 86
Tetanus 146
Tetrodotoxin 142
Thalmann, Edward Captain 27
Thermal protection 76
    clo 69
    three dog night 69
Thirst 190
    hypovolemic 190
    osmotic 190
Three dog night 69
Tiny bubble group 28
Tiny bubble model 28
Tissues 8 *see Compartments*
Travel mix 33

Trimix 32-33

U

U.S. Navy (USN) Standard Air
    Decompression Tables 20, 22
Undersea and Hyperbaric Medical
    Society (UHMS) 119
Urinating on marine stings 145
US Naval Medical Research Institute
    (NMRI) 24

V

Valium 16
Valsalva maneuver 40, 99, 115
Van Liew, Hugh Ph.D. 25
Vann, Richard Ph.D. 89
Varying permeability model 28
Vasoconstriction 58, 72
Vasodilation 73
    hunting reflex of Lewis 73
Vasopressin 45 *see Antidiuretic hormone*
Venom 142
Venous pooling 39, 44
    body position underwater 40
Ventilation *see Breathing rate*
Vitamin C 130, 131, 132
Vitamin E 130, 131, 132
VO_{2max} 92 *see Aerobic capacity*

W

Washout curves 9
Water vapor 187
Weathersby, Paul Ph.D. 24
Weight lifting 154, 160, 163, 164, 171
    hernia 99
    reduce effects of aging 170
Weight loss 176-179
Weights
    ankle 166
    wrist 166
    weight belt, slipping 99
Wells, Christine Ph.D. 92
Wienke, Bruce Ph.D. 28

Whales 37, 59
Wilmshurst, Peter M.D. 90
Wind-chill factor 55
Women divers *see Gender*
    mammary implants 86, 89
    oral contraceptives 89
    pregnancy 89
Work
    breathing 36
    external 91
    internal 91
Work load 91-92, 98, 104
Workman, Robert D. M.D. 22